EILUNGKIANG

U.S.S.R.

AMUR R.

SUNGAI R.

Harbin

KIRIN

Vladivostok

Mukden

LIAONING

YALU R.

K O R E A

Dairen

Seoul

N

SEA OF

JAPAN

Tokyo

J A P A N

YELLOW

SEA

tao

su

Shanghai

EAST CHINA

SEA

KIANG

J

PACIFIC

OCEAN

FORMOSA

A

FIRST EDITION 1948

China: *The*
Land and the People

China: *The Land and the People*

GERALD F. WINFIELD

Issued in cooperation with
THE AMERICAN INSTITUTE OF PACIFIC RELATIONS

WILLIAM SLOANE ASSOCIATES, INC.
Publishers - - - - - - - - - - *New York*

First Printing

Acknowledgements

The groups and individuals, both in China and America, that made possible the opportunities that provided the stimulus to write this book are too numerous and varied to be individually acknowledged. Among them, however, are several of such dominant significance as to demand mention. They are the Board of Foreign Missions of the Presbyterian Church in the U. S. A. which sent us to China during the depth of the depression; Cheeloo University where my interest was directed to the problems of the common people; the Rockefeller Foundation which provided the research grants that made that interest fruitful; and finally the charm and challenge of the land and people of China itself.

For assistance in the final preparation of the manuscript I am indebted to Mr. William H. Dennis and Mr. Eric Swenson.

The Institute of Pacific Relations is an unofficial and non-partisan body founded in 1925 to facilitate the scientific study of the peoples of the Pacific area. It is composed of National Councils in eleven countries besides the United States.

The Institute as such and the National Councils of which it is composed are precluded from expressing an opinion on any aspect of national or international affairs. Opinions expressed in this study are, therefore, those of the author.

Contents

China: *The*
Land and the People

China, Key to Peace

A LL THE SIRENS AND WHISTLES IN CHUNGKING LET GO at ten-thirty on the morning of September 3, 1945. After eight years, one month, and twenty-seven days of resistance, China was free.

Domination by outside powers had ended. The country that had been carved into a series of economic colonies by the world powers of a few decades before was now emerging as a great nation. The shrill din of victory echoed against the high cliffs of the Yangtze.

I was standing with two friends waiting to cross from the South Bank of the flooded river into Chungking proper. We were part of a crowd of thousands waiting for the ferry that would take us into the city for the official three-day victory celebration just beginning. Mingled with this crowd that was living a great moment in Chinese history were other thousands carrying household possessions—a solemn, weary group fleeing the ravages of uncontrolled flood. The Yangtze was ninety-nine feet above low-water level, the highest in seven years. The houses that huddled on spider-leg stilts against the steep riverbanks were disgorging their occupants as the waters rose. The stone paths connecting the South Bank villages and the ferry landing were crowded with refugees.

An incongruous multitude, part flood victims, part holidaymakers, jammed the approaches, the steps, and the improvised walkway to the ferry float. With the first blast of the sirens, most of the crowd broke into a cheer and surged forward toward the landing. We fought to keep our footing at the edge of the six-foot drop into the ditch that flanked the steps.

Whistles were blowing lustily when our ferry nosed into the debris of the floodwaters. Churning to keep its course against a nine-knot current, it picked its way past floating strawstacks, the wreckage of houses, a long line of empty gasoline drums, and past one of the gunboats that were China's claim to a navy. At regular intervals the gunboat boomed out a salute to victory from its specially mounted brass cannon, and with each boom a wave of excitement passed through the crowd on the ferry. China's navy, making up in emotion what it lacked in size and power, was saluting the first victorious war of China's modern history.

The ferry edged up to a float now raised by the flood almost to Chungking street level, and the crowd poured ashore. To avoid the congested main streets, we turned down an alley that runs along the top of the old city wall on the Chialing River side.

The alley, like the paths along the shore of the South Bank, had been blocked by refugees until only a narrow lane remained open between rows of mat sheds erected during the night. Each shed barely covered a single bed of boards raised on sawhorses, yet in each were piled all the pitifully few items of furniture, pots and pans, clothing, and other family possessions rescued from the rising waters. Only a few feet below the street level, beneath the crenelated parapet of the city wall, the muddy river sucked at the piles and planks of the houses from which those victims had fled. Here and there stacks of boards that had been ripped from floors and hastily tied together were floating at the ends of tethers. Huge gray rats scrambled across the floating debris or perched on the tops of projecting piles.

We passed scores of men and women sprawled on beds or

sitting in folding canvas chairs, asleep in spite of screeching whistles and booming cannon, too exhausted from their long night struggle with flood to be aware of the momentous celebration going on around them.

On one board bed a sallow-faced woman lay with a newborn baby on her breast, exhausted from the labor of childbirth in the midst of disaster. Her baby would have to take its poor chances of survival, like so many of China's children throughout the centuries of war, flood, and famine.

After a few blocks we turned left toward the city, away from the ancient winding alleyways near the river, and entered one of the broad new avenues built after the first devastating bombings of the war. It was a solid mass of happy people moving toward the center of the city or finding positions from which to watch an endless string of parades. Dragon lanterns danced gaily, even though they were out of season. Already floats and representatives of dozens of organizations were assembling. Uniformed children marched in groups carrying school banners. Police and military units went by in close order drill. Members of every conceivable organization streamed past, all intent on celebrating the victorious end of the long war and all moved by an awareness of the new importance and dignity of their country.

Within a block of each other on this the first day of peace and freedom two violently contrasting factors in China's present problem were caught up in one dramatic and symbolic moment. One was a free China with a new political consciousness, with internal unity and the security of political progress at last within reach. The other, the age-old China, was gripped by problems of physical environment symbolized by raging flood, by debris and wreckage, by bone-weary thousands who had fought all night to escape with a few belongings. The one a struggle for new political forms; the other the old, weary struggle for existence—political problems versus human problems.

These are the bases for the great struggles of our time. On the one hand, we attempt to extend the industrial revolution so that all peoples may approach the higher standards of living already achieved in the Western world. On the other, we attempt to determine the type of political organization that shall govern this new, productive industrial society. In so doing we try to resolve the cultural conflict between the old prescientific wind, water, and muscle technology, with its medieval social forms, and the advancing front of industrial technology and modern social forms. While fascism, private-enterprise democracy, socialism, and communism contend for control of the emerging world society, the development of these basic struggles and the speed with which acute human problems are solved will determine whether or not global war will come again.

What are these fundamental human problems? Hunger is first. Even before the destructive forces of World War II forced much of Europe's population down toward the starvation line, two-thirds of the human race, concentrated for the most part in Asia, lived at or around the survival line where the main preoccupation was the grim effort to live. These two-thirds of the human race are scourged by famine and pestilence, clothed in poor and often unhygienic garments, housed in hovels and firetraps, fed scarcely enough to maintain life, and are almost completely uneducated. The miserably low industrial production of this great segment of the human family is limited by hand methods aided by only the simplest of tools.

Most of this two-thirds of the human race is crowded into overpopulated, rural areas that are 80 per cent dependent on agriculture. They are either under a colonial government or have just escaped from the status or threat of being subject peoples. For many of these peoples, civil war is the most common method by which power within the state is sought. All of them know exactly what evils they wish to abolish, but few have constructive ideas or plans to substitute for old ways. International wars evolve from the struggle between more powerful states for control of the undeveloped resources of these backward peoples.

Any solution of these human problems must answer fundamental questions. Can the technical knowledge now possessed by mankind put an end to famine and pestilence and raise living standards of this backward two-thirds of the world's population quickly enough to prevent dissatisfaction from becoming violence? Can these underprivileged peoples who live in the overpopulated and underdeveloped parts of the world become strong enough within a single generation to attain internal unity and maintain external respect? Can the wide gap now existing between their starvation standards of living and the high standard of living of North America be diminished before tension between the two embroils us in a third World War?

The two-thirds of the human race now lacking bare necessities have observed the Westerners living among them. They know that large groups of people can live in cleanliness and health. They have seen the expansion of individual creative capacities made possible by education. They want these things for themselves. They want access to the resources of the globe and to the knowledge that has accumulated during the past hundred fifty years. They want the potential productive capacity of the world's two billion human beings utilized to ensure the production and distribution of goods and services which contribute to a rich life. If they cannot find peaceful means of moving toward an era of greater abundance they will try force, or they again will become the bones of contention that tempt others to break the peace.

These backward peoples of the earth are determined to

solve their human problems and raise their standards of living. They are determined to develop their own nations in which freedom and security can be attained.

Americans have an enormous stake in the success or failure of the Asiatic peoples who are trying to raise themselves from the survival line to a minimum of health and decency.

For nearly a hundred fifty years American religion, American philanthropy, and American education have helped the people of Asia to obtain the techniques and material necessities for better living. In many instances such activities have contributed directly to student exchange and to the improvement of public health and education. The unselfish purposes behind these efforts are valid expressions of the fact that we owe the backward peoples of the earth our respect and assistance because they are fellow human beings, equals under the principles of justice and order that control the universe. In such activities we still believe that all men are created free and equal. Our ideals force us to recognize our stake in the advancement of backward peoples. Our economic, governmental, and missionary activities in Asia have served to acquaint these peoples with a higher standard of living and to inspire them with new hope and desire.

Then, too, we have a political stake in their success. Much of the driving force behind their desire for freedom has been inspired by a growing knowledge of us, of our history, and of our political ideas. This huge mass of humanity, when stabilized, must play an important part in the world political structure in which we are assuming increasing responsibility and leadership.

We have an economic stake in the success of these people. Our economy is based on the machine and upon a mass production system which cannot produce necessities or luxuries for the many without world-wide sources of raw materials and world-wide markets. To work best for us, our economy must keep pace with expanding world production and commerce.

The peoples of Asia must assume an increasingly important share in a world-wide economy. If they succeed in solving their problems and thereby reduce the risk of war, then we, as American individuals, gain. If they fail and war comes again, we will be involved. World War II proved beyond a doubt that the lives of men, women, and children everywhere are bound together. Our personal lives are more determined by what happens in the foreign capitals of the world than they are by what happens in the next town or the next county, in New York or Chicago, in Dallas or San Francisco. By no stretch of the imagination could any domestic event affect our lives more deeply than could global war. Nothing that could happen in any American town or city could possibly tear apart as many American families as could a war that forces so many of us to lay down our normal chosen careers in order to destroy men and property in other parts of the world.

Our recent war began to brew in a world that lay outside our local spheres. Never again can we feel safe in ignoring brewing pots stirred by other nations and other peoples. It may appall some of us to realize that we are so closely linked with a huge group of people whose backgrounds are so different from our own. Yet this is an inevitable price we pay for our own cleanliness and comfort, our extensive control of power, and our freedom for development of our personal and group life. The forces that have given us the economic wealth that has produced these freedoms, both material and social, are also the forces that bind us to the rest of mankind. The energy we know how to generate and control, the technology that produces the things we want for physical comfort and for mental and spiritual growth, the means we command for the spread of knowledge and the production of entertainment and enjoyment, all these are the same universal forces that create increasing interdependence and make it impossible for the world to exist one-third modern and two-thirds medieval.

Deeper than the demands of charity, philanthropy, and religion, more fundamental than political expediency or economic needs, our stake in Asia has now become a matter of the survival of our democracy and our standard of living, even our very existence as a free people.

Our way of life, our democracy, our standard of living, our freedom, are all the products of six basic factors. First, there are the ethics and concepts of Judaeo-Christianity, with emphasis on the universal value of the individual. Second, there is the democratic form of social and political organization, which releases the energies of all types and classes of people and sets and modifies the rules by which their activities are carried on. Third, there is the scientific revolution and the modern technology it has created. Fourth, there is the private enterprise system of capitalism, which fosters competition under democratically applied checks and controls administered by our system of government. Fifth, there are the vast natural resources of the world's richest continent, which we began to develop precisely at that moment in history when science was creating the new technologies. And, sixth, there are the skills and abilities of every race on earth that have come to our shores and joined in building the American way of life. That way of life could not survive without all six of these basic factors, and several of them are vulnerable to repeated global wars and subject to destruction by constant ideological corrosion.

As an example, we can maintain our high standard of living because we have always had more than ample quantities of coal, oil, iron, timber, fertile land, and quantities of other resources permitting us to produce all kinds of goods inexpensively and in abundance. Yet some of these important resources are reported to be approaching exhaustion. The monumental study published by the Twentieth Century Fund, *America's Needs and Resources*, states: "The supply of some of our most valuable resources is likely to become deficient in one or two decades, and will, therefore, present serious problems in the 1950 decade. Supplies of most of our high-grade metallic ores are in this class. The known zinc, lead and bauxite reserves that are now commercially feasible to utilize will be exhausted by 1960, even with the rate of extraction at half the wartime rate. It is estimated that our own high-grade iron ore reserves would last only eleven years at the 1943 rate of use." According to this study, our estimated oil reserves probably would last only fifteen years if continually extracted at the 1940 rate; our natural gas reserves might last half a century. These quotations need not be interpreted to mean that our economy is in immediate danger of exhausting raw materials without hope of substituting new sources or new materials. Rather, they point to the fact that another war as destructive as World War II would seriously affect our ability to maintain our high standard of living. We cannot expect to avoid direct destruction of our resources in future wars.

The constant tension caused by the wide gap between our economic level and those of Asiatic peoples could do more than exhaust our resources. Under the impact of additional wars and the pressure of huge armament burdens, the free enterprise system of production, which has been a major factor in raising our standard of living, would be one of the first casualties. Centralized planning and control would be required for maximum efficiency in arming and fighting. As more and more dictatorial methods were required to meet exigencies, the democratic process itself would soon be curtailed. As we sought to ferret out and eliminate all enemy ideologies within our society, our basic freedoms of speech, assembly, and belief would be destroyed, together with our ability to learn and absorb the experience and skills of other peoples.

The American way of life can survive and provide the standards we desire for ourselves and for our children only if (1) major global wars are prevented and the conflicts that cause them are lessened to the point where expenditures for armaments may be drastically reduced; (2) the standards of living of the backward peoples of the world are raised to levels nearer to our own in order to lessen their dissatisfaction and to provide them with the means of security from more powerful neighbors; (3) the democratic way of living, working, and solving problems is steadily extended to encompass the globe as a whole. On the achievement of these goals depends our survival.

Force alone cannot protect our way of life. The atomic bomb can be a Frankenstein monster if used to the saturation point anywhere on the globe. The economic, social, political, and spiritual condition of Europe proves that no highly developed industrial society can withstand the frightful destruction of modern war even when atomic weapons are not used. We are presented with a choice of fighting our way into poverty or of building our way into a lasting prosperity.

China is a most important key to the peace and prosperity of the world. The human problems that are the source of the cultural and political struggles of our time have come to a focus within her borders. The outcome of China's conflicts may determine the fate of the human race in the second half of the twentieth century. Her size, her enormous population, and her resources magnify the importance of her internal developments. She is a guide and an example to other undeveloped peoples and a potential power among other great nations.

Of all the Asiatic peoples, China, in spite of current failures and conflicts, probably more than any other of the backward nations has the best chance of solving her fundamental human problems. She is the nation in which the "critical experiment" of our time is being made to determine whether or not all the human race can free itself for an abundant life. We cannot be sure that the overcrowded, underdeveloped parts of the world can raise their standards of living and maintain them at a high level until one of them succeeds in doing it.

The fact that Europe has had fairly high standards, and that Russia, with her immense resources, will someday achieve high standards is not sufficient proof that Asiatic peoples, with the handicap of overgrown populations, can do the same thing. If China can succeed, then the other backward peoples can hope to do likewise, and all of us can hope for a stable and workable world society. If China fails, then we and our children will almost certainly have to pay the price in conflicts and in wars.

There are several reasons why China has the best long-term chance of rebuilding her life. First, she has a racial and cultural homogeneity. Although it also sets in motion forces that are liabilities to the task of solving her problems, this ancient culture binds her into a nation more unified than any of the other large and backward groups in Asia or Africa.

Second, China has a population containing many strains highly endowed with natural ability. The long centuries of national existence, the many public works, and the culture and literature of China indicate the quality of the Chinese race. It is no exaggeration to say that China constitutes the greatest reservoir of undeveloped human ability now existent. While this ability will be put to rigorous test in the years ahead, its existence is one of the strongest reasons for believing that China can be rebuilt.

Third, China occupies a territory that is modestly well supplied with natural resources. Although the resources of China are not so abundant as those of the United States, they are sufficient to provide the basis for a solution to her problems if they are carefully used.

Fourth, much of China's territory lies in the Temperate Zone, where the climate is favorable for the development of a robust people. She also has extensive areas in the subtropics, where the application of modern methods in medicine and industry can be expected to increase production and improve life.

Fifth, China has a better chance of succeeding in her task than other Asiatic peoples because she has apparently passed beyond the danger of being reduced to colonial status by other powers and is free to develop her resources for the benefit of her own citizens. To educated Chinese, the greatest achievement of World War II was the abrogation of the "unequal treaties" that resulted from her long resistance to Japan. They had been in effect for one hundred years from the signing of the first in 1842. With the abolition of the last in 1943 China was freed from her semicolonial position.

Finally, China has hope of success because she is assured of the co-operation of more advanced peoples in applying modern methods to the solution of her problems, a factor of prime importance. For the first time in history such help is available and can be requested with impunity. China is already receiving assistance from member states of the United Nations who possess the knowledge and means of applying technical processes to human problems. The fact that China can avail herself of such assistance gives sound reason to believe that she will succeed.

Of all the Asiatic nations, China is the most important to America because she is likely to regain her former position of leadership in Asia, a position already enhanced by American money and American blood spent in crushing Japan. She is the most important to us because she is the largest Asiatic nation, and in size of population the largest nation in the world. Our political fate in the Pacific is closely bound to that of China.

Since the solution of these human problems and the reconciliation of opposing forces in China are of fundamental importance to the stability of our own personal lives, it is desirable for us to understand the issues and the possible means of solving them to the best advantage of those involved, including ourselves. We need historical perspective to understand the forces at work. We need to understand what kind of people the Chinese are, for it is important that we know the human and social as well as the economic and political significance of these problems.

This book is an attempt to draw in broad outline the picture of China as she is and to sketch some of the important problems and processes involved in her rebuilding. It is primarily concerned with the struggle to harness the Chinese environment with modern methods, but the implications of the political struggle cannot be avoided.

The rebuilding program outlined in Part II is designed to serve as a standard against which the magnitude of China's problems may be judged. The time scale is necessarily long. Hope of success, in spite of the failures and near collapse of present day Chinese society, lies in the vitality of the Chinese people, and in their ability to think and act in terms of such a long term program.

The task of presenting the "over-all" China of the Chinese is by no means simple. Too frequently it is necessary to reduce the millions of families and individuals to statistics which can be used as factors in appraisal. In the process it is inevitable that much of the truth, and particularly the personal, human truth, will slip through our fingers and be lost. But we shall have to try to extract the central truth, in so far as it can be found, from the whole rich multiplicity that is China.

Nor is the task of marshaling such statistics an easy one. One of the basic facts about China is the scarcity of available facts. Much of the land, even in the densely populated areas where Chinese culture has made its greatest advances, has not been surveyed or classified. Governmental statistics are incomplete and notoriously inaccurate. There is wide variance in figures from different sources concerning such things as landownership, crop yield, income, and vital statistics.

Many Chinese agricultural statistics used here are taken from surveys made by the University of Nanking's Department of Agricultural Economics under the direction of Dr. J. Lossing Buck, who has compiled the data into a three-volume work entitled *Land Utilization in China*. These data are based on surveys of only 38,256 farms in twenty-two Chinese provinces, a tiny fraction of the more than 56 *million* families estimated as composing China's rural population. Yet Buck's studies are probably the most reliable picture of Chinese agriculture now available.

In spite of the admitted inaccuracies that may exist in these statistical data, there is enough reliable information to warrant discussion and conclusions that will provide a sound guide for formulation of policies. America and Americans, if they are concerned for the future, must gather from the most reliable statistics and observations available some understanding as to how China can be rebuilt. Before we can plan effective assistance in that rebuilding, we must acquire a picture of China as she is.

Part One

THE LAND AND THE PEOPLE

Chapter 1

Geographic and Human Foundations

THE CHINESE ARE INCENSED, AND RIGHTLY SO, BY THE commonly expressed opinion that China is not a nation, but a geographical area. Such a conclusion is frequently reached by those who have glimpsed the geographical stage, the climate-born scenery, and the human actors, but who have failed to see the great drama in which China has evolved her national characteristics.

China is the dusty Shantung plain in springtime—a green and brown patchwork of diminutive fields stretching as far as the eye can see, broken only by clumps of new-leafed trees screening scattered villages. China is the thousands of half-naked Shantung farmers bobbing over hand windlasses, drawing water to irrigate their garden-crop wheat. China is the long roads through the Shansi loess, rutted and sunken by the passing of countless carts through endless years. China is the pungency of the Tsingtao fish quay, where seagoing junks bring squid and shark to market. China is the kaleidoscopic fantasy of Szechuan in midwinter, where soaring mountains are terraced with the mirror waters of rice fields reflecting shrine and bamboo clump and palm and winter peas as they descend in liquid steps from the heights to the lush valley. China is the full harvest moon shining over houseboats on Soochow canals. China is the turgescent stench of rotting *kaoliang* (grain sorghum)

drowned in miles of flooded countryside. China is the Peiping
dust storm that hides the sun and turns the sky a rich ma-
hogany. China is the urgent three weeks of spring on the
Chengtu plain, when winter wheat is harvested, the fields
plowed, fertilized, and flooded, then plowed again, harrowed, and reharrowed before spring rice is transplanted.
China is the silhouette of camel trains bearing coal from the
Western Hills or the rhythmic chant of rivermen on hands
and knees, straining and clawing at towpaths to drag their
boats through the rapids of the Yangtze gorges. China is ten
thousand pictures of people and places. It is countless re-
cordings of the impact of nature. It is visual evidence of the
survival of the old and the struggle of the new.

China *is* a nation, and this nation has a unique physical
foundation—the geographical stage on which the drama is
enacted. The dominating facts about this geographical area
are that it is continental, it is coastal, and it is rugged.

The Geographical Area

Greater China—including Manchuria, Mongolia, Sinkiang, and Tibet—occupies the center portion of the Asiatic
continent. It is divided into thirty-four provinces. In the
northeast are the nine provinces of Manchuria. Beyond the
Great Wall are the four provinces of Inner Mongolia, the
two western provinces of Nearer Tibet, and the single, far-
northwestern province of Sinkiang (formed of Chinese Tur-
kestan in 1878). South of the Great Wall are the eighteen
provinces known collectively as China Proper. Before World
War II, Manchuria was divided into three provinces instead
of the present nine. At that time Greater China consisted of
twenty-eight provinces and two territories. By recent acts
and treaties, the two former territories of Outer Mongolia
and Farther Tibet have become independent.

These thirty-four provinces of Greater China constitute

the second largest sovereign area in the world, being exceeded only by the Soviet Union. Altogether they constitute a continental mass of 3⅓ million square miles, more than 300,000 square miles larger than continental United States. They support a population three or four times as large as that of the United States.

The United States has oceans to the east and the west which temper her climate. China, a continental country with Asiatic Russia, India, and Europe to her west, has vast variations in climate, population distribution, and national economy. The spaciousness of China does not mean that her physical base is as rich as that of the United States, nor does it mean that her ability to produce is as uniformly distributed geographically.

The United States is approximately 3,000 miles wide, east to west, and approximately 1,500 miles long, north to south. The result is an east-west orientation that Americans frequently apply to other countries. The main axis of China runs from north to south. From the northernmost border of Manchuria to the southernmost tip of Hainan, China extends in a north-south line for more than 2,500 miles. Her western border is barely 2,500 miles from the eastern sea at the widest point. All the great populated areas and the entire national economy of China are located within 1,000 miles of the eastern coast line along the Yellow Sea, the East China Sea, and the South China Sea. During World War II much was heard of the great Chinese cultural migration to the "west"—but this "west" is well within the 1,000-mile-wide coastal strip.

On the accompanying map, showing China superimposed on the United States, no cities of importance appear as far west in China as is Oklahoma City in the United States. Lanchow, Chengtu, and Kunming, China's large western cities, are within the 1,000-mile coastal area, falling along a line

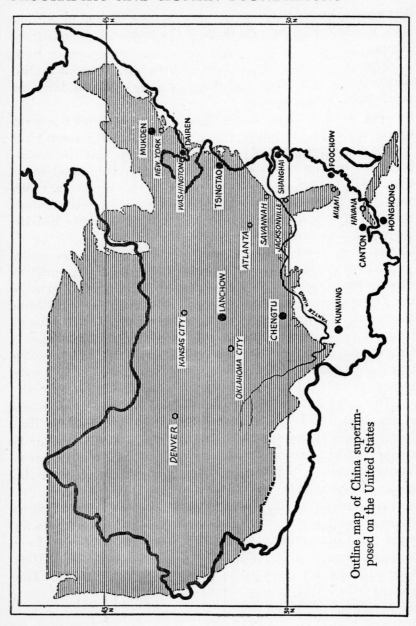

Outline map of China superimposed on the United States

that runs from north to south through Oklahoma, and Texas, with Kunming to the southeast of the most southerly tip of Texas.

The two coast lines run northeast and southwest, the northeastern provinces of China extending much farther north than New England, and the southeastern provinces extending much farther south than Florida. It is in this north-south coastal belt that most Chinese live.

On these superimposed outlines, the comparison of important city sites may suggest variations in climate, production, and cultures. Mukden and New York are in about the same latitude, as are Dairen and Washington. Tsingtao falls between Washington and Atlanta. Shanghai lies between Savannah and Jacksonville. Foochow falls near Miami, and Canton is as far south as Havana, Cuba.

China's great artery is the Yangtze River, which, on our superimposed outlines, appears to rise in New Mexico, follow the Texas coast east along the Gulf of Mexico, and empty at Shanghai, between Savannah and Jacksonville. Four of China's most important cities are located on this river—Chungking, Hankow, Nanking, and Shanghai. Because one-third of China's north-south axis lies south of the Yangtze, most of South China is superimposed on the Gulf of Mexico.

The great land mass of China is rugged, with 60 per cent of the area 6,000 feet or more above sea level. Only on the North China plains of Hopei, Honan, and Shantung can one travel without seeing rolling hills or high peaks. In the Yangtze valley the downstream traveler is constantly aware of mountains and hills, except in the Hankow area and the mudflat delta. For one hundred miles the Szechuan basin is fairly level, but the valley is only forty to fifty miles wide. All China south of the Yangtze is either hilly or mountainous, penetrated by narrow river valleys. Even the North China plain cannot compare with the long stretches of gently rolling Mississippi valley where one sees no real hills in days of traveling.

In the far west, surrounding Tibet and thrusting eastward along the thirtieth parallel to within 700 air miles of the coast, is a great mountain mass of which the Himalayas form the southern prong. This rugged easterly range, known as the Tsingling Mountains, dividing the country into North China and South China, is the reason for an overpopulated coastal area and a sparsely settled interior. It is this mountain mass that has turned the greater portion of the continental interior into agriculturally useless plateau and desert.

While China appears, on the map, to have continental proportions, the people and their culture have evolved in an area squeezed between the ocean, the deserts, and the mountains. Even this coastal area is rugged. Sikang, Chinghai, and Sinkiang, with more than one million square miles of territory, support a population approximating only six million. Slightly more than 1 per cent of China's people live in this one-third of China's land area extending deep into the continent! Most of the Chinese people live south of the Great Wall in the one million square miles commonly called China Proper, a region covering only 30 per cent of Greater China, and only 43 per cent the size of continental United States.

The Climate

Just as her topography is the stage on which China's drama is enacted, so the climate is the agent providing the scenery on that stage, determining how rocks shall be weathered into soil, what vegetation shall cover the hills and the mountains, what crops men may plant and harvest.

At the risk of oversimplification, it might be said that the climate of China is bred by three main geographical features and varies with the yearly changes of temperature. These three great factors that determine where life shall be lived and how are the Pacific Ocean on the east, the high Eurasian desert heartland to the northwest, and the mountain masses on the west and south.

These three factors produce a monsoon climate—a hot, rainy summer carried inland by winds from the Pacific, and a cool, dry winter carried eastward by winds from the Eurasian heartland. But the Tsingling Mountains thrusting eastward from the Himalayas and separating North China from South China interrupt this regular flow of air. The result is a wet south and a dry north.

During the winter months, the slow-cooling Pacific Ocean forms a low-pressure area that sucks cold winds from the rapidly cooling Eurasian heartland. These cold, dry winds sweeping eastward over North China produce a clear, cold winter. When the winds are strong they also bring the heartland's desert dust that in ages past has covered north China with a loess soil, deepest on the northwestern edge of China Proper, nearest the source.

To reach South China the winter winds must pass over the Tsingling Mountains. When they hit Szechuan province and the lower Yangtze valley, they cool the moisture-laden air of the south and form clouds, creating a dismal, chilly winter season. Chungking, the key city of Szechuan province, is as far south as New Orleans but has a much more disagreeable winter. The sun is invisible for weeks at a time, while temperatures hover in the fifties. It is warm enough to cause perspiration during a brisk walk, but damp and cold enough to penetrate thick clothing and unheated rooms and drain away body warmth.

The summer rainy season is caused by the reversal of these processes. The deserts of Central Asia heat more rapidly than the waters of the Pacific. A high-pressure area develops over the ocean and a low-pressure area over the heartland. The moist winds from the ocean rush inland, dropping most of their moisture as rain on the China coast. The Tsingling Mountains cause the last of the wind-borne moisture to precipitate, delivering great quantities of water to the upper reaches of the Yangtze and leaving no moisture for the northwestern provinces.

The result is an arid northwest with an annual rainfall ranging from zero to six or seven inches, a semiarid North China with an annual rainfall of seven to ten inches on the western edge to twenty-four and twenty-five inches near the coast, and a humid South China with annual rainfall ranging from forty inches in the upper and western limits to sixty-five or a hundred inches along the coast near Canton.

Because of the effect of the Tsingling Mountains on rainfall, Greater China can be divided into a nonagricultural interior comprising two-thirds of the entire country, and an agricultural coastal area embracing only one-third. Agricultural China, in turn, is divided into the humid south and the semiarid north. Fortunately her wet season coincides with the summer growing period.

The contrast between the south and the north can be seen graphically on an airplane trip from Chungking or Chengtu to Lanchow or Sian. This flight is the more dramatic because it goes over the Tsingling Mountains, which cause the contrast.

Taking off from Chungking in March or April one looks down on the well-watered, highly cultivated hills and valleys of Szechuan, already richly clad in new greens even brighter than the winter foliage of the higher slopes. There are many trees along the hilltops and steep mountainsides. There are streams everywhere, running low but filled with water. Flooded rice fields have the appearance of segmented lakes. The sky is overcast, and a haze hangs on the hilltops and shrouds the valleys. The air smells damp and cold. There is no wind.

For an hour the plane climbs steadily in order to clear the mountains, at times flying blindly through clouds. At last it bursts from the silvery blanket and one can look down on the Wei valley of North China. Here there are no clouds. The sun pours brilliant light on the sear, brown earth below. Much of the valley is fairly flat, traced here and there by roads dug deep into the loess soil by cart wheels and incessant wind. A few trees are in villages or along dry stream beds, their limbs bare. There is no green to be seen. Even winter wheat plants in many of the dry fields are more brown than green.

When one steps out of the plane one is met by a gusty wind. Dust drifts across roads and fields and the air is cold and cloyed with a dusty smell. As the sun drops lower and its radiant warmth declines, the wind suddenly becomes colder. In a matter of hours, one has come from the humid south to the dry north. The difference between south and north is almost as obvious on the train trip from Shanghai to Peiping, but the wartime routes that crossed the Tsingling Mountains can never be surpassed in imparting the contrast of China's geographic foundations.

Besides the effect on seasons and rainfall caused by the mountains, the heartland deserts, and the Pacific Ocean, China experiences a cooler winter and a hotter summer than do most land areas in similar latitudes, with local variations far from the norm. Peiping in the north experiences 100° heat every summer and frequently has temperatures higher than cities in the south.

The description of average seasons, rainfalls, and temperatures does not indicate local variations that plague the farmer and affect his harvest. Indeed, Buck* estimates that the climatic hazards of agriculture in China are greater than in any other equally large agricultural area in the world. Droughts and floods occur frequently. Semiarid Honan, in North China, has received eighteen inches of rainfall in one day, while a Kwangsi town in the humid south, normally

* *Land Utilization in China*, Chicago, 1937.

receiving a 50-inch annual rainfall, once received only eight inches in the course of a year. Moisture-laden air stagnating over the Han valley in 1935 dropped fourteen cubic miles of water in six days, and produced the great Yangtze River flood.

The Chinese People

The geographical area is the stage. The climate provides the scenery. The actors that dominate the stage and produce the drama are men. No matter where the traveler may go in China, he is constantly aware that Man dominates the Chinese scene. Almost nowhere in the whole expanse of agricultural China can one be alone.

Even though the topography is more rugged than that of any other nation of comparable size and importance, no valley is too remote to be inhabited. Human feet have worn trails across every hill and mountain, and human hands have hewn the stones that pave many of these trails. The dusty lanes of North China villages, the narrow stone-flagged streets of South China hamlets, the roads that lead to market, and the streets and *hutungs* of Chinese cities repeat the constant sound of human feet. On the plains, in the valleys, and high on the mountain slopes, every foot of available soil is patiently cultivated. Everywhere one can hear the call of human voices. Man dominates the scene.

Who are these people, these Chinese, who through the centuries have so thoroughly occupied and developed this vast area along the eastern coast of Asia? Where did they come from and what are they like?

The Chinese are a people who developed from prehuman species in the territory where they now live. In 1928 a group of bones five hundred thousand years old were discovered near Peiping. These were the bones of Peking Man, given the scientific name of *Sinanthropus pekinensis*, believed to represent a human species of the early Stone Age. It may be that present-day Chinese are the direct descendants of this primitive man. There is no conclusive evidence indicating that the Chinese came from any place outside of China.

The earliest written records of China date from 1200 B.C., but archaeological discoveries show that the culture from which China has grown had begun to develop on the dusty plains of North China, along the Yellow River, long before that date. From this center the Chinese slowly spread out and assimilated other groups until, many centuries ago, they occupied the territory they inhabit today.

As they expanded they retained certain characteristics and practices which made it possible for them to dominate new environments and absorb other peoples. They carried with them a system of intensive hoe-culture agriculture which developed irrigation as a means of increasing production. They maintained a diet that was basically vegetarian and closely adapted to their type of agriculture. They had a written language and had amassed in their body of literature the ideas and customs of the sages, particularly of Confucius. This language and common acceptance of ideas, customs, and philosophies created a basic unity and homogeneity which has been binding in spite of differences in topography, climate, and even in spite of variations in spoken language brought about by the absorption of new racial groups. As a part of this common culture, they developed the family system that has been a major factor in their survival as a racial group and as a nation.

The absorption of other racial groups is still in process. Today in Greater China there are three major nationalities plus minor remnants of tribes not yet fully assimilated. The three major nationalities are the Chinese, the Mongols, and the Tibetans. The unabsorbed tribes are found in the mountains of the southwestern and southern provinces, but of the total population of Greater China well over 90 per cent are Chinese.

While the Chinese have a basic homogeneity in race and culture, many of their characteristics show wide variations. For example, the "almond eye" feature, which was probably absorbed from a South China tribe, now occurs in about 36 per cent of the people in the Canton area, 23 per cent near Shanghai, and only 11 to 21 per cent in the north. Again, while the basic physical type known as Chinese is common to the whole country, there are many characteristics which vary between north and south and frequently between different provinces. Northerners are larger and more stolid and emotionally stable than southerners. The Chinese themselves distinguish different temperaments from different parts of China, just as we recognize differences between New Englanders, Midwesterners, and Texans, but the disparities of Chinese temperaments are more apparent because the provinces are much older and because there has been less contact between them.

The spoken language used in China also shows many variations. Mandarin, or *kuo-yü*, the most widely used dialect and the one now being taught as the national language, varies from place to place. Within this dialect, the Pekinese variety, considered to be the most melodious and cultured type, is commonly known as Northern Mandarin and is spoken in the provinces of Hopei, Shantung, Honan, Shansi, and Shensi, each province having distinctive variations. These variations are in many cases merely brogues, particularly in the speech of the peasants, but occasionally differ sufficiently to become other dialects.

In the lower Yangtze valley around Nanking another common variant of Mandarin may be called Southern Mandarin. The language of the upper Yangtze valley and of Yünnan province may be called Western Mandarin. People who speak different versions of Mandarin can communicate without much difficulty.

From the lower Yangtze valley below Nanking along

the coast to a point as far south as Canton, there are many dialects differing so radically from Mandarin that they may be called different languages. Of these there are at least two major groups, the Wu dialects of the lower Yangtze and the Cantonese of Kwangtung province. Fukienese and many other dialects spoken in these coastal areas bear little resemblance to one another.

With all their variations of spoken language, physical features, and temperament, the Chinese as a people retain many important traits that are widespread and common to all.

The Chinese are energetic. Prodded by necessity and tradition, they work steadily for long hours. The diligence of many generations is apparent in the terraced fields, in complicated systems of canals, in cities, and in the Great Wall itself.

The Chinese are good-humored. They like to tell stories and are especially fond of mother-in-law and henpecked husband jokes. Their language lends itself readily to puns, a favorite source of Chinese wit. A combination of curiosity and good humor causes Chinese to gather to watch a hot argument over a business transaction or to witness a family quarrel. The contestants play up to their audience, frequently judging their success by the amount of laughter provoked. Of course there are crabbed and ill-tempered Chinese, but by and large they are good-natured. They must be to live as they do, always crowded and frequently in uncomfortable circumstances.

The Chinese are honest. In general, their word is as good as a written contract. There are unreliable individuals, especially conspicuous during times of turmoil, but extreme honesty is an innate characteristic of the Chinese. Americans who hear of "squeeze" sometimes look askance at the practice. Actually it is commission, the normal Chinese means of doing business; a small assessment on the money that passes through the hands of the parties to any transaction, whether it is a purchase or a tax collection. It resembles a brokerage fee and in many instances serves in the place of advertising. It is an accepted practice, and in no sense is it dishonest.

The Chinese are shrewd, astute in evaluating the advantages or disadvantages of a situation or a transaction. Often they carry shrewdness to such an extreme that they tend to be penny-wise and pound-foolish. Because they have lived on so little for so long it has become essential to squeeze the most out of everything.

The Chinese are self-respecting and equalitarian in their attitudes. They have an ingrained sense of personal dignity. No one is prevented from rising because of birth or connections. There is no such thing as caste among the Chinese. It is this trait that prompts people to say the Chinese are basically democratic, and it is this sense of dignity within themselves, together with a desire to respect it in others, that is a component of that quality called "face." Face is preeminent in the practice of etiquette. When one man first meets another, he must show by his actions that he respects him as a person. Each must indicate that he considers the other a prosperous, well-educated individual of considerable social importance, even when both know it is not true. We all like to feel important, and the Chinese have developed many subtle ways of making people feel that way.

The Chinese are "familyistic." We Americans like to think and speak of ourselves as being individualistic, and we strive for individual satisfaction and advancement. The Chinese, however, are conscious of family loyalty above all, and may be called "familyistic" in much the same sense that we are individualistic.

The Chinese are loyal. As an outgrowth of their family system and their devotion to the family group, they have developed a deep sense of personal loyalty, to family, to friends, and to employers. If domestic servants or other employees have been accepted as trusted members of the family, there is established an almost unbelievable capacity for loyalty. I know of one servant who remained with his Chinese mistress and her two children during the siege of Hongkong, who helped them escape through the Japanese lines, and who worked for money to feed them as they traveled inland toward Chungking in unoccupied China.

The Chinese have a genius for friendship. Friends will go to incredible lengths to help one another, and a friend in need may turn to the friend of a friend for almost any kind of assistance. One middle-school boy was punished repeatedly for coming back to his dormitory late, against the rules. He never explained that he was going to the hospital night after night to teach a sick friend the day's lessons so that the friend would not fall behind in his work. This friendship is a two-way street. Your friends will do anything they can to help you, and they will turn to you without hesitation if they need your help.

All these characteristics and many others add up to make the Chinese a friendly people, sufficiently human, of course, to include a share of rascals. Particularly when one can speak their language, and can more readily share their thoughts and feelings, one finds them most lovable and kind.

While the Chinese tolerate no immutable caste system and an individual is free to evolve his own occupation and destiny, there were five major "classes" in the old society, each meriting a different degree of honor and respect.

The scholar has always been accorded the position of greatest honor in Chinese society, for he is the teacher, the man who has mastered the Chinese language, the classics, history, and philosophy. Because for many centuries examinations were the only means of acquiring high official position, the scholar was also the government official.

The second most honored position in Chinese society was accorded the farmer. It was he who fed the nation. On his labor and production all else depended.

In third place came the artisans, for they too are producers and merit the esteem of the community.

Below the producers came the merchants, who, theoretically at least, did not deserve quite the same respect due the producers. Perhaps this relatively low position accorded to people whose livelihood came from trading was because trading is a matter of wits, with the result that the merchant is sometimes a rather unscrupulous individual.

Finally, at the bottom of the list, was the soldier, a position quite in accord with the old Chinese adage: "Good iron is not used to make nails; good men are not used to make soldiers."

These degrees of respect are still deeply rooted in Chinese thinking, although they have been modified by impact of war, modern technology, and contact with the outside world.

How Many Chinese?

Although no one knows exactly how many Chinese there are, it is probable that about one-quarter of all the people on earth are Chinese. For years the population has been estimated at four hundred millions. In 1926 the Chinese Postal Administration compiled an estimate of the population by *hsien* [county] and placed the figure at 485,508,838 for the 28 provinces existing at that time, but omitted Outer Mongolia and Farther Tibet. Dr. George B. Cressey in his *Asia's Lands and Peoples* gives an estimate of 473,992,369, using figures published by the Ministry of the Interior in 1938, which included estimates for 23 provinces, to which Cressey added estimates for the other provinces and territories. From Buck's studies of rural population it would appear that the total may reach nearly 600 million. While his surveys provide no actual census totals, he shows an average farm population in the eight agricultural regions studied of 1,485 persons per square mile of cultivated land. As there are some 340,000 square miles of cultivated land in the 22 provinces studied, we might conclude that there are 504,900,000 rural people in this area alone, to which must be added the population of the northeastern provinces. On the basis of these figures, it may be reasoned that an estimated population of 500 million living in Greater China is not too high.

How do these 500 million make their living? What kind and how adequate a living do they make? To understand China as she is, we must seek answers to these questions.

Chapter II

Agriculture

SECOND ONLY TO THE SCHOLAR IN SOCIAL HONOR AND primary to the life of China is the farmer. An understanding of the land he cultivates and of the agricultural system under which he works is essential to an understanding of China as she is.

During the first forty years of the twentieth century in the United States, the percentage of total population living on farms steadily decreased. At present only 23 per cent of the American population lives on farms. The average American, who has become accustomed to this progressive urbanization, finds it difficult to understand how thoroughly rural China is or how basic agriculture is to Chinese national production and wealth. In China, more than 79 per cent of the population are farmers. An additional 11 per cent live in market towns in which the leading occupation also is farming. Only 10 per cent live in cities.

The total area of cultivated land in agricultural China, exclusive of Manchuria, is approximately 340,000 square miles or 217 million acres. Including the Manchurian provinces, the arable land in all Greater China is less than 10 per cent of the total land area. Even in densely populated agricultural China the terrain is so rugged that only 27 per cent of the area of that region is in crops. This 217 million acres under cultivation in China compares with 365 million acres cultivated in the United States. Stated in other words, a total of about 500 million people in China depend for sustenance on the products of 217 million acres of land worked by 65 million farmers, while in the United States 140 million people have first claim on production from 365 million acres that require the labor of only 6.5 million farmers.

This paucity of arable land in China, limited by climate and topography, combined with a vast population almost entirely dependent on agriculture could have but one result: an overwhelming pressure of population on the land.

Just what does it mean to have about 400 million farm folk living on the small area of land that China has available for cultivation? It means that there are approximately 1,500 persons actually living on every square mile of arable land. The comparable figure for the United States is about 53 persons to every square mile of cultivated land. Moreover, most American farmers add to their income by the use of uncultivated pasture and forest land. This figure for China is an average—in many localities the population density far exceeds the average to balance the many places where it falls below. In the locality with the greatest population density studied by Buck's investigators, 4,372 persons live on each square mile of plowed land. The least populated locality investigated had 212 persons to each square mile. Even an average of 1,500 persons per square mile of cultivated land means that between two and two and a half people actually live on each acre of cultivated land!

The increasing pressure of population through hundreds of years has enforced intensive land utilization. The farm population has been squeezed into the confines of every little valley, up the slopes of every hill where any soil can be found, and onto marginal lands where scanty and erratic rainfall is a constant hazard. It has caused a modification of the terrain greater than that of any other area of equal size in the world. Nearly half the land under cultivation is irrigated; about a quarter is terraced.

This intensive agriculture is both a cause and an effect of the pressure of the population on the land. On the one hand, this massive population came into existence because systems of agriculture were developed that could supply enough food to keep it alive and furnish enough energy to make possible the production of more food. Conversely, these systems of agriculture came into being because there were hands and backs to do the work required, and because there was a constantly increasing number of mouths demanding a greater yield from the soil. The whole interaction between land, water, and people that is agriculture in China has resulted in a unique synthesis of man and nature.

The adaptation of man to nature in China has assumed many different forms to fit different natural conditions existing in a large and varied geographical area. Innumerable variants of crops and rotations, of methods of tillage, and of storage and transportation have been developed. Among them are two dominant types of human adaptation to the demands of nature—the systems of agriculture characteristic of the northern wheat region and those of the southern rice region.

Wheat Region Agriculture

The North China wheat region extends from about one hundred miles north of the Yangtze River to the northern boundaries of the nine Manchurian provinces in the northeast. The agricultural practices of this region are illustrated by those of the Shantung plain.

Three major factors determine the substance and practices of agriculture on the Shantung plain: the land is nearly flat, with some rolling or broken hills outlying; the climate is semiarid, with an annual rainfall ranging from twenty-five to thirty inches near the coast to less than fifteen inches farther inland; the growing season is comparatively short, followed by a cold, dry winter.

From the train window of one of the two railway lines that traverse the Shantung plain, the gently rolling land appears to stretch as far as the eye can see. During most of the year it is dry and dusty with an over-all brownish cast. In many places where there are low hills the rains have washed out deep gullies. Every inch of land is planted to crop except that which has been spared for essential roads and trails or is occupied by the houses and threshing floors of villages. The tiny fields that form a crazy-quilt pattern over the land are separated by ridges of soil thrown up as boundary markers. Here and there along these boundary ridges are stunted and pruned mulberry trees, planted as permanent living boundary "stones" but kept down to the height of a low creeping bush so as to avoid shading the crops.

Dotted across the plains are the grave mounds of ancestors, standing sometimes alone, sometimes in little groups, but occupying valuable crop land that nourished the ancestors in life and now supports their children. Through the years these graves are slowly plowed back into the fields. They range in size from fresh mounds ten to fifteen feet high and twenty to thirty feet across to those of long-dead ancestors which have been reduced to the size of inverted bushel baskets.

In the early spring the land is bare and brown. More than half the fields are under winter fallow waiting for the spring planting of millet or kaoliang. The rest are striped with brown soil and dark-green rows of winter wheat still hugging the ground. The villages too are drab, with brown mud walls and thatched or gray tile roofs. Above the straight ridgepoles of the houses bare trees lift limbs swelling with new buds but still devoid of color. Much of the time a warm wind blows, carrying dust from the roads and trails that crisscross the countryside and from the dry, fallow fields.

AGRICULTURE

Throughout the windy spring the air is almost never free from the smell of dust.

As spring advances, the Shantung farmer begins his annual struggle to conserve and utilize that most precious of all his resources, moisture. If it has been a good year, there were rains during the preceding September or even as late as October, and there may have been one or two snows in the cold months of December and January. But now the hot, dry winds of spring are blowing, and the chances are that there will be no rain to speak of until the end of June, or early in July. The wheat must be brought through to harvest, and the seed of summer crops must be germinated with the limited amount of moisture available in the soil or deep down at the level of the subsoil water table. If, by chance, showers do fall, the farmers are out as soon as the soil surface is dry enough, cultivating their wheat. Stroke by stroke, swinging goose-necked hoes made to cut through soil like the blade of a cultivator plow, they break down the capillary structure of the soil surface to prevent the warm winds and blazing sun from sucking up precious moisture. It is hoe culture with a vengeance as they hurry to form a dry, surface mulch for the wheat.

When wheat begins to grow, whether showers come or not, farmers bring in portable windlasses and commence the laborious drawing of irrigation water from wells. Wells have been dug so as to have one convenient to the corner of every four or five fields. The windlasses are simple, cleverly constructed machines, efficient but backbreaking tools for raising water from wells thirty to sixty feet deep. They are made portable so they can be carried home each night to avoid possible theft.

During the lengthening hot days of April and May, sweating farmers, their bare backs burned to a rich sorrel, toil hour after hour at the windlasses, while sons, daughters, or wives guide the hard-earned water along the furrows to the deep, wide-spreading roots of the wheat plants. Because wheat has an extensive root system capable of foraging for water several feet below the soil surface it is the dominant crop in this semiarid region. Maturing of the grain is a triumph of both the plant's biological skill and the hard labor of the peasant with his simple windlass and bucket.

After the wheat has been given its boost of moisture by hand irrigation, the farmers turn to their next task. The remaining fallowed half of their land must be seeded with summer crops. The fields were plowed the preceding fall, and during the early spring the farmer hauled fertilizer and dumped it in little piles which by now have dried and been spread. If it rains, the farmer may plow again, but if moisture is scanty, he will plant in the seedbed already prepared by the fall plowing and harrowing.

In planting his millet, kaoliang, or cotton, the farmer makes sure of his germination by opening a furrow, dropping his seed by hand or from a simple two-row planter pulled by an ox or a donkey, and then quickly covering the seed and packing the damp soil with his feet or by pulling after him a roller made of two flat-edged stone disks about three inches thick and a foot in diameter. By rapid opening and closing of the soil and by tamping the earth so that the damp soil envelops the seeds, the farmer has prevented unnecessary evaporation of moisture and has lessened the possibility of dehydration by wind. He has planted everything in rows, both to ensure full use of limited moisture for germinating his seeds and to facilitate frequent cultivation. But in spite of his deference to moisture, during dry years the farmer may have to carry water or replant his summer crops several times before the seeds germinate and bring forth a stand.

Soon after planting his early summer crops the Shantung farmer must be busy about his wheat harvest. By now the grain has filled the head, and the heads have turned from green to gold. The average farm is not likely to have more than two or three acres in wheat, yet at harvesttime every man, woman, and child in the countryside is mobilized to harvest, by hand methods, an aggregate crop that is three-fourths that of the wheat harvest of the United States. So intense is the pressure on the land that for many nights before harvesting a member of the family must sleep in the fields to keep pilferers from making away with the ripening grain.

Threshing floors have been prepared as they have been for untold centuries past—first dug, then harrowed, then watered and rolled time and again until they are packed concrete hard. Threshing floors are permanent features of the villages, but some are temporarily prepared in the corners of fields from which the wheat is first harvested, to be returned to crop when the annual threshing is completed.

The wheat is either cut with a small hand sickle or pulled up by the roots and piled along the rows to be withed into bundles by hand. It is carried from the fields to the village threshing floors on shoulder poles, by pack animals, or in wheelbarrows. If the wheat has been pulled up by the roots, the latter are lopped off with a knife and carefully preserved for use as fuel in the cook stove. The upper half of the straw and the head are spread on the threshing floor, where the grain is crushed from the heads by a stone roller drawn by man or animal. Then the straw is removed with long-tined wooden pitchforks and long-toothed rakes, leaving the chaff and wheat on the floor for the slow, laborious job of winnowing.

It is this careful hand labor that makes the yields of wheat per acre higher for China than for the United States, in spite of other deficiencies. But it is also this careful hand labor and lack of equipment that force the Chinese farmer to put in a total of twenty-six man-days of work on each acre of wheat. In the United States, only 1.2 man-days of work are required for an acre of wheat.

After the wheat harvest, the spring rush continues. The Shantung farmer must now plow his wheatland and seed it to a summer crop. If he has harvested his wheat by pulling it up by the roots, he begins his plowing immediately. If he has cut his wheat with a sickle he must first dig out the heavier parts of the stubble for use as fuel. In any case, he must clear his land of most of the stubble, both because it is needed for fuel and because, if left to rot in the ground during the summer, it will compete with the summer crop for the limited amount of nitrogen in the soil and so diminish the crop yield. The farmer prudently removes it.

The summer crops that follow winter wheat are usually soybeans and corn interrowed, although other combinations may be used. The regular planting of soybeans following winter wheat is one of the major methods evolved by farmers through the centuries to maintain the total amount of nitrogen in the cycle of food, fertilizer, and soil. After this summer crop of soybeans is harvested, the land is winter fallowed.

When his summer crops have been sown, the farmer can slacken his pace a bit. He still must cultivate his field to keep the weeds down, but he has done about all he can to alleviate his moisture problem. If heaven is good, summer rains will begin at their normal time in late June or early July, and he will have enough moisture for the summer growing season and perhaps enough to give his winter wheat a good start in the fall. If heaven happens to be ill-humored and the rains are late, he will turn to his Taoist doctrines and conduct the extensive ceremonies that he believes will influence the Old Man of Heaven to make rain.

In the fall the farmer has to harvest his summer crops and do his fall plowing. When he plants his winter wheat he again will use his system of packing the seedbed cover, for again he is moving into the part of the year when lack of moisture becomes one of his great problems.

AGRICULTURE

Dearth of moisture is the factor that has resulted in an unusual type of specialization among Shantung farmers, particularly during the spring and fall months—the specialized growing of vegetables. Most North China farmers buy rather than grow their vegetables.

Vegetables, unlike wheat, have limited root systems requiring large quantities of moisture near the surface. Consequently, most of the vegetables produced in North China during spring and fall must be irrigated. Those villages, or sections of villages, fortunate enough to be located near a permanent stream or in an area where water is sufficiently near the surface to be raised with comparative ease, specialize in growing vegetables for the farm population living for miles around. Since the value per acre of vegetables is considerably more than that of wheat, all farmers would grow their own vegetables if they could, and many do produce as many vegetables as possible during the rainy summer months. So great is the problem of limited moisture that one area with well-water five to fifteen feet from the surface can grow dry-season vegetables profitably, while an adjacent area with well-water more than twenty feet from the surface cannot.

The wheat region farmer has adapted his cropping system and his methods of cultivation to the conditions set by the dry climate in which he lives.

Another major resource demanding conservation is heat. We have already noted the frugality with which the farmer preserves the stubble of his fields in order to cook his food, but he has many other strategies for coping with the winter's bitter cold. He is aided, in part, by a climate that provides him with clear sunshine while temperatures remain below freezing for many consecutive weeks, permitting him to take full advantage of the warming power of the sun's rays. Many centuries before Western architects had developed solal architecture, the courtyards and houses of North

China were oriented to trap the winter sun's slanting rays, not because of any erudite or scientific reasoning, but in accordance with a complicated set of beliefs concerning local wind and water spirits. The result of this mysterious system of house orientation is homes built around courtyards with north-south axes. During cold weather the most comfortable place in a North China home is outofdoors, in front of the main living room, which always faces south. Here one may sit in reasonable comfort even when the air temperature is below freezing, with the sun beating in and the cold winds barred by surrounding buildings and courtyard walls.

One of the chief uses of the "south-pointing needle," a Chinese invention never much used at sea, was for the orientation of buildings. A by-product of this precise architectural orientation on this predominantly flat land is that the country people always give directions by the points of the compass, never by referring to right or left as we do. Should you ask a farmer the direction to the next village, he might tell you, "Go north to the next trail, then turn east—that will take you there," or "That is the village you want—off to the southeast there." On the North China plain, one is never confused about directions.

In spite of the meticulous use of fuel and the exact solal orientation of their buildings, the padded garments common to North China are the chief defense against cold. Chinese winter clothes are functionally designed to retain warmth, and both men and women wear much the same fashions during the season. Recent U.S. Army tests have proved that two separate light garments retain more heat than a single layer of double thickness. It is not surprising to find the utilitarian Chinese wearing padded trousers and jumper under a long gown padded or lined with fleece or goatskin, and under these several layers of jackets, with accessories such as copious sleeves that serve as muffs and padded shoes that are thicker and warmer than any Western counterpart. Since the chief source of energy available is the grain that is eaten, it is good economy to dress so that the heat produced by the burning of the grain in the body is caught and held in the air space of quilted cotton garments.

Another expedient by which the Shantung peasant conserves heat consists of running the flue from the stove through the mud brickwork of the family's communal bed. The preparation of meals warms the bed, and the family may retire to solid comfort, each person wrapped separately from toes to head in heavy cotton quilts.

The third major resource that the Shantung farmer must conserve is fertilizer. He doesn't know it, but what he is desperately trying to accumulate is nitrogen in a form that his plants can use. In his campaign to save fertilizer, he is limited to the conservation of organic fertilizers. In order of importance, his sources of nitrogen are the excreta of the family, the manure produced by his animals, and, strange as it may seem, the country roads. The third source suggests the reason why, during all seasons of the year, one may see farmers and farm boys wandering along the country roads, a shallow basket on one arm and a long-handled, four-pronged fork in hand, picking up the droppings of departed draft animals, of dogs, and of wayfarers. Nitrogen to feed their crops is precious and scarce.

To conserve this fertilizer and to prepare it for the land, the farmer has devised an unusual structure usually located in one corner of the courtyard and frequently not more than thirty feet from the rooms in which the family lives. A combined animal shed, pigpen, and latrine, it contains a large, stone-lined, hard-bottomed pit. Into this organic matter sump goes all the precious nitrogen-bearing waste of men and animals to wait for the spring fertilizing of the fields.

Because vegetable matter is too scarce to be used as animal bedding to absorb urine and to increase the manure content, the farmer hauls large quantities of subsoil from his fields, stores it in piles along the village street, and uses it to spread under his animal. Each day he shovels the used, urine-soaked earth, together with the animal droppings, into the adjoining pit-latrine and spreads a fresh bed. Since the animal and its bed are beside the pit, this daily chore is quickly accomplished.

The single pig kept by the average farm family lives in the mud and muck of the pit itself, obtaining part of its sustenance from the freshly passed stool of the family and adding its own droppings to the steadily gathering hoard of fertilizer. The pig is fed slop from the kitchen and other available roughage such as chaff from wheat threshings or grass dug from the fields during the summer. The gleanings of manure from the roadsides, the ashes from the cookstove, and other farm dross, all find their way to the fertilizer pit —and to the pig.

During the year the pit slowly fills with a mixture of manure and mud, and each spring the farmer digs out this laboriously gathered hoard of plant foods and hauls it to the field by wheelbarrow or two-wheeled cart. An analysis made of fertilizers thus prepared showed that they were no more rich in plant foods than is a rich garden soil. Yet it is only by such careful husbanding of fertilizer that the Shantung farmer gives his soil the capacity to produce year after year.

If he lives near a city or on one of the few waterways providing cheap transportation to a city, the farmer has another source of fertilizer—dried human feces. The collecting, drying, and selling of the feces of a North China city is a big business. In the days before World War II, when the exchange was approximately three or four Chinese dollars to one American dollar, the annual dried feces business of Peiping amounted to several million dollars Chinese money.

The flow of nitrogen and other plant foods in the form of grain and produce from farms to cities and the return flow of feces from the cities back to the farm for use as fertilizers has resulted in a series of zones of fertility around the cities. As one approaches a big city one becomes aware of an increased fertility long before the city is entered. The crops grow greener the closer they are to the city. From an airplane, the city appears to be the center of a green oasis which fades gradually to the brown of the distant countryside. For centuries soil fertility has been built up near cities at the expense of foods brought to market from more distant zones.

Through hard work and constant conservation of moisture, heat, and fertilizers, the North China plain is coaxed to support its vast population, a regional population almost equal to that of the entire United States, a population which has become an organic part of the semiarid, gently rolling plains.

An aerial photograph of an Illinois or Iowa farm district is a panorama of rolling fields on which farmsteads are scattered at intervals of a half mile to a mile or two. If one can imagine a village of from twenty to two hundred *families* living on each of those American farms, and if one can imagine those American fields of twenty, forty, eighty, or a hundred forty acres broken into strips and rectangles each about a half acre in size, one can begin to grasp the density and distribution of population on the Shantung plain. The intense pressure of population and the organic union of man with the land are facts basic to an understanding of China.

Rice Region Agriculture

Rice is a hot-climate crop that must be grown in a flooded field, conditions met in South China where the climate is tropical or subtropical and where there is an abundant rainfall. Sixty-six per cent of the area of Agricultural China lies in this rice region, but it contains only 49 per cent of the total cultivated land. From the Yangtze valley southward the terrain is mountainous.

The region as a whole is divided into five subregions, each named by Buck after its dominant crops. The lower Yangtze valley is called the Rice-Wheat area. Here the fields are drained and sowed to wheat in the winter and are flooded for rice in the summer. Farther south and along the coast is the Rice-Tea area. In the hills of this part of the country tea is grown on the high ground above the rice terraces. Still farther south is the Double Cropping Rice area where the growing season extends through the greater part of the year, permitting two crops of rice on each field. To the west and north, inland from the Double Cropping Rice area, is the Southwest Rice area. Farther north, on the upper reaches of the Yangtze and in the foothills of the Great Snowy mountains, is the Szechuan Rice area.

Two localities in Szechuan province serve to illustrate the relation of man to his environment on a plain and in a hill area in the rice region.

Agriculture on the Chengtu Plain

The fundamental difference between rice culture on the plains and in the hills is the method of irrigation, flooding and draining at will being possible on level land, while in the hills water must be stored the year around.

There is some flat or nearly flat land in the rice region, although there are few extensive plains. The largest expanses of flat ricelands are located in the lower Yangtze valley from Ichang to Shanghai, especially in the area of the big lakes; on the lower delta of the Pearl River around Canton; and in the Red Basin of western Szechuan province around Chengtu. The Red Basin may be chosen as illustrative.

The irrigation system of this basin is one of the great engineering feats of the ancient world. The basin itself is a deep north-south valley encircled by the red earth hills of western Szechuan and overshadowed to the west by the peaks of the Great Snowy mountains in Sikang province. During most of the year, the people of these flat lands have no visual proof that these mountains exist, for they are almost continuously hidden in banks of clouds. A few times each year, in the early morning or late evening after rain, the clouds clear, and for a while the serrated snowy peaks are visible. When this does occur, even those who have lived there all their lives are likely to pause and stare in fascination at the mountains in the sky.

The heart of the Red Basin is the rolling Chengtu plain, a triangular area about sixty miles long on each of its three sides. Down the western side of the plain flows the main course of the Min-kiang, the westernmost of four rivers that give the province of Szechuan, "Four Rivers," its name. Through the Min-kiang each year flows a great volume of water from the melting snows of the northwestern Szechuan mountains. The entire valley of 500,000 acres, more than 700 square miles, harnesses these waters by means of a single irrigation system.

This system was first put into operation about 250 B.C., while the Great Wall of China was under construction. China had been unified under the Chin dynasty, and Li Ping was the governor of Szechuan province. Li and his engineer son created an irrigation system by placing a division-head in the Min-kiang at the northwest corner of the valley and by cutting a diversion canal through the nose of the mountain that forms the east bank at that point. In this manner the river could be divided and its water distributed over the plain as needed.

The system they created still functions. Its series of two main feeder channels, nine canals, 526 laterals, and 2,200 sublaterals, add up to a total length of 728 miles. The fish-shaped division-head, which splits the waters and turns them into the two feeder channels, is still much the same as it was twenty-two hundred years ago when it was first invented. The structure itself consists of nothing more permanent than "rock sausages"—long, loosely woven bamboo tubes filled with cobblestones from the bed of the river, the basketry being the casing, and the rocks the stuffing.

The division-head and the walls of the weirs and canals are strengthened against the rush of summer waters by multiple rows of rock sausages piled one upon the other to form stone-faced embankments. Since basketwork is subject to rotting as well as to wear and tear, and since the channels regularly accumulate silt, the waters are diverted each year for repairs and dredging. Regularly, from October 20 until February 15, the western channel is blocked for repairs. Then, on February 15, the waters of the eastern channel are diverted. The coffer dam used for this diversion consists of a series of huge wooden tripods covered with sheets of matting. Other materials are stacked against the matting until the water is excluded and diverted to the other channel. The words "Dig the channel deep; keep the banks low," among others of Li Ping's admonitions, have guided thousands of farmers through twenty-two centuries as they restore the sausages and dig silt from the channels, canals, laterals, and sublaterals in order to maintain the system that brings them life. Each year on April 5, after the repairs are finished and just before the spring freshet, the "waters are opened" with elaborate ceremonies, conducted at temples erected to the memory of the two Lis whose genius created the life-sustaining abundance for a hundred generations of descendants. And each year the waters pour out on the plains to nourish rice crops for one of the most densely populated and fertile valleys in the world.

This public irrigation system in a land of abundant waters is typical of the flat lands of the whole rice region. It permits a system of agriculture that can best be seen during that rushed four to six weeks of spring when winter crops are harvested and the foundation for summer crops is laid.

Rape (used for forage and cooking oil) and wheat are

the major winter crops of the Chengtu plain. They are grown in conjunction with a series of minor crops—winter beans and peas and several hardy vegetables. In the fall, after the rice fields have been permitted to dry out while the rice matures and is harvested, the land is made ready to receive wheat and rape. In low fields requiring drainage, deep ditches are dug inside the paddy dikes. Peas and beans are planted on the dikes and in some of the smaller fields.

Rice is a more productive crop than wheat, contributing almost three times as much food to the acre. As it must be grown for many months in a flooded field, the first act of the spring agricultural drama is the preparation and planting of nursery beds in which rice plants are started many weeks before the wheat and rape are harvested. Nursery beds are located close to the farmhouse and near one of the irrigation canals for convenience in fertilizing and watering. They are dug, fertilized, seeded, and immersed as the young rice plants begin to grow. The water level is slowly raised until the young plants are growing in water several inches deep, following a time schedule calculated so that the wheat ripens and is harvested two or three weeks before the rice plants are ready to be transplanted.

Rows of wheat are never pulled out by the roots in South China. They are cut with a small sickle, and the remaining stubble is usually not removed before plowing for rice. Threshing is done almost entirely with bamboo flails, although one may see wheat being threshed by beating the heads on a plank supported by sawhorses. After threshing, the women go over the straw by hand to ensure the removal of every last grain.

The major spring work of transplanting rice begins with the plowing under of stubble as soon as the wheat and rape are removed from the fields. Underslung water buffalo, geared by nature to perpetual slow motion, pull single-handled, iron-shared, wooden plows through the gummy

fields, turning over huge clods of soil. Then, before flooding, the accumulated liquid fertilizer is applied.

All the human and animal excreta accumulated since
the fertilization of the wheat crop in the fall goes into this
liquid feculence. If the farmer lives near a city he may go
into town each morning and return with two brimming
buckets of night soil on his shoulder pole, or he may contract to buy solid feces or urine from the regular night-soil
dealers, delivered to his farmstead for an agreed price. To
this potpourri in a huge vat, is added a generous supply of
water so that the mixture is quite dilute.

Fertilizer is applied to the field before it is flooded in
order that the farmer may have firm footing to carry his
load of liquid and see to spread it evenly. With a long-
handled, wooden dipper, he skillfully douses each of the
clods with a coating of manure. This process continues
simultaneously in hundreds of fields, and the whole country
is redolent with the stench of well-ripened sewage.

Then the swift irrigation waters are permitted to enter
through a breach in the dike, and as the water spreads over
the level field the clods melt away and the stench is slowly
drowned. The field is harrowed after the desired water level
is reached, by dragging a six-foot, tooth-studded, rectangular device back and forth across the field, working the clods
into a deep sticky mud and smoothing the bottom of the
field. After repeated harrowing, the field is at last ready
for the young rice plants.

By this time the nursery beds have produced rice plants
about a foot high and sturdy enough to be pulled out of the
mud by the roots, withed into bundles, and taken to the
fields where they will mature. The transplanting is all done
by men. Each clump is placed by hand, a backbreaking job
like the one I remember as a boy picking cotton from the
scrawny, low plants that grow in spite of the poor, sandy
soil of East Texas.

AGRICULTURE

Once the rice is transplanted and the last straw from the wheat harvest is stacked away, the greater part of the hard spring work is finished. During the rice-growing season the fields are cultivated several times by the simple expedient of wading through the mud barefooted, churning up the soil about the roots of the plants and tramping down weeds. This form of foot cultivation frequently is done by a group of men who form a line across the field and amuse themselves with small talk as they wade back and forth.

As the rice grows and the level of the water in the field is gradually raised, the whole countryside appears to be one vast lake broken into a series of little ponds by the dikes that surround individual fields and traversed by the stone-paved trails that serve as roads. The watery surface of the lake is soon obscured by the rapidly growing grain, and at the end of the summer the water is permitted to seep away and be used up by the rice plants busy in the fundamental creative process of filling out the starch and proteins in their kernels. By the time the grain has filled out the awn, the soil around the roots of the rice is dry, and the fields are ready for the harvesters. It is at this time, when the waters have disappeared, that the effects of the rice borers, tiny worms that cut the stems of rice stalks near the ground, can be seen. All through the fields, scattered among healthy, well-filled plants are shrunken heads of grain that have turned white. The extent of damage caused by these borers varies from year to year and from field to field, but it is always present and frequently serious.

When the fields are dry and the rice is at last ripe and ready to reap, the harvesters come with sickles. They cut the rows and lay them flat until the whole field is shingled with rows of drying rice. For threshing, a wooden box, four or five feet square, two feet deep, and fitted with handles at the corners, is carried to the field, where two men beat the cut grain against the inside walls. A piece of reed matting hung on poles at the two back corners of the box catches the flying rice grains as they bounce. The box is dragged along the field until the contents become too heavy to be easily moved. Then there is a pause while the unhusked rice is dipped up into sacks and carried to the farmhouse. In the wake of the box the straw is tied into bundles and made into small shocks to be used later for thatch and fuel.

When the rice has been harvested the year's cycle is complete, and the farmer starts all over again, plowing his land for the winter wheat and rape. This system of flat-land rice culture represents the most intensive utilization of land in the world. It was the invention of this system of agriculture by the ancient Chinese that permitted the growth of China's population. And it was the development of this system of agriculture that has created most of the vast human problems now confronting China as a nation.

Agriculture on Terraced Hills

The second fundamental variant of the rice-region system of agriculture is the system that has grown up with the cultivation of rice on terraced hill land.

Not too far from the Chengtu plain is a terraced area, north and west of Chungking, a high, rolling valley of the clouds that I first visited one November when the year's farm activities were at an ebb. A new motor road had just been completed, an alien thing of the twentieth century that winds its way into a world of the past to which the population has slowly adapted itself and which, in turn, has been modified to fit the needs of the population. Except for an occasional bus or truck, the road has done little to change the age-old pattern of transportation in the valley. The farmers own absolutely no wheeled vehicles. Most of the freight and traffic of the area still moves on human backs or dangles from the shoulder poles of men and women walking over paved trails that wind through the paddy fields up and over the hills, connecting field with field, house with house, and valley production with village market.

Leaving Chungking early in the morning, when the road and hills were hidden in mist, we drove up the winding shore of the Chialing River some miles from Chungking, where the road leaves the valley and winds upward through the mountainous hills. An old round stone fort sits high on one of the peaks, a landmark toward which the road twists and turns, then passes and ignores, as it climbs to the heights above. Below us the last gray wisps of fog drifted in the valleys. All the land that could be leveled had been terraced, and the rest, too high and steep to hold water, was laid out in sloping fields. Even in late November the panorama was dominantly green. Along the dikes between the rice paddies and on all the steep dry fields were new crops of peas and beans and wheat, and the hills were crowned by green trees. Where the soil was not covered with water or green plants, it glistened a wet, rich red.

We drove along the mountain crest for some distance, and then descended toward a valley floor as the road plunged downward in looping turns. Stretching right and left were repeated and varying views of the valley below, a veritable fairyland, a land of ten thousand mirrors. The valley floor and the lower slopes of the rolling hills were covered with thousands upon thousands of paddy fields filled with water —little liquid shelves that emerged from the mountain mists to reflect the shapes of trees growing beside the fields or on the hilltops. Clumps of bamboo, rows of cedars, pines, and palms appeared in each clear and placid mirror. Here and there floating water plants had scummed the surface as though some of this array of fabulous mirrors had lost its silver backing. These hill rice fields can grow no winter crops because they are too high to be refilled if the store of water collected from fall rains is drained away. Each field must act as its own reservoir against the spring planting.

At last we left our car and set off by foot along a well-worn path paved with hand-hewn stones worn thin by the tread of uncounted generations. Then indeed we were in the fairyland of ten thousand mirrors which we had looked down on from the mountains. The mirrors themselves presented an endless variety of shapes. Many were half-moons that fitted the curve of the hillside on which they formed terraced steps. Some were almost square and some were rectangular with one or more sides molded into sweeping curves by the contours of the hills. They fitted together into a mosaic of shining water surfaces, cut by terrace walls and dikes, studded with the fresh green jade of newly sprouted peas.

The trail wound back and forth along the terrace dikes between the fields. In the distant background on either side were the high mountains that held the valley suspended in the moist chilly air of November like fabled hanging gardens, and formed a backdrop for innumerable fantastic and charming pictures that changed with each turn of the trail. Mists of cloud and fog mingled together about the peaks, now shrouding them, now framing them against the sky.

In every direction, the foreground was spread with paddy fields reaching up the lower slopes and occupying every foot of usable soil. Here, against the brow of a low hill, stood a farmhouse of bamboo lathe and mud plaster, surrounding three sides of a court paved with large flat stones. The ends of the ridgepoles and the eaves swept upward in graceful curves against a background of the rich red-brown earth of the hill behind. There, a small stone shrine housed two pygmy earth-gods not over a foot high. Another shrine, made of a square stone column twelve or fourteen feet high, housed a god within a niche near its top. Against another hill stood the carved gravestones of many ancient but well-tended ancestral tombs.

On the rising slope above the water-field level, the tender

green of newly sprouted wheat and peas blended with the drenched red soil. In clumps about the farmhouses and along the hilltops bamboos lifted their long stems and slender finger-leaves in delicate traceries. On the crests of the slopes stood symmetrical lines of cedars, black-green against the sky and distant mountains, some festooned with great clumps of sweet-potato vines hung out to dry. A line of palms lifted their fronds in a stolid row, while along the upper terrace a line of gnarled and misshapened deciduous trees twisted bare branches against the sky.

Across a paddy field along another path, three old peasant women stumped along on the tiny, bound, and crippled feet that are vestigial remains of an old era not yet forgotten. Like school children anywhere, several groups of youngsters half walked, half skipped their way to school, dressed in long robes of bright blue denim, book satchels swinging carelessly from their shoulders. All these vivid impressions of robust life in a vigorous country were reflected, upside down, in one of the thousands of liquid mirrors that stretched away from our feet.

His trouser legs rolled to his thighs, a farmer across the way waded through his rice field, fishing. In one hand he carried a long, sharply bent bamboo pole. In the other he carried a basket open at top and bottom. With the bent end of the pole he made sweeping half circles before him. When the fish, driven toward him, darted near enough he dropped the basket over them, reached through the open top, and caught them with his hands. Fish, together with fresh-water shrimp that are individually tiny but in the aggregate no small addition to the Chinese diet, are the winter harvest of the hill rice fields.

In the cold water of many fields water buffalo and their reflections moved slowly, plowing or harrowing back and forth, turning and stirring the deep mud for the spring transplanting of rice, still many months off. As we strolled past one such field, one of our number called, "What plowing is this?"

"The third," came back the answer.

With one hand on the single handle, the farmer rolled his plow over for the turn at the end of the row. He pulled the single rein connected with the pierced nose of the great, wide-horned beast and shouted to turn it slowly about for the next furrow. The clumsy animal's huge splay feet sank deep into the mud, its belly cruising the waters like a scow, and the man waded in cold water halfway up his thighs.

As the light changed from dull grayness to brilliant sunshine and the clouds drifted away from the face of the sun, I could not feast my eyes enough on the loveliness of each picture above for the urge to gaze at its image in the placid waters below. Nowhere on earth is there a more photogenic landscape. Nowhere on earth is one more gripped with the revelation that the very landscape is man-made. Nowhere on earth is man more completely and organically integrated with his natural environment.

This valley has struck a biological balance, and, with minor variations, its methods represent huge stretches of similar hill country throughout the rice region. The soil is completely developed and utilized, even on steep slopes. Wheat and beans grow on sloping, dry land, peas along the dikes in winter, rice in the terraced land, and corn, sweet potatoes, and other vegetables on the sloping land in summer. Storage of water in the rice fields each winter utilizes and conserves rainfall to the maximum. Winter harvesting of fish crops results in year-round production from the rice fields. Conservation of all human and animal manure in liquid form results in maximum utilization of available plant foods. The effect of all this is a very rich agricultural yield, just about the maximum that the prevailing prescientific system of hoe culture can achieve. On the other hand, this region is even more densely populated than dry North China. The average farm size is smaller, and the number of persons per square mile of cultivated land is greater.

How Efficient Is Chinese Agriculture?

Both in the drier northern wheat region and in the wet southern rice area, Chinese agriculture has developed the capacity to support a huge farm population. The effect of this huge population has been to make it inevitable that the farm size be small. The average farm size for the entire country is 4.18 acres, and this acreage is divided up into many fields so that each farm has an average of 5.6 separate fields.

Some comparisons may help to visualize the relation of the farm population to land areas in both China and the United States. The average Chinese farm is 4.18 acres; the average American farm is 157 acres. There are 3.76 acres of crop area on the Chinese farm; 66 acres on the American farm. On the smaller Chinese farm, 6.2 persons live, while only 4.2 live on the larger American farm. There are 15.7 acres of land in crop for every person living on the American farm, but in China there is only 0.6 acre in crop for each person living on the land. The individual American living on the farm actually has twenty-six times as much land in crop as the individual Chinese farmer has. And this is not the whole story.

On his tiny farm, the Chinese farmer must produce three-quarters of the food he consumes and enough of some cash crop to pay his taxes and purchase the things he does not produce. He normally buys about one quarter of his food —his salt, sugar, vegetable cooking oils, and meat. Then, too, he buys most of the cloth from which his clothes are made, although some home spinning and weaving still exists. And, in addition to food and cash crop, the Chinese farm must produce fodder for work animals and many of the materials from which the farmstead is built, repaired and maintained—straw for bricks, thatch for roof, bamboo and kaoliang stalks for fencing material.

Finally, this small farm must produce its own fuel. Search for fuel has led to the stripping of the trees from the hillsides in many parts of China. In most of the country every wisp of wasteland grass is gleaned, and every leaf that falls finds its way to the firebox of the kitchen stove. Still, there is never enough fuel, and much of the crop residue, the stalks and the straw, which should go back to the soil, must be used instead for cooking. "The fuel under the pot is more costly than the food in it" is a common saying in many parts of China.

But if the average farm size is only a little more than four acres, surely there are at least a few large farms? When all the farms studied by Buck were classified as to size, about 7 per cent were called "very large farms." The average size of these very large farms was only thirteen acres! By American standards there are no large farms in China.

One must conclude that there are too many families in China who make their living from farming for the amount of arable land available. This means that competition for use of the land is heavy, land values are excessive, and rentals are frequently much too high. Consequently, both production per farm and production per man are low. It is not easy to state the value of Chinese farm production in terms of currency, particularly since Chinese money has been robbed of all stable meaning from time to time and from place to place. It is more meaningful to calculate production values in "grain equivalent," a method used by professional agricultural economists by which everything produced on the farm is given a value in terms of grain rather than money. This system of translating farm production into grain equivalent on a basis of food or energy value is particularly applicable to China, where for ages stored grain has been the real measure of wealth.

When Buck made his calculations for the Chinese farms he investigated, he found that the per capita production for the entire farm population averaged 980 pounds of grain equivalent. In other words, the entire average productive capacity of the farming people of China amounts to only fifteen or sixteen bushels of wheat per person per year. This total includes that used and that sold to pay rent, taxes, and all other expenses.

Stated in terms of labor, one adult male (man equivalent), working for one year on a Chinese farm, produces an average of 3,080 pounds of grain. In the United States, one man working for one year produces 44,000 pounds of grain equivalent, over fourteen times as much.

From one viewpoint, Chinese agriculture is quite efficient. The very fact that has been able to feed the millions dependent upon it for survival is no small achievement. The fact that it is entirely prescientific in method and was developed by centuries of empirical experience largely by illiterate peasants is another aspect of Chinese agriculture that cannot be brushed aside lightly. Even though much land has been rendered useless by stripping of forests and overworking of soil, the fact that systems have been developed which do preserve much of the soil and do maintain a high level of production generation after generation is a great achievement. The fact that yields per acre from these overworked soils compare favorably with the yields of the relatively virgin soils of America speaks volumes for the prescientific garden-plot type of intensive hoe culture that the Chinese peasant has developed.

These comparative yields are interesting, especially for basic grains. The average production per acre for China as a whole is higher than that in the United States. China produces an average of 67 bushels of rice per acre as compared to our 47 bushels, and 16 bushels of wheat to our 14. We produce 25 bushels of corn to China's 21, 22 bushels of barley to her 19, 108 bushels of Irish potatoes to her 87, and 177 pounds of cotton lint to China's 168 pounds. This is not a bad record for an agricultural system that has been established for thousands of years and has undergone no major changes for centuries, especially when the record is compared with America's extensive scientific agriculture.

On the other hand, yields per acre in Europe, where intensive scientific agriculture is practiced, are considerably higher than those of China. For example, Italy produces 93 bushels of rice per acre compared to China's 67 bushels. England produces 32 bushels of wheat to China's 16 and 244 bushels of Irish potatoes per acre to China's 87.

China's yields per acre are comparatively good and, judging by European experience, probably can be increased greatly by the application of scientific methods. However, production per man is very low, due in no small part to the fact that population pressure has forced division of land into farms that are too small. An indication of this is to be found in Buck's figures. The production per man equivalent for all farms averaging 4.18 acres amounts to 3,080 pounds of grain equivalent. The production per man equivalent on "very large farms" averaging 13 acres is just double this figure, or 6,160 pounds of grain equivalent. We may conclude that even with present methods of cultivation and without any improvements in fertilizers, strains of seed, or use of insecticides, the production per man could be doubled if the farm size were to be increased from four to thirteen acres, and this without any loss in yield per acre. A major reason why the Chinese farmer is poor and his yield per man low is because China is overpopulated.

Chapter III

Diet, Clothing, and Shelter

IT IS PERHAPS NO PARADOX THAT A PEOPLE WHOSE AVerage diet keeps them close to the starvation line should raise feasting to a position of honor among the arts. Both in spite of and because of the fact that her agriculture produces the bare nutritional necessities of life only through the ceaseless manual labor of her millions of farmers, China's feasts embrace a variety and range of dishes beyond the imagination of more plentifully supplied peoples. Fish and fowl, meats and mollusks, sweet things, sour things, dishes spiced and flavored in a hundred ways, dishes soft and smooth, dishes crunchy and crisp, are blended into an elaborate sequence of taste, texture, and color.

At such meals one is scarcely permitted to remember that coarse and common things like vegetables exist. Four-fifths of all the food served is meat or fish, crab or fowl. A visitor who is entertained only at the homes of the wealthy can travel through China without realizing that vegetables, rice, and wheat are consumed in any quantity.

A great body of literature has been written about foods and feasting. Famous cooks of the emperors occupy places of national honor in both the legends and the written history of China. Yet the basic diet of the country as a whole is a far cry from this famous and wonderful feast food. The diet of the common people of China is closely integrated to its type of agriculture and is restricted by the demands of its huge population on its limited land area. In contrast to the feasting of the wealthy, the diet of the rural population is confined almost entirely to plant food. It is nearly 98 per cent rice, wheat, millet, soybeans, broad beans, peas, and other plants. Only 2.3 per cent is of animal origin—meat, eggs, fowl, and fish.

In China 91.8 per cent of the calories contained in the average diet derive from seed products, compared with 38.2 per cent in the average American diet. While only 2.3 per cent of calories in the Chinese diet come from animals, 39.2 per cent are derived from this source in the United States; 5.2 per cent of the calories in the average Chinese diet derive from vegetables, 9 per cent in the United States; $\frac{2}{10}$ of 1 per cent of calories comes from fruits in China, 3.0 in America; $\frac{1}{2}$ of 1 per cent comes from sugar in China, 10.1 per cent in America. In addition to these dietary discrepancies, there is no milk in the Chinese diet.

It is no accident that the Chinese are vegetarians and that pork stands first among the limited amount of animal products consumed. Without her dietary adaptations, even her intensive development of all available land would not serve to keep China's millions alive. The Chinese diet is what it is simply because many more people can be fed on a vegetarian diet than can be fed on the animal-product rich diet of the West.

Plants eaten directly yield far more energy than plants eaten indirectly in the form of animal products. For example, a quart of milk contains only one-seventh as much food energy as the fodder required by the cow to produce it. The chicken feed required to produce a dozen eggs contains nineteen times more food energy than the eggs. The plant energy lost to man is used to keep the cow and the chicken warm and moving. From the energy utilization point of view, therefore, it is more efficient to feed grain straight to man rather than waste the greater part of it keeping animals warm and active.

DIET, CLOTHING AND SHELTER

There is no evidence that animal products ever played an important part in the Chinese diet, although the total animal population of the Chinese countryside is considerable. If all animals are calculated in basic animal units equivalent to one ox, there are 0.34 such units per acre of crop in China as compared with only 0.23 per crop acre in the United States. Although there are actually more animals per crop acre in China, three-fourths of them are used for work, compared with 10 per cent used for work on the American farm. Ninety per cent of American "animal units" are raised for food. Only 25 per cent of Chinese "animal units" are so used, and most of these units are made up of pigs.

Since the life cycle of wheat and rice has been traced from seed to table, it would be unfair to neglect the pig, which, in its lifetime, occupies several important positions, eventually becoming the most prized meat. The place of the pig in her food economy indicates how much like a balanced aquarium China really is. In a balanced aquarium plants utilize carbon dioxide and the energy of the sun to create food and oxygen for animals living in the water. The animals, in turn, break down the food and oxygen and produce carbon dioxide and waste, thus creating a reciprocal life cycle with the plants, each depending on the other. Yet in a balanced aquarium there must be some snails—scavengers to eat up and break down waste and to prevent the collection of debris. The pig is the snail in China's balanced aquarium.

Because the main position of the pig in Chinese food economy is that of a scavenger, its life is totally different from that of the pampered American pig. Nowhere in China is there the huge hog lot typical of a midwestern American farm on which scores or hundreds of hogs are fattened on full ears of corn. Indeed, it is a rare thing in China for a hog to be raised from piglet to pork chop by a single farmer, and it is equally rare for a Chinese farmer to raise more than a single hog at a time. The pig's life is tailored for a single purpose: pork from waste.

The biography of a Shantung pig is typical of all Chinese pigs. Pig breeding is a specialty practiced by farmers who have special experience or special sources of rough or waste food. Not that these men raise hogs. They do not. Their profit is in piglets. The typical pig is born in a litter farrowed by the single brood sow owned by such a specialist. He is a thin-snouted, long-eared, homely, black piglet, and his mother is a sow that resembles the almost extinct Arkansas razorback.

When weaned, this little pig goes to market, but not before the farmer has rendered him sexless to protect his breeding business. Prewar he brought a dollar or two Chinese currency, which was ample return on labor and cost of maintaining the sow. The transaction, of course, separates the pig from his sisters and brothers, and henceforth he faces life alone in his private pigpen-latrine. Because he is able to digest roughage which the human system discharges partially digested, he represents a short cut in the total food cycle.

The second owner of the pig keeps him from six to ten months. Then, when he has become a full-grown but lean shoat weighing from sixty to one hundred twenty pounds, he again appears in the market. The farmer pockets about ten Chinese dollars, having fed his pig on waste plus small quantities of good bran and soybeans, and having accumulated a lot of good pig fertilizer. The outlay in bran and soybeans is balanced by the money received plus the fertilizer produced.

The third owner usually has a special food supply with which he can fatten his charge for the meat market. He may have an especially fine crop of soybeans, or he may have made a batch of kaoliang wine and wishes to use the spent mash to full advantage. After several months of this superior indulgence, the hog is betrayed to the butcher.

The farmer himself does not butcher. He could not afford to feed his family a whole hog, even if he had the means of preserving the meat. The butcher sells his pork by ounce tidbits to those who wish to add a little meat flavor to their cereal foodstuffs. Because even a butcher is faced with the preservation problem, he must sell the entire pig within twenty-four or thirty-six hours of slaughtering.

The first time I visited a Chinese abattoir, I was surprised at the ease with which one of the butchers was carrying what appeared to be a two-hundred-fifty-pound freshly scraped hog. The mystery was solved as I watched the operations. After stunning and sticking a loose-skinned hog in much the same manner as that used in Texas during hog-killing time, he had cut a hole through the hide on the inside of a hind leg and inserted a long iron rod to separate skin from fat and muscle. Then, putting his mouth to the hole in the leg he blew the pig up like a toy balloon. The floppy skin became smooth and taut, and an ordinary-sized pig assumed the proportions of one twice as large. An inflated pig, I learned, is easier to scald and scrape.

In addition to its function as the major meat producer, the Chinese pig has an export value. Pig bristles have been one of China's more valuable products for the past fifty years. Until recently most American toothbrushes were made with Chinese bristles. Even when China was blockaded in World War II, bristles were flown out over the Himalayas.

Although to most Chinese animal foods are prized delicacies, pigs, chickens, and ducks are the principal animals raised for food. No others are self-sufficient enough to fit into farm life without upsetting the close balance of China's food economy. The biochemical fact that more food energy is produced by plants than animals, acre for acre, demands that almost all arable land be used for crops that can be eaten directly by men. Of Chinese farm land 89.6 per cent is in crops. The remainder is divided as follows: 7.3 occupied by farm buildings, roads, ponds, and graves; 1.0 in forest; 0.7 in pasture; 0.7 in fuel plants, chiefly grass; 0.4 in wooded pasture; 0.3 in productive fish ponds.

The diet of the Chinese peasant varies according to regional crops, and the bulk of every meal is that kind of breadstuff which is produced in his region. In the north, the major sources of energy are wheat, millet, and a grain sorghum called kaoliang, or "tall grain." Proteins are derived from soybeans, peanuts, and sweet potatoes, plus the meat and eggs that are the festive fare of the dozen annual holidays. In areas where the wheat is sold, the country population eats a coarse breadstuff of mixed millet, kaoliang, and soybean, which is fairly efficient from a dietary point of view.

For breakfast in North China turnips and carrots pickled in brine are usually served with steaming bowls of millet porridge. The scalding mixture is wolfed with great whistling gulps that cool it to a point of gastronomic safety. Salted peanuts may add delicacy to the breakfast menu.

There are either one or two additional meals during the day, both consisting largely of either rough millet-kaoliang-soybean bread, steamed wheat bread, noodles, or dry, unleavened pancakes a foot across and an inch thick, together with hot vegetables. For variety, baked or boiled sweet potatoes or even a soupçon of meat or egg cooked with the vegetables may be added.

Although wheat is a dietary staple consumed by two-thirds of Chinese families, rice is dominant in the central and southern sections and has a larger total tonnage. In some southern hill sections, where rice cannot be grown, corn and sweet potatoes are staple foods. Everywhere there are quantities of legumes, including soybeans. The protein content of soybeans takes the place of meat in the Chinese diet. So long ago that no one knows exactly when, the Chinese learned to make bean curd from soybeans. Bean curd is the coagulated protein of the beans prepared by grinding, washing out the starch, and suspending the proteins in water to precipitate them in a cheeselike mass. Of the many hundreds of kinds of bean curd, some are allowed to ferment like cheese and acquire the same pungent taste. Mixed with vegetables or made into soup, these curds are the Chinese poor man's meat.

As all solid foods are eaten with chopsticks, they are first cut into bite-sized pieces that may be served at table without further cutting. Vegetables are either pickled in salt or prepared as hot dishes. The most common type of stove is a simple affair with a large cast-iron pot some two feet in diameter and about six inches deep, set over a simple mud or brick firebox that may or may not be equipped with a chimney. The chopped vegetables are fried or boiled in a minute quantity of fat or water, using straw or other quick-burning fuel that gives such a brief hot flame that the pot must be constantly stirred to prevent the contents from scorching.

Recent studies prove that Chinese methods of cooking are unsurpassed for the preservation of vitamins, because vegetables are never permitted to linger over the fire or in water. Perhaps these quick-cooking methods are in part a result of the type and scarcity of fuel, but from the point of view of taste and, accidentally, nutrition, the method is excellent. Vegetables, however, are a minor, flavorful addition to the main bulk of the meal, the local breadstuff.

On a score of annual feast days, such as the New Year and the spring and fall festivals, everybody who possibly can prepares special dishes that add much to the nutrition of the population.

The New Year Festival, governed by the lunar calendar, comes at the beginning of spring and resembles the American Christmas and New Year rolled into one. It is the longest rest period of the year. For the poor there are at least five days of complete leisure, for the great mass of families fifteen days, while the well-to-do celebrate for an entire month. During this time shops are closed and no work of any kind is done. Since it is thought to be bad luck to cook noodles or rice during the first five days of the New Year, even women get a rest from their incessant cooking.

In the north the special dish for New Year is *chiaotze*. It is served on most occasions of celebration but especially at "passing the year." Chiaotze are steamed or boiled meat and vegetable dumplings made by folding any one of a number of mixtures into a small, rolled piece of unshortened pastry-like dough. There are a dozen interesting and artistic ways of fluting the edge of the dough where it is pressed together around the filler. On the last days of the old year every family folds dumplings by the hundreds and sets them aside to be cooked quickly and easily at any time during the five to fifteen days of the celebration. To the North China child New Year and chiaotze go together like Thanksgiving and turkey in America or Christmas and plum pudding in England.

Chiaotze is not the only special dish for the New Year. There are *hung shao jou*, beef cut into chunks and roasted in a rich soysauce that turns it a deep red; *jou wan tze* or meat balls; and *tsa tsai*, a mixture of a dozen or more kinds of vegetables and meats. Then there is *huo kuo*, cooked on the table in a little brass stove that gives the dish its name, "fire-pot." In the latter, a charcoal fire burns in a chimney that runs up through the bottom of a pot in which vermicelli, sliced vegetables, and meats are cooked in chicken broth. The stove sits in the center of the table and raw ingredients are added as the cooked tidbits are consumed.

Then there are the symbolic *nien kao*, or year cakes, made of glutenous rice molded around dried fruits. Like so many of the symbols of Chinese culture, this one is dependent on the fact that two characters with the same sound have quite different meanings. The word pronounced *kao* means both "cake" and "high" or "exalted." The same sounds stand for "year cakes" or "exalted year." So year cakes are eaten both because they are good and because they are thought to bring good luck.

On the fifteenth of the first month, when the New Year celebration ends for most families, comes the *yuan hsiao* festival. On this day dragon lantern dancers and stilt walkers are in the streets, and sweet glutenous rice yuan hsiao dumplings are eaten.

On the second day of the second month the birth of the rain dragon is celebrated by *lung tai tou* or the "dragon lifts his head" festival. It is women's holiday from sewing because it is believed that if they sew they will go blind. The special dish is *ho yeh ping*, or thin pancakes in which numerous meats and vegetables are wrapped.

The next festival is the feast of the tombs, or *Ch'ing Ming*, which, like Easter, varies as to date. On this day the tombs of the ancestors are visited, and special foods like those eaten at New Year are prepared both for departed spirits and for living members of the family.

Then, on the fifth day of the fifth month, a festival is celebrated in memory of Ch'ü Yuan, a famous statesman who drowned himself in despair over the corruption of his time. On this day the ghost of the great Ch'ü is fed by dropping glutenous rice cooked in lengths of hollow bamboo in the nearest stream. From this practice has evolved the delectable *tsung tze*, a three-cornered, glutenous rice dumpling steamed in wrappings of broad reed leaves and eaten in honor of the departed Ch'ü.

Ch'iao Nü Chieh is celebrated on the seventh day of the seventh month. This is the day on which marriageable girls display their skills in sewing and housekeeping. The special meat dishes of the New Year appear again, and, in order to be seen in their new dresses, girls go to a play at the village open-air show grounds.

The fifteenth of the seventh month is the Festival of the Lost Spirits, a day on which lighted candles are set adrift on the waters of rivers and lakes and Buddhist scriptures are read for the ghosts of those who have no descendants left to mourn them. Recently it has become a memorial day for the soldier dead, but, like the other festivals, it is an occasion for eating better food than the daily fare.

The fifteenth of the eighth lunar month is the midautumn festival called *T'uan Yuan Chieh*, or festival of family fellowship. On this day all fathers and sons who are working away from home return to eat the *t'uan yuan ping*, a special fellowship rice cake eaten by members of the immediate family. Parents and sons, unmarried daughters, and daughters-in-law, together with the grandparents eat the cake. Married daughters are excluded, since they belong to the families of their husbands. If, by any mischance, a family member must be away at this time his portion of cake is sent to him.

On the ninth day of the ninth moon everyone goes for a picnic on the highest place they can find. *Teng Kao* this is called and it means "ascend high." Among foods consumed are special cakes bearing ideographs meaning "step by step ascend higher."

So through the year the Chinese break the monotony of their limited daily diet by festive days on which better food is part of an intimate family and community life.

In terms of over-all nutrition, the Chinese diet is better than a description of its average simplicity and lack of animal products might indicate. Generally speaking, enough calories are consumed to provide the energy necessary for heavy muscular labor. Proteins are more limited. Wheat-eating northerners get more proteins than rice-eating southerners, accounting, at least partially, for the difference in stature. Since wheat contains more proteins than rice, the people of North China frequently achieve a height of six feet or more, while many southerners are less than five feet tall and weigh less than one hundred pounds.

The most consistent shortage in the Chinese diet is calcium. Since milk is rarely, if ever, consumed after the age of two or three years, when the Chinese child is finally weaned, the chief sources of this important bone-and-tooth-forming element are the leafy vegetables, which average only 5.2 per cent of the entire diet. As a result, rickets is a common disease, especially in Central and South China where the diet contains less calcium and the persistent cloudy weather permits less exposure to vitamin D-forming sunlight. Another disease, osteomalacia, peculiar to Shansi province in the north, is caused not only by the normal calcium deficiency but also by a strange and vicious postnatal custom.

Osteomalacia is characterized by the softening of a mother's bones to such a degree that the pelvis becomes too weak to hold the weight of the body and tends to cave in, a result of giving a mother nothing but thin rice gruel almost completely devoid of calcium during the first month after childbirth. Since the calcium intake from the normal diet is low, a Shansi mother is partially robbed of her own calcium by the growth of the unborn child. Then, during the month after the birth, her body continues to plunder calcium from her bones in order to maintain the calcium content of her milk. By the time the second or third child is born the mother's bones have become so damaged and deformed that parturition is impossible, resulting in death or invalidism.

In other parts of China, however, it is frequently the custom to give pregnant mothers specially prepared pig ribs cooked in a sweet and sour sauce of sugar and vinegar. This method of cooking ribs has proved to be an efficient way of supplying calcium. The acid in the vinegar makes the calcium in the bones digestible. Custom, therefore, conspires in one district to cripple and kill women by robbing their bodies of calcium, while in others it prescribes an excellent source of supplemental calcium.

Iron is another important element in which the average Chinese diet is deficient. Again the intake is on the borderline between enough and too little. An increase in the quantity of leafy vegetables consumed would do much toward relieving both calcium and iron shortages.

Protective foods supplying basic vitamins are so limited as to make all too prevalent such deficiency diseases as scurvy and beriberi. Pellagra is common in the south, and keratomalacia, a deficiency disease of the eyes due to shortage of vitamin A, is widespread, particularly among shop apprentices in Shantung province.

For the past thousand years, one of the greatest killers in all China has been famine. Dr. George Cressey, in his *Asia's Lands and Peoples*, estimates that a hundred million people have died of famine in China during the past century. Both flood famines and drought famines, with locusts added for good measure, carry death across China's hills and plains, with neither a Tennessee Valley Authority to control flood and prevent drought nor an adequate transportation system to alleviate suffering.

Over and over again, the Yellow River, "China's Sorrow," has burst its dikes and flooded out thousands or millions of people. Times without number, the Yangtze and a dozen smaller streams have drowned whole districts and destroyed grain reserves, leaving survivors to starve. In most of the drier northern and northwestern provinces droughts occur every few years. Sometimes famine comes to great areas because population pressure has pushed humanity too far into marginal lands where soil and rainfall fail.

In 1939 I saw one of the worst floods to strike North China in this century. North China at the time was dominated by the Japanese, but Americans were still comparatively unrestricted. War clouds were rising in Europe and there was unrest and uncertainty throughout the world. Early in July, I accompanied my wife and children to the seaside resort at Peitaiho, northeast of Tientsin, and returned to Cheeloo University at Tsinan, Shantung, where I was engaged in agricultural sanitation research which could be completed only during the summer months.

Toward the middle of August, while Shantung and most of Hopei provinces were parching in drought, heavy rains fell on the western mountains, and swept through the nine rivers that converge on Tientsin, flooding the countryside and washing away a portion of the only railway between me and Peitaiho. Letters stopped coming as rail service was suspended. The radio brought word of the nonaggression pact between Hitler and Stalin. Since no one knew how the Japanese might react toward Caucasians when their European partners went to war, it seemed imperative for me to go to Peitaiho.

It was understood that the Japanese, trying to maintain emergency operations on the railway, had established a boat service connecting the two points between which the railway had been washed out. But I found it impossible to obtain a ticket. From the railway station I pedaled my bicycle to the Japanese Consulate to look up a vice-consul I had known in more peaceful days.

"Mr. Yawata," I said, when the vice-consul came to the reception room, "I believe this pact between Germany and Russia means war in Europe. My wife and children are in Peitaiho, and because of the flood only a few special tickets to Tientsin are being sold. I don't know what may happen here if war breaks in Europe, but I want to be with my family. I tried to buy a ticket just now but, because everything was being handled in Japanese, I failed. Can you help me get a ticket?"

"I shall be glad to give you a letter to the commander at

the station, but"—and a wry smile twisted Mr. Yawata's lips—"I don't think the Japanese Army would be much impressed with your anxiety about their inability to keep things peaceful in Peitaiho. Don't you think I should write in my letter that one of your children is seriously ill?"

All night long I sat hunched up on the hard bench of a third-class coach on the "boat" train in which we crept through darkness without lights, proceeding cautiously over temporary bridges in guerrilla country. Dawn disclosed the two great famine breeders. To the right were the prematurely ripening summer crops scorched by drought. To the left stretched a hundred miles of water. The flood casually lapped against the raised railway bed that separated inundated crop land from sun-baked fields.

Soon after daybreak I found myself the only Westerner embarking on a fleet of sampans which were to ferry us from the train to diesel barges tied up at a nearby walled village.

As soon as the sampan left the station, some of the Japanese unpacked lunches and began to eat, arousing consternation among the Chinese boatmen, who pointed out in no mild manner that we were passing over their ancestral graves now buried under the flood. After agitated pleading, the food was put away and the villagers kowtowed at the prow of each boat to propitiate the offended spirits of their dead ancestors, all the while keeping the boats going forward by taking turns at poling.

As we climbed from the sampans to the west wall of the village, it became apparent how North China towns have survived such periodic floods. Huge earth-filled stone-faced walls, twenty feet thick and thirty feet high, surrounded the village. When the floodwaters rose, the gates had been closed and sealed with sandbags. Outside, the water was ten to fifteen feet above street level; inside, the village was dry.

We landed on the wall as though it were a dock and walked along it to the diesel barges. They were Japanese, of a type used ordinarily for transport in the misty and calm Inland Sea of Japan, but now on military duty as landing craft. They were covered with clean matting, which necessitated the removal of our shoes, and shaded with tarpaulins from the hot sun. There were about a hundred people in each of the six or seven barges.

Backing away from the village wall, we chugged along the railway where the bed had been washed away and the rails left suspended, half submerged in the swirling waters. Between us and the horizon was an expanse of water dotted with villages behind and beneath barricaded walls. For nine hours we wound back and forth among village walls, clumps of trees, and ceremonial arches marking graves beneath. Villagers in boats were trying to harvest the unripe heads of the ten-foot kaoliang still projecting from the water. Everywhere there were piles of uprooted kaoliang clinging to obstructions. Rotting, its sourish smell, very like that of ensilage, assailed my nostrils. There was no sign of the huge quantities of millet and soybeans that were decaying beneath the surface. The food supply of the countryside was destroyed.

All morning and until well past noon the barges chugged past the villages, the trees, and the rotting kaoliang. At last we pulled up to the platform of the West Station in Tientsin, as though it were a dock instead of the first of three railway stations in a city of over a million people. Along the platform were seagoing tugs which had come up from the river and were now moored miles away from any normal watercourse.

Before long we were again aboard a train, proceeding slowly along a high embankment from which we could look down on the flooded city. Here and there people were roosting on housetops, but in many places the houses had collapsed, their mud walls dissolved in the eddying waters. Cautiously our train crept across the big steel bridge that spans one river, now a great muddy torrent carrying bloated bodies of drowned men and animals.

At the Central Station we stopped while every available space was loaded with swarming citizens of Tientsin, each carrying what he could to the flood-free areas to the west, toward Peiping, or to the north, toward Mukden and Pei-taiho. At the East Station more people jammed in, standing, reeking, cluttered with possessions. After a four-hour wait, the train crept forward through the flood with scores of huge wooden coffins bobbing along on either side, caught in blind alleys, bumping and jostling together as though delighted to be washed free of the suburban grave mounds that had held them.

On each side of the track huge supply dumps of Japanese Army equipment lay ruined by water, and great piles of baled cotton awaiting shipment to Japan were now swelling and rotting in foul water. Now the water on the right side of the roadbed was actually higher than the tracks, with sand-bags delaying the inevitable washout. Rushing waters had already started to undermine the concrete piers supporting a bridge across an underpass, sweeping through it in a four-foot waterfall. The train stopped, then jolted forward to falter across the bridge. Twenty minutes after our crossing, the bridge collapsed. There were no more trains for three weeks, but I was with my family when the European phase of World War II began.

In spite of the vast area drowned in the 1939 flood, in spite of the huge quantities of food destroyed while still unripe in the fields, in spite of the damage and waste in Tientsin and other cities when barrels of dried eggs swelled and burst like huge stench bombs and grain in elevators turned to slimy, putrid jelly, there was still no widespread famine as there would have been a hundred years ago. This particular area was bisected by railways and was near coastal docks, permitting importation of food as soon as floodwaters subsided. With adequate transportation and sufficient organization, China need not have another famine, but transportation and organization are still very much in the future. Until these two services exist, there will continue to be famines when floods, droughts, or grasshoppers destroy the precarious balance of China's food economy.

The life and economy of the vast rural population of China is too much like that of a balanced aquarium. The food habits and diet of the population have become closely adapted to the crops the land can best produce, and land utilization has been empirically adapted to produce those things providing the most food for the largest number of people. It is thus that the huge population can be fed on the relatively limited land area available in China, provided the delicate cycle is not interrupted by destruction.

China's Clothing

Food alone accounts for about 60 per cent of the value of all goods consumed by the rural population of China. Rent, clothing, fuel, and light represent an additional 24 per cent. These five items compose 84 per cent of rural Chinese living standards, a fact which means that the rural population lives just at the subsistence level.

The fundamental garments worn throughout China, with slight variations in cut and weight, are trousers, jumper-like short jackets, outer gowns of ankle length (buttoned down the right side and split to the knee to provide freedom for walking), mandarin hats (hard black skullcaps topped off with a button), straw hats for work, cloth or straw shoes, and cloth or knitted stockings. In recent years knitted stockings have appeared on the market but frugal Chinese do not wear them until cloth soles and heel guards have been sewed on. Underclothes are worn by comparatively few, although they are becoming more popular each year. For ceremonial occasions, the Chinese man dons a black vest over his long gown. When he is dressed in his best bib and tucker, the average Chinese peasant is a man of dignified and harmonious appearance.

Chinese clothing is primarily utilitarian, both style and tailoring being determined by limitations on the quantity and the types of material available. For example, most Chinese garments are equipped with "buttons" made from rolled and knotted pieces of the garment cloth. "Buttonholes" consist of loops of the same cloth. While it is true that Western-style buttons are used on the Western-type clothing sometimes worn in cities, they are not typical of Chinese clothing.

Trousers worn by both men and women are made without buttons of any sort. Cut full at the waist, they are secured by the simple expedient of taking a reef in front and tying a cloth string belt. Leather belts are still a curiosity.

Leather shoes are increasing in number, but most Chinese feet are shod in cloth or straw. Throughout the north, cloth shoes are hand-made and homemade, with cloth uppers. Soles are built up of many layers of old cloth stuck together with flour paste and heavily stitched with rosined string, which takes the abrasion. Such cloth shoes may last for three or four months of normal wear, but they are obviously averse to rainy weather. North China countryfolk solve the problem by staying indoors when it rains, which is seldom. In the rainy south such shoes are obviously impractical. Southerners, therefore, weave straw into soles, heels, and straps that may be worn without stockings. While southerners frequently go barefooted, northerners consider naked feet shockingly immodest.

Statistics regarding clothing gathered by Buck referred only to the number of garments owned by the heads of the households on a group of better-than-average-sized farms, but even these figures represent a clothing situation that is meager enough. Nine-tenths of all work garments owned by the heads of farms surveyed were made of cotton. The remaining tenth included some silk, some wool, and, in the northwest, some fur. The family head by direct count possessed an average of 8.8 work garments, with an average of 4.3 coats and jackets, 3.3 pairs of trousers, 1.0 long gowns, 1.1 pairs of socks, 0.9 hats, and 1.4 pairs of shoes. People in the hot humid south were found to have more garments than those of the north, a reflection of both the higher standard of living in the south and the greater need for changes of clothing.

Dress garments owned by family heads were predominantly cotton, although there was a larger proportion of silk than in other garments. Since these limited numbers of work and dress garments must include thin ones for summer, warm ones for winter, and special ones for occasions, it is obvious that even the heads of not-so-poor families have little more than one change of clothing.

The story is told of a Chinese woman who had two sons, the older tall and rawboned, the younger short and slender. The mother was partial to the younger son because his clothes took less cloth, and on many occasions she reminded the elder that he was expensive to clothe. One day, as the two brothers were working in the fields beyond a creek some distance from their home, a torrential rain came up and both started for home on the run. By the time they reached the creek it had become too deep to wade. The taller brother plunged in, his chin barely above water, while the younger brother was left stranded. When the elder brother reached home, the anxious mother rushed out and demanded, "Where is your younger brother?"

"Oh, he's over on the other side of the creek saving cloth." The great mass of Chinese people have always been poorly clad, and now, after years of war and economic inflation, they are even more so.

China's Housing

Northern buildings are closely integrated around solal courtyards (like the Shantung homes already described), and villages are intimately grouped, while the warmer rice regions permit a more open type of farmstead and village. It is natural that methods of construction vary to meet different climatic needs and types of building material available. Because wood is expensive and scarce, construction is usually limited to earth products—tamped earth, stone, brick, and tile—frequently superimposed on a wooden framework. Nearly half the walls of farm buildings are constructed of earth itself, either as raw tamped material or as adobe. About one-fifth of farm building walls are made of burnt brick, and another third include variations such as the rice region's woven bamboo lathe plastered with mud. Most floors, about 87 per cent, are made of earth, with some 8 per cent of brick, and the rest of other materials including a few of wood. Buck found that 28 per cent of farmhouses had thatched roofs, 48 per cent were roofed with tile, and 24 per cent used other materials such as the flat mud roofs and cave houses with loess roofs common to the northwest. Thatch is more common to the wheat region, while tile is preferred in the rice country partly because it offers protection from heavy rains.

By modern standards, Chinese houses are poor affairs with few windows—one to every two rooms—and these sealed. Most window openings are covered with translucent oiled paper, and, if they open outside the courtyard, heavily barred to discourage thieves. The only apertures permitting ventilation are the doors. To multiply discomforts, the stable and privy (completely equipped with pig) are frequently located next to the kitchen. The floors are usually damp.

DIET, CLOTHING AND SHELTER

The average farmstead consists of 5.0 *chien* (areas of floor space under a more or less standard section of roof, which may be divided up into varying numbers of rooms) for residence only, 1.6 chien for mixed residence and farm use, and 3.1 chien for farm purposes only. Residence and farm use includes that space used for grain and implement storage and also for sleeping quarters. Of the rooms used exclusively for residence, three-fifths are bedrooms, one-sixth kitchens, and one-tenth guest rooms, while on 16 per cent of the small farms bedrooms and kitchens are combined. Separate dining rooms exist on about 11 per cent of the large farms, but on only 3 per cent of small farms. Separate kitchens occur on two-thirds of the large and on one-half of the small farms.

Floor space available for each person averages 174 square feet (less in the colder wheat region, more in the warmer rice region), of which 91 square feet are used for residence only, 36 square feet for combined residence and farm use, and 47 square feet are limited to farm use. The per capita residence share is about the size of an American prison cell.

These data on rural buildings add up to a low average value, approximately US$137 per farm (less in the north, more in the south, again reflecting a slightly higher living standard in the south). Another division by averages, stated in U.S. dollar exchange values, shows the buildings on small farms to be worth $54, on medium-sized farms $124, and on large farms $259.

Furnishings in rural homes are equally poor. On a per capita basis there are 0.6 beds, 0.6 tables, and 1.2 benches, of which only 36 per cent are painted or varnished, and a total of 22 per cent left totally unplaned and rough.

The food, clothing, and shelter of this vast rural population add up to one fact—*poverty*.

Chapter IV

Commerce, Industry, and Transportation

EVEN THOUGH 80 PER CENT OF HER PEOPLE LIVE IN rural communities, no picture of China as she is can be complete without a description of her urban population. Including those living in market towns, China's city dwellers form a vast group of over 100 million people— equal to more than two-thirds the entire population of the United States.

Most Westerners know the names of China's big coastal cities—Shanghai, Tientsin, Canton, Peiping, Nanking, and Hongkong. (Although Hongkong is a British colony, it plays an important part in China's economy.) Of the inland cities, Hankow, Chungking, Chengtu, Kunming, Kweiyang, and Kweilin are well known in the West, largely because of World War II activities. All these cities have populations ranging from 600,000 to several millions. Shanghai is a modern city with a skyscraper sky line and four million inhabitants. In addition to these twelve well-known cities, China has at least fifty more with populations ranging from 100,000 to 400,000, and at least one hundred cities of from 25,000 to 100,000. In addition, there are several hundred market towns, essentially rural in economy, with populations of from 10,000 to 25,000.

Most of China's towns and cities were, until a few decades ago, completely contained within their ancient walls, and many of them still can be locked up tight at twilight. Cities and walls have played such important roles in the development of their respective districts that it may be of interest to recount some of the historical details and legends connected with the city of Soochow in Kiangsu province as they are set down in the *Chronicles of Wu Hsien* (the Soochow district) and translated by David Gray Poston.

In 514 B.C., when China was still an aggregation of many small states, Ho Lu styled himself the King of Wu and assumed regency over the kingdom that is now the city of Soochow. Desirous of organizing his new territory, he called in his prime minister, Wu Tzu Hsü, and said, "Our country is in a remote corner; furthermore, this southeastern land is damp and trying. There is the ever-threatening danger of the [Yangtze] river and the sea and within the kingdom we have no means of defense. The people have nothing to depend on—there are no granaries, and the fields are not under cultivation. What suggestions have you to offer?"

Wu Tzu Hsü replied, "The country must expand from within in order that you may establish yourself firmly, rule your subjects wisely, build up a strong kingdom, and become a powerful ruler. Hence, the first step is to build a city wall with eight land gates, following as a pattern the 'Eight Heavenly Winds.' When that is done, the city must be placed under military officials. Finally, granaries must be built and an arsenal constructed."

Ho Lu nodded in approval. "Good," said he. "But building a city wall and constructing granaries require certain 'geographical adaptations.' May there not be some heavenly 'force' which will enable us to triumph over our neighboring countries?"

"Certainly."

Whereupon Ho Lu concluded, "I hereby place these matters in your hands."

Wu Tzu Hsü consulted certain sorcerers, who began to

"study the soil and taste the water," to "imitate the heavens," and to "model the earth," these being the correct methods of sorcery and geomancy.

Shortly thereafter, Wu Tzu Hsü built a city wall, following the advice of his sorcerers, with eight land gates placed along the four sides of the wall, the method of placement being the pattern of the "Eight Heavenly Winds." Each of the winds corresponded to a direction of the compass; thus, the cardinal points and the four bisecting points within the angles of these cardinal points formed the eight directions. Each wind had a name, the meaning of which designated the special characteristics of that wind.

According to one scholar of the Han dynasty, Hsü Shen, the names and characteristics of the Eight Winds are as follow:

Northeast—YUNG	—mild
East—MING SHU	—bright
Southeast—CH'ING MING	—pure and bright
South—CHING	—scenic
Southwest—LIANG	—cool
West—CHANG HO	—prosperous
Northwest—PU CHOU	—unsymmetric
North—KWANG MO	—wide and endless

In accordance with this pattern, Wu Tzu Hsü constructed eight gates, two west gates, two south gates, two east gates, and two north gates, and according to Poston's translation of the *Chronicles of Wu Hsien* these eight gates and their subsequent histories were as follow:

One of the west gates was the Chang Men, so named because it permitted the Chang Ho wind to enter. Thus, the autumn wind, has its origin in the west and represents the "masculine force" that causes all things on earth to materialize. King Ho Lu, wishing to destroy the Ch'u Kingdom to the northwest of Wu, thought that this gate would enable prospering winds to enter, thus ensuring the success of his endeavors. Through the centuries the Chang Men has been repaired many times and still stands as one of Soochow's most important gates.

To the south of the Chang Men was built the second of the western gates, the Hsü Men, named after Wu Tzu Hsü who lived near by. It is recorded that after the death of Prime Minister Wu his eyes were hung on this gate.

There is considerable confusion regarding the original name of Pang Men, the southwestern gate, because of two Chinese characters with practically the same sound and meaning—*pang* (pronounced bang) and *p'an* (pronounced pan), both meaning "coiling" or "winding." It is said that this gate was first known as the "Coiling Dragon Gate," there having been affixed a wooden plaque with a coiling dragon on it as a charm against the Yüeh Kingdom. Another explanation of the gate name is that, being half on land and partly in water, it had a winding entrance. In any case, both the gate and its towers were destroyed by a typhoon in the autumn of 1227 and were rebuilt to even greater grandeur two years later.

The southeastern gate was She Men, or Snake Gate, built as an exit for King Ho Lu's soldiers on their way to inaugurate a campaign to annex the Yüeh Kingdom, southeast of Wu. For unknown reasons the Snake Gate disappeared, perhaps in the thirteenth century, and in November, 1938, the Japanese planned, but never built, a new Snake Gate at some point along the southern wall toward the east.

One of the eastern gates was the Lou Men, originally known as the Liao Men, because it opened toward a village named Kuliao where flowed the Lou Creek.

The Chiang Men, or Artisans' Gate, was constructed in the eastern section of the wall where King Ho Lu asked Kan Chiang the artisan to set up a forge for making swords inasmuch as the mud in that vicinity was especially suitable for forging iron. While making the king's swords, Kan Chiang's wife, Mo Yeh, cut off her hair and fingernails and threw them into the fire, whereupon the ore was melted. Two swords were then forged, and the name Kan Chiang was given to the male sword and the name Mo Yeh to the female sword. In Sui times (A.D. 581–618) this gate was closed, not to be reopened until 1936 when the Soochow city government cut the Hsiang Men through a section of the eastern wall south of Lou Men.

In 504 B.C. King Ho Lu conquered the Ch'i Kingdom to the north of Wu, and the Prince of Ch'i sent his daughter to Ho Lu as a hostage, signifying that the prince had pledged himself to peace. Ho Lu desired that the girl should become the wife of his eldest son, Wu Po, but the young princess wept day and night for her native land and finally became quite ill. Ho Lu then built a north gate, naming it the Wang Ch'i Men, or the Gate Overlooking Ch'i, where the princess might have a commanding view in the direction of her far-off home. But a mere view did not satisfy her and she dwindled to death with yearning.

When Ho Lu was about to conquer Ch'i, he led a large army through one of the northern gates, giving it the name of P'ing Men, or the Gate of Pacification.

These were the eight original gates in the walls of the city of Soochow, the city famous for beautiful gardens and beautiful women. This city wall, like hundreds of others, is rich with folklore and through the centuries has played an important part in the history of its region.

The Chinese city walls that had dominated the countryside for so many centuries decreased in usefulness in the twentieth century as larger cities burst from their confinement under pressure of growing populations, modern transportation systems, and a degree of industrialization. During the early days of the Sino-Japanese War, scores of city walls were demolished by the Chinese themselves. Walls were no obstacle for Japanese heavy artillery, but once Japanese garrisons were inside, light-armed Chinese troops and guerrillas were unable to recapture the city.

City walls in unoccupied China were either partially or totally torn down for another reason. During the course of the war every town in China with a population of 25,000 or more was bombed. With the exception of Chungking, where the soft bedrock permitted the digging of effective air-raid shelters, the bombed cities were forced to depend on dispersion for the protection of their people. For instance, in Chengtu, a walled city with seven narrow gates, each air-raid alarm provoked pandemonium as 600,000 people fought to escape. Many were trampled to death, and many others were trapped inside and killed by bombs. Because water lies three feet beneath the surface at Chengtu, no shelters could be dug. The alternative was to tear down the city gates and construct wide new streets through gaps in the walls. War and enemy bombs have destroyed, directly and indirectly, many ancient bulwarks, yet all the changes of war and modern industrialization have had but little effect on the majority of Chinese cities. Many remain the medieval boroughs of centuries past.

The population density of Chinese cities is almost unbelievably high, especially since almost all houses are limited to one story. In Chengtu, some 600,000 people live in an area of less than twelve square miles inside the city wall, creating a density of 50,000 persons per square mile, as compared with about 22,500 per square mile in New York City. There are no such things as housing standards, and the accommodations in the worst slums of any American city are palatial compared to those occupied by the average Chinese city dweller. Conditions have been made even worse by the destruction and subsequent crowding that have resulted from years of war.

COMMERCE, INDUSTRY, AND TRANSPORTATION

Except for relatively small portions of some coastal cities, all Chinese towns and cities consist, like Chengtu, of one-story buildings. Residences are built around courtyards much like those of country houses, but are arranged on narrow, dirty alleys flanked by high walls. These alleys become muck-filled rivulets when it rains. In any weather one can wander for hours through the ugly lanes in large Chinese cities and never see the slightest hint of beauty. Yet over the wall there may be a lovely old garden or the spacious rooms of the wealthy.

The great majority of city people, like those in the country, are poor. A family of four to six lives huddled up in one or two rooms, with from four to ten families sharing a single courtyard.

Sanitary conditions are primitive. For the women of the typical poor families living in a single courtyard in North China cities, there is a single toilet of the most archaic sort. The men use nearby public latrines, most of which are equally primitive and unsanitary. It is common for small children to defecate at their convenience within the courtyard or in the alleys. There is no such thing as a family bathroom for personal cleanliness, and 60 or 70 per cent of the city dwellers can afford no more than two or three baths a year at one of the cheaper public bathhouses.

Very few Chinese cities have modern water supplies and even in Peiping, where running water does exist as a public service, less than 10 per cent of the population obtains water from a tap. Those who can afford this service use a daily average of only eleven gallons per person for all purposes. The great majority still obtain water as they have for centuries, by the shoulder-pole load, two buckets of about five gallons each, purchased from professional water carriers. From wells or city taps the carriers fill two large, wooden tanks mounted on a wheelbarrow. At the customer's door, water is drawn into the shoulder buckets and delivered to the household water jar. The daily consumption per person averages only one gallon—for washing, drinking, bathing, cooking, and laundry. The normal daily consumption of water in an American city varies from thirty to fifty gallons per person.

This is not to say that there are no clean and spacious homes in Chinese cities. The lovely homes of the old, wealthy families are both beautiful and comfortable, but with a comfort that is based on the service of many hands rather than the comfort of modern conveniences. Many coastal families live in gardened mansions embodying the best in Chinese and Western architectures and equipment and decorated with the lush blue and gold rugs of old China and many of the ancient gems of Chinese arts and crafts. Particularly in the coastal cities there are large modern apartments the equal of any in Europe or the Americas. Yet the total number of people who live in these desirable quarters is small indeed compared to the great masses of humanity living under conditions far below minimum health requirements. Well over 90 per cent of the people of China need to be rehoused.

Commerce and Industry

In China as she is today, there are about 1,500 country people living on every square mile of cultivated land. When more than 100 million city dwellers are added to this rural population, the number of persons who must obtain food from the land becomes 1,875 per square mile of crop area.

What do all the people who live in towns and cities do? How do nonfarmers make their living and gain their daily bread?

A majority depends on trade for livelihood. There are merchants of many kinds, and 95 per cent or more of the trade of China is still maintained by the old-type specialty shop handling one commodity exclusively, although modern department stores already are flourishing in the large coastal cities. Shops are usually grouped together on one street and are always organized into trade guilds. Many streets are called Silk Street, Fur Street, Cloth Street (cotton cloth), Tea Street, Pottery Street, Lime Street, Metal Street, Rice Street, Horseshoe Street, Medicine Street, or even Little Embroidery Street, representing both the business and the guild.

Finance in China is of major importance as a source of livelihood, from the large modern banks, which before the war were gradually stabilizing the economic life of China, to the pawnshops, where loans are made with great frequency against every conceivable kind of property. Between these categories are literally thousands of small private banks which range from reliable institutions of considerable size to alley-sized money shops dealing in petty exchange transactions and usury, with fantastic interest rates as high as 20 per cent a month for "personal" loans.

In every city there is a large group that makes its living from government—city, county, provincial, and national. Socially, these are the elite. Since, by centuries of tradition, officials are also scholars, they are given a doubly reinforced prestige. Also by centuries of accepted usage, the official class enjoys wide financial perquisites so that wealth is usually added to the prestige of position and scholarship. To become a scholar-official is still, as it has been for three thousand five hundred years past, the very acme of success, and such successful people usually live in cities.

Another class of city dwellers is composed of landlords, who may also be merchants or officials, or both. They own varying amounts of farm and city property, and not a few of them can depend on property income for their support.

With the spread of modern education, larger numbers are filling positions as teachers, doctors, and lawyers, either as part of the educational system itself or as products of it. These professional groups, however, are still in the minority. The old-fashioned herb doctor and the purveyor of drugs and remedies are still more common, even in the advanced coastal cities, than are the modern doctor and the pharmacist.

Since in every large city of China there are now modern factories of one kind or another—cotton mills and machine shops, flour mills and auto repair shops—another large group of city dwellers is engaged in manufacturing. For every person employed in modern industrial establishments there are still hundreds engaged in the old handicraft production. Well over 90 per cent of China's industrial production is still the result of premachine-age handicrafts.

The old crafts usually are carried on in small family shops organized into guilds like the merchant shops. Blacksmiths and coopers make the wooden tubs and water tanks popular throughout China. Cabinetmakers turn out all kinds of furniture, from the most exquisitely carved and jade-inlaid treasures to the crudest and simplest stools and tables used by the poor to furnish their crowded, dirty homes. Silversmiths, tailors, jade carvers, jewelers, glassmakers, and glassworkers. In Peiping there is a whole street of jade-tree makers, plying the craft, of course, on Jade Tree Street. There are special shops for fluffing cotton fillings for the thick cotton quilts in which all China rolls up to sleep on a winter night. There are potters and artisans who can make beautiful porcelains. There are shops that produce exquisite cloisonné. There are many types of workers in bamboo—those who make bamboo furniture, who tie split bamboo for awnings, shades, and screens, who weave split-bamboo mats, make bamboo musical instruments, writing brushes, sedan chairs, or plait bamboo into long towropes by which junks are towed up hundreds of rivers and streams. In the cities of China there are stonecutters and stonemasons, brickmasons, and carpenters, who build humble homes or fine temples. Very little such work is done by machine.

For centuries China has had a large printing and lithography industry. For many centuries the books of China, both classical and popular, were printed by means of wooden plates on which a whole page of characters was carved. This method is still in use, although it has been almost entirely replaced by movable metal type in dozens of small, busy printing shops in every Chinese city.

"Women weave cotton, men weave silk" is an ancient saying from the time of Confucius which seems to govern activities in the textile industry. I remember hiking out to the edge of Nanking one day to watch a group of male master artisans weaving silk tapestries. In a crowded house with mud walls and a thatched roof, three ancient hand looms were set up on the bare earth floor. Strings lifting the warp threads ran up to the top of the frame ten or twelve feet above. Pushing down a treadle which alternated the warp threads, the weaver pulled a cord which made the shuttle fly back and forth between the lifted and depressed filaments. At one side of the frame there was an endless chain of heavy paper pattern guides which seemed to me similar to a player-piano roll and which, in some way, determined the threads to be lifted as the shuttle flew through the maze and created a rapidly growing tapestry. For generations the knowledge and skill required to make these heavy silk brocades has been passed down from father to son in this family of silk weavers.

On another occasion, I visited a cotton weaver's establishment near Tsinan in Shantung. Here the looms were set up side by side in a dugout sunk below ground level in order that the workers would be warm in winter and cool in summer with neither fire nor fan. Over each a small skylight admitted just enough illumination for the work to be visible. Although most cloth is woven on power-driven machines today, a good deal of hand spinning and weaving remains.

Throughout China there are large and flourishing fermentation industries, with one group of shops engaging in the production of wines and stronger alcoholic drinks, and another making soybean sauces. Both are highly skilled types of work. What the Chinese call wine ranges all the way from mild fruit wine to grain alcohol distilled to more than 100-proof liquors. The more powerful of these so-called wines hit straight and hard and undoubtedly have been an important contributing factor to the creation of much of China's most famous poetry.

Soysauces, the table salt of China, are produced by thousands on thousands of families who make a living by fermenting this most widely used of all Chinese condiments. The production of a prize soysauce is a lengthy and complicated process requiring the same amount of skill as the production of famous European wines. Mash is made of wheat bran, soybeans, and salt, with each skilled producer using different proportions and adding many other materials. Large quantities of salt present in the mash prevent rotting and provide the conditions under which specific organisms are able to form the sauce. The fermentation of the best grades requires from five to seven years, during which time the fermenting mash is carefully tended. At the end of the fermentation period the completed sauce is leached out by the addition of measured quantities of water.

China still carries on many industrial processes which, like agricultural methods, have been evolved empirically over centuries of time. One of these processes is the extraction and production of salt from the wells of Tzeliuching in Szechuan. When war cut off regular communications with the seacoast, salt production assumed great importance and was accelerated to meet unprecedented demands. Some of the Tzeliuching salt wells are three thousand feet deep, having been drilled by primitive means for centuries. Drilling is done by a heavy metal bit which slowly pecks its way down through soil and rock to the salt brine far beneath the surface. The bit is suspended on a rope of woven, split bamboo from one end of a long beam. The beam is balanced near the bit end in much the same manner as the well sweeps of early

New England. Along each side of the beam there is a scaffold on which twenty or thirty men stand. When they step on the beam their weight raises the bit, and, as they step off, the bit drops a few inches and strikes the bottom of the well. After days of pecking away at the rocks, the bit is removed and the pulverized rock is washed out by water and bailers. Then the bit is returned to the hole and the process continues. After years of drilling, the well finally breaks through to salt water and the brine is drawn up.

Raising the brine is an impressive achievement, for it is not easy to raise liquids from several thousand feet underground without the aid of pumps. Each load is scooped up in a 20-foot long bamboo bucket suspended from a bamboo rope and powered by a capstan turned by three, four, five, or even six yoke of oxen. When the lift first starts, and the weight of three thousand feet of bamboo rope is added to the bucket and its contents, all available oxen are required to budge the capstan, straining round and round. As the bucket nears the surface and the weight of the rope diminishes, successive yoke of oxen are unhooked and permitted to rest, until at last only a single yoke is needed. More than half an hour is required for the drawing of one bucket of brine from the deeper wells.

Once the brine has been brought to the surface, it is evaporated over natural gas flames and produces a very pure quality of salt. Since salt is a daily necessity for the flavoring and preservation of food, there is no more certain source of government revenue than a tax on salt. Hence its production is a government monopoly.

Most of the mines of China—and there are a good many of them—are similarly primitive and largely operated by manpower. Tin, tungsten, and antimony are found in abundance and purity, and there is great demand for their export, but many of the mines are still worked by methods which have not changed for three hundred years.

In Yünnan province tin mines are working deposits laid down in long tunnels that were once underground streams which gradually silted up with a tin ore that is far above the world average in purity. Ore is brought out in sacks on the backs of young coolies who frequently have to crawl on hands and knees to squeeze through the narrower tunnels. Sometimes the tunnels are so long that a man can carry out only one or two sacks of ore a day. Methods of extracting the tin from the ore are so crude that the ore is still rich in tin when it is discarded as slag. The introduction of modern flotation refining will make this slag profitable to rework.

China's iron and steel production is still tiny compared with that of other nations chiefly because a large part of the industry, in organization and method, is reminiscent of the ironsmiths of Europe's Middle Ages. When the North China Rural Christian Service Union wished to help the farmers of Shansi learn to be better iron producers, they were forced to go to the British Museum and study blast furnaces that became obsolete in England more than a century ago. The Shansi iron producers, like those in most of China, work with small and simple crucibles in which only a small percentage of the iron content is smelted from the ores. Such work is done by men who farm during the summer and turn miner and refiner during the winter, producing a brittle, low-grade iron which was and still is the basic material from which thousands on thousands of small blacksmith shops hammer out farm tools, crude square nails, and the thousands of simple iron tools necessary even to a relatively primitive society. It is from this kind of iron that the big shallow pots which form the tops of most Chinese stoves are cast.

During the Sino-Japanese War, most of China's modern iron- and steel-producing sites near Shanghai, in Manchuria, and other places, were captured by the Japanese. Before evacuating, however, the Chinese managed to dismantle and ship much of the machinery to unoccupied China, where no large iron and steel industry had existed before. There plants were set up, and late in the war American technicians supplied by the United States government as a wartime measure advised on how to improve them. The Japanese, on the other hand, because they possessed limited iron resources of their own, rebuilt and re-equipped the captured plants in occupied China and developed new industries in Manchuria and other coastal regions. Some were destroyed by bombs, some were destroyed by excited Chinese troops returning in victory, and some were dismantled by Russians. The effect, however, has been an introduction of modern methods and ideas in areas previously untouched, affording the industry an opportunity to rebuild on a larger national scale.

Most Americans have heard their grandparents tell, or they have read, how lye was extracted from wood ashes when the virgin forests of the American continent were being burned to clear the land. Lye is being produced in Chengtu and other places by the same method today, taking advantage of the fact that almost all cooking done in that city uses wood as fuel. Because of the ready market for wood ashes, thrifty Chengtu householders are meticulous in saving them and in keeping them uncontaminated until the ash buyer arrives. Several hundred people are employed in the lye-extraction business, beginning with the ash buyer who goes about the streets with a wheelbarrow purchasing raw materials for his employer. The equipment of one of these plants is rudimentary, consisting of a few large wooden tubs, in which ashes are leached with water, and the pots for recovering the lye by boiling off the water. The fuel used in this latter operation is straw, fed to the fire a wisp at a time, the ashes of which are recovered and, in turn, leached to provide more lye. This quaint vestige of an ancient chemical industry was revived by the war blockade, but it is representative of many other Chinese industries.

Another of the ancient chemical industries still practiced made possible the invention of the firecracker in the ninth century—the extraction of saltpeter, or potassium nitrate, from the floors and brick beds of North China. Potassium nitrate is formed slowly from organic matter by microorganisms in the mud floors and in the mud bricks which are the beds of North China peasants. For centuries men have made a living by buying up old brick from these beds and by digging up floors from country houses to provide raw materials for saltpeter extraction. The firecrackers which a dozen of us once set off at the Press Hostel in Chungking to celebrate the first American air raid on Tokyo were made from saltpeter extracted in this manner.

When the Sino-Japanese War assumed most bloody proportions in 1937, many new industries were being built up in the areas later occupied. Among them was the China Industrial Gas Company, organized by a group of enterprising Shanghai businessmen under the leadership of Y. C. Lee, a competent industrial chemist, who had decided it was about time for China to produce her own oxygen and acetylene for use in oxyacetylene welding. They assembled the necessary capital and, with the assistance of an American importing firm, sought the necessary machinery. There was no trouble in obtaining equipment needed to set up a plant to produce oxygen by liquefaction of air, but when they wanted to make calcium carbide and produce acetylene they ran into cartel trouble. When they tried to purchase a complete carbide plant in America they were referred to a French firm. The French firm would be glad to sell them all the carbide they wanted, at a fee, but regretted that no plant for the manufacture of carbide itself could be sold. Whereupon Mr. Lee resourcefully consulted his chemical reference books on the subject of carbide manufacturing, sought more financial assistance from his friends, and designed an electric furnace.

Just a year before war struck Shanghai with a vengeance, China was producing her own acetylene gas, the new plant turning out four tons of carbide a day.

As the Japanese advanced through the city, both the oxygen and the acetylene plants were dismantled and crated, parts were shipped inland immediately, and the remaining crates were hidden in warehouses while fighting raged. After the city was occupied, the remaining crates (with the connivance of American friends) were "exported" to Manila for "repairs," landed in Hongkong, taken by junk to the Chinese mainland, and shipped up through the Yangtze gorges to Chungking, where they became mainstays of the war effort. Many American and Chinese airmen have breathed oxygen from Mr. Lee's oxygen plant, and time and again when electricity failed, Chungking and other inland cities were lighted with carbide lamps supplied from his electric furnace.

These little plants represent the beginnings of modern industrial development in China, for they, with scores of others like them, are the seeds from which new patterns of production and new ways of living for China's city populations will grow.

Impetus may be added to China's industrial growth by Chinese graduate students who have, for the past decade, been studying by the thousands in the United States—as many as five thousand during a single year. A majority of them seek technical knowledge. In addition, beginning in 1946, hundreds of Chinese with some technical background have been sent to the United States annually for periods of practical training with American commercial and industrial firms. The China of the future will be better supplied with professional men and technicians, but whether or not these additional resources are used for the welfare of the Chinese people as a group, to raise the living standard of the common man, depends not so much on technology itself as on how it is applied and how Chinese social developments keep pace with commerce and industry.

Transportation

Not only is most of China's manufacturing still in the handicraft stage, but her transportation is still largely dependent on wind, water, and muscles. Almost everything is still packaged for transportation in units small enough for one or two men to carry on shoulder poles.

Throughout China the most common means of transportation is muscle. At least half the tonnage moved in all China is moved on men's backs. One survey of the movement of agricultural products to market showed that 5 per cent was transported by train and truck, 45 per cent by man-pulled junks and handcarts, and 50 per cent by human carriers.

Means of moving things by manpower are numerous and ingenious, so varied indeed that there are different Chinese verbs to describe each different method. *Na* means to carry in the hand; *pei*, to carry on the back; *k'ang*, to carry on the shoulder; *t'iao*, to carry suspended from the two ends of a shoulder pole, and *t'ai* means for two or more men to carry an object swung on a pole between them.

Just to carry people, a half dozen different kinds of sedan chairs have been developed to suit different conditions, both physical and social. In the chairs on which people ride up the thousands of steps leading to the 5,000-foot peak of sacred Taishan in Shantung the passenger sits with his feet hanging out over one of the carrying poles, and the carriers walk side by side on the same step as they mount the broad stone stairway with their cargo between them. In West China, where chairs are used largely for traveling over stone-paved trails winding over mountainous terrain, the passenger sits between the carrying poles, with one or two carriers in front and one or two carriers behind, permitting the negotiating of steep, narrow, winding trails. Formerly the number of chair carriers reflected the social position of the passenger —the higher the rank the bigger the chair and the more carriers. During the time the American Embassy was located in Chungking, the American ambassador could not appear in a chair with less than four carriers, even when he was making a private trip to his cottage in the hills outside the city.

The human freight bearers of China daily perform prodigious feats of endurance. An average West China carrier bears a load of 104 pounds over twenty miles of hill and mountain trails daily. However, if two men carry a load on a pole between them, they carry only 156 pounds. Part of the secret enabling a single man to carry 104 pounds is the elasticity of the shoulder pole from which the load is suspended, the spring of the pole taking part of the weight off his shoulder while one foot is in the air, the whole weight descending only when the foot is firmly on the ground. Carriers using shoulder poles develop a particular gait which causes the upper body to remain erect and move forward in a straight line while the hips swing to minimize bouncing. At the salt mines in Yünnan, men carry loads of 135 to 140 pounds in this manner, while in some places in Szechuan province men regularly carry weights heavier than their own bodies. Even in swank Shanghai apartment houses one may see a grand piano being delivered through the corridors swung on poles, the carriers gasping a weird and rhythmic chant as they move in unison. In peace or war, long lines of these carriers form China's most important transportation system.

In addition to carrying things bodily, many other means of using manpower for transportation have been developed. On the northern plains wheelbarrows move millions of tons every year, and there are as many kinds of wheelbarrows as there are kinds of sedan chairs. Most North China wheelbarrows are mounted on a single, central, wooden wheel, built so that the load may be divided and balanced on both sides of the wheel. As the weight is resting directly on the wheel, one man can transport single barrow loads of almost half a ton. Another type is called a "two-handed barrow," because it has a man in front and a man behind; capacity, one ton.

On long cross-country hauls the barrowmen cover a regular run over a definite route so often that they can gauge the amount of energy needed for each stage of the journey and buy enough noodles to meet their needs at each stage. One uphill part of the journey may require eighteen ounces of noodles, while the next may require only sixteen. The barrowmen buy accordingly, just as an American motorist purchases different amounts of gasoline for journeys of different lengths.

In Central and South China, where there are thousands of miles of canals and navigable rivers, there are hundreds of thousands, if not millions, of boats, ranging in size and capacity from small sampans used by individual farmers to large junks with a cargo capacity of several hundred tons. While sails are frequently employed, the chief motive power is supplied by human muscle, rowing, poling, or pulling on a towrope. Goods are transported for long distances by inland boats on one of the connecting arteries such as the Grand Canal which links the Yangtze and Yellow rivers and provides inland water passage between Tientsin and Peiping in the north and cities of the lower Yangtze valley in the south. This canal is one of the great engineering feats of the ancient world.

Mules, horses, and cows are used as pack animals in many parts of the country, and camels are still common as beasts of burden from Peiping north and west. There are also underdeveloped modern transportation facilities—steamships that ply the coast and great rivers; a growing network of highways for buses, automobiles, and trucks; airlines; and railways—but the development of these comparatively new media were curtailed seriously by the Sino-Japanese War.

In 1927 China had only 7,683 miles of railways; in 1932, she lost 3,726 miles when the Japanese took Manchuria. By 1937, agricultural China had built 11,035 miles of rails; two years later she lost 80 per cent of these. At the peak of Japanese penetration, only a few hundred miles of railway lines remained in Chinese hands. Including those lines which were hurriedly built in unoccupied China, and those built by the Japanese in occupied China, there should be a total of well over 12,000 miles of railways in all China when the country is finally at peace and all destroyed trackage is replaced. This amounts to 27 miles for each million population, or 274 miles for each 100,000 square miles of territory. The comparable figures for the United States are 1,940 and 7,970, respectively. There are still eight Chinese provinces which have never boasted of a single mile of railway track.

Lack of modern transportation facilities in China is a limiting factor in the type and rate of agricultural development. Mr. Chang Kia-ngau, former minister of communications, states that 19 per cent of agricultural produce is sold locally, 44 per cent is sold in nearby villages, 29 per cent is sold in towns or cities of the same district, and only 8 per cent reaches more remote areas. In other words, China's flow of trade is still largely confined to the distance a man can walk in a day.

This is China as she is: a huge population crowded on a limited amount of arable land distributed over a mountainous terrain; an agriculture which is relatively effective but still a prescientific, intensive, hoe-culture system; a method of industrial production essentially in the handicraft stage; a system of trade and merchandising dominated by guilds; a transportation system largely dependent on human muscles. A nation that is poor.

Chapter V

Health

THE DEVELOPMENT OF A NATION'S RESOURCES, NAT-ural or human, cultural or financial, is deeply affected by the state of health of its people. An analysis of China's agricultural, industrial, or social problems or a discussion of her rate of progress toward their solution and toward a higher standard of living would not be complete without an examination of the health conditions under which her people labor.

There are several basic statistics that measure the state of a nation's health. The most general and fundamental of these is the crude death rate, which states the number of deaths per year per thousand population. Next in importance is the infant death rate. When the age at which deaths occur is known, it is possible to calculate "life" tables that show the life expectancy by sex, age, and occupation. The vigor of a population is measured by morbidity rates defining the number of illnesses per thousand of population per year. Both death and morbidity rates are further broken down to provide specific rates, which show the number of deaths or illnesses due to a specific cause. To complete the picture it is necessary to know the number of births that occur each year in each thousand of the population.

A modern nation is characterized by a low crude death rate, a low infant death rate, a low morbidity rate, a low birth rate, and a long life expectancy. Against these standards China's position among the nations may be determined.

The data necessary for the compilation of the rates and tables mentioned are scant and relatively unreliable in China. Most Chinese who fall ill and die are never seen by a trained physician, nor are the circumstances recorded. Even in Peiping, which possesses a good municipal health service, which has been the home of a group of strong medical institutions for the past thirty years, and which has had competent medical services for nearly a hundred years, more than three-quarters of all who die are never seen by a physician. Diagnoses of death causes are, therefore, unreliable in most places. Moreover, the common people of China are so accustomed to death, particularly that of infants, that many deaths are not reported, even in those few places where modern agencies for recording vital statistics exist.

However, mortality records have been kept in enough places and with enough thoroughness to present a fairly accurate indication of Chinese death rates. Buck, in his rural studies, collected data on the number of deaths occurring in specific localities in the years 1929–1931, a period of relative peace and security above average in the life span of a Chinese generation. He reports an average annual death rate of 27.1 per thousand for all localities studied, with 24.1 for North China and 30.0 for South China. The Mass Education Movement at its rural experimental area in Tinghsien, Hopei, found an average death rate of 27.6 for the years 1932 to 1935. The experimental health area at Kiangyin in Kiangsu province reported an average death rate of 43.6 for the years 1931 to 1934. The death rate recorded in Peiping ranged between 25 and 26. From these data a death rate of about 30 per 1,000 annually for times of peace is probably not an excessive estimate, with the probability that there is an increase during times of war, natural calamity, and famine.

A death rate of 30 per thousand would mean that China has the highest death rate of any large nation. Next to her comes British India with a death rate of 24.9 in 1931,* followed by the Soviet Union with a 1928 rate of 18.8. Next in order come Japan with 18.2; France with 16.3; England and Wales with 12.3; Sweden with 11.7; the United States with 11.3. Lowest death rate is that of Australia, 8.7. The death rate of China, using the above figures, is over three times as high as that of Australia, two and a half times that of the United States.

Infant mortality rates, showing deaths before one year of age per thousand births, give a similar result. India has an infant death rate of 248.7 for males, 232.3 for females. China has an infant death rate of 161.5 for males and 154.9 for females. Japan's record approximates that of China. Rates for England and Wales and the United States are less than half those of China, and New Zealand has the lowest infant mortality rate of all, with only 38.4 for males and 25.5 for females.

These death rates, infant and general, indicate low life expectancy for Chinese. At birth the Indian has the lowest life expectancy—males 26.91 years, females 26.56 years. The average Chinese may look ahead to a slightly longer life, 34.85 years for males, 34.63 years for females. Comparative figures for other countries are: Japan, 42.06 for males, 43.20 for females; England and Wales, 58.74 for males, 62.88 for females; United States, 59.31 for males, 62.83 for females; New Zealand, 65.05 for males, 67.88 for females. In other words, the life expectancy of a Japanese in 1921–1925, the period covered by the above data, was about equal to that in Massachusetts fifty to fifty-five years ago, while life expectancy in China, 1929–1931, was not much different from that in Massachusetts at the time of the American Revolution.

It is even more difficult to compile a reliable picture of the frequency and extent of illness in China. However, since

* Rates for years comparable to those for which Chinese data are available are used.

the known case fatality rates for most diseases responsible for known deaths in China are usually less than 10 per cent, it does not seem unreasonable to estimate that there are from ten to twenty illnesses for every death. On the basis of a death rate of 30 per thousand population, we may estimate that there are from 300 to 600 cases of illness per year among every thousand population, or a total of 150 million to 300 million illnesses per year in the nation as a whole. In other words, from one-third to two-thirds of the entire population is sick at least once in the course of each year. If the lower figure is taken and it is assumed, from known figures, that the average hospitalization period is six days, then 25 million hospital beds would be required constantly to care for Chinese illnesses.

An analysis of the causes of death adds to the health picture of China. Again the data are not too abundant, but they serve to indicate the relative importance of various disease groups.

The most important group of diseases in China contains those spread through human wastes, the fecal-borne diseases that cause about one-quarter of all deaths. Since this group of diseases is so important and because a number of them are peculiar to China and depend on special conditions with wide ramifications in the social and economic life of the country, a more complete discussion of fecal-borne diseases will follow this general discussion of China's public health.

After the fecal-borne disease group, the second most devastating disease of China is tuberculosis. Tuberculosis is appallingly widespread, and it is probable that almost every person in China contracts a tiny primary infection before the age of twenty. The number of instances in which the resistance of the individual is insufficient to check the disease is enormous, resulting in deaths that total at least 10 to 15 per cent of the entire death rate. The annual slaughter of approximately 1,500,000 Chinese by tuberculosis is not surprising in view of the inadequacy of proteins and protective foods in the Chinese diet, the crowded conditions of both country and city, and the fact that the Chinese custom of eating from common bowls with chopsticks is tantamount to a constant exchange of bacilli between family and friends. Since the average Chinese has no knowledge of how the disease is transmitted, spitting is completely promiscuous in the home, on the street, and even in the modern office buildings of Shanghai. Although treatment for tuberculosis is available, open cases of the disease, undiagnosed and untreated, serve as foci of infection in every community. There is no general preventive education.

The prevalence of tuberculosis among students is particularly distressing. Between 1939 and 1942, 5.1 per cent of all college students examined in Peiping were found to have active cases. By 1946, wartime conditions had forced the incidence so high that 60 per cent of the Chinese applicants for American student visas at Shanghai were found to have active cases, preventing their further study in the United States.

The third most deadly group of diseases in China includes those communicable diseases transmitted directly from one person to another, usually by droplets from the nose and mouth or by contact with objects such as chopsticks or teacups which have been contaminated by an infected person. In spite of the fact that the Chinese were the first to practice vaccination for smallpox, it is the most important of the third group, killing tens of thousands every year. After smallpox come measles, diphtheria, scarlet fever, and, for small children, whooping cough, all of which take a steady toll. This third group of diseases is responsible for 8 to 12 per cent of all deaths.

Next in order come the diseases that are associated with childbirth. The most important of these is tetanus neonatorum, closely followed in incidence by childbed fever and other causes of death associated with parturition. Puerperal, or childbed fever, and tetanus neonatorum are caused by lack of cleanliness during birth.

Almost every day in most of the modern hospitals of China pregnant mothers give a history of from five to twelve, or even fifteen, pregnancies from which they have one or two children still alive, and frequently none at all. In a great number of these cases these women will say, when asked about the circumstances of the deaths, that the children died in tetanic convulsions eight, nine, or ten days after birth. The cause is obvious. The umbilical cord of the newborn child was dressed with dirty rags and herb medicines, if not with a salve of road dust as is the habit in some places. Tetanus germs were thereby inoculated into the child's navel, where in eight or nine days enough toxin was generated to cause death. This disease is so common that the Chinese call it the "nine-day disease."

In addition, many maternal deaths occur in those cases in which any one of many complications, such as the previously described osteomalacia of Shansi province, prevent the mother from delivering the child. In every hospital in China there are women who were brought in after having been in labor for days, unable to deliver their children. In many of these cases a forceps delivery or a cesarean section may save the mother, but in a great many cases they come too late. There are thousands on thousands of mothers who never reach a hospital, and who die at home. About 6 to 8 per cent of all deaths in China occur as a result of childbirth.

Already the knowledge of and demand for modern obstetrical service has spread far and wide throughout China, but until trained midwives and doctors become available in sufficient numbers many hundreds of thousands of mothers and babies will die, as they have for ages past, infected by the dirty hands and bad customs of those who seek to help them.

HEALTH

The fifth most important group of diseases is the insect-borne group. Important in this group are malaria, typhus, bubonic plague, and relapsing fever. Although malaria occurs almost everywhere, it is unusually prevalent in the rice region from the Yangtze valley south, and especially prevalent in western Yünnan along the Burma Road. Some steep-walled valleys are so infested with malignant malaria that they have become almost depopulated. Typhus is widespread, particularly common in rural areas throughout the country where bathing is rare in cold weather and large populations of lice accumulate on the people. Bubonic plague is endemic along the Fukien and Chekiang coasts, where it survives in rats that live in the thick mud walls of houses. Fortunately, it has not yet spread into areas deep in the interior. With the increase of modern transportation systems there is a definite possibility that plague will become a much more serious problem than it is at present. Careful watch was kept on the Burma Road during World War II to prevent spread from India. Relapsing fever is transmitted by the bites of ticks and lice, principally in the north, but it does not occur with the frequency of the other three diseases in the insect-borne group. This group probably accounts for 3 to 5 per cent of the deaths of China.

The sixth group includes respiratory diseases other than tuberculosis. Most important causes of death from this group are the pneumonias, which are widespread and common. However, the entire group is not so common in China as it is in the West, due principally to the fact that China is predominantly agricultural and not subject to the degree of industrial hazard found in the West. The group may account for 2 to 3 per cent of Chinese deaths.

The seventh important group includes the venereal diseases. Both syphilis and gonorrhea are quite common and widespread in all parts of China, for every city and town has a fair number of prostitutes who play major parts in the spread of these diseases. The group probably accounts for 2 to 5 per cent of deaths.

The remaining deaths are the result of diseases or accidents which are not controllable. In this group are heart diseases, kidney diseases, apoplexy, and cancer, as well as accidents and suicides. In the advanced countries of the West diseases belonging to this group cause most of the deaths because medical science has not yet learned how to prevent them and has established controls over preventable diseases.

Seventy-five per cent of all deaths in China are due to preventable diseases that are under control in the West (there are about 15 million deaths each year in China, of which 11,750,000 are due to preventable causes). One of the great tasks facing the medical-health services is the prevention of these deaths.

So much for a brief survey of illnesses, deaths, and their causes. What about births? Only the Soviet Union, with 42.7 births per thousand population, has a higher birth rate than China, with 38.3 births per thousand population, although the actual rate may be somewhat higher due to failure to report some births. Comparative rates are: India, 34.3; Japan, 32.4; United States, 18.9; Australia, 18.2; France, 17.4; England, 15.8; Sweden, 15.4.

The health status of China is extremely low. Although today only India can approach her poor record, it is important to remember that healthy populations living in clean environments with low death rates are comparatively new in the history of the world. London constructed her first sewer just over a hundred years ago. Death rates in New England during the time of the American Revolution were comparable to those in China today, and the death rates and causes of death in New York City in 1890 differed little from those of Peiping in 1934 and 1935. We in America, with a whole new continent for development, are not far removed in time from health conditions similar to those prevailing in China. The difference is a result of application of knowledge discovered in the past seventy-five to one hundred years. Someday this same knowledge will be applied in China.

The Fecal-borne Diseases

Reference has already been made to the fact that the equilibrium that has been developed between man and nature in China is like a balanced aquarium. The ramifications of this balance between man and his environment are extensive. The part the pig plays in the food cycle has been cited as one example. Fecal-borne diseases are another outstanding example of this biological integration, although, from a human and humanitarian point of view, they represent an unhappy, injurious, and evil factor in that equilibrium.

The size and importance of this group of diseases in Chinese life can be measured by the fact that one-quarter of all deaths are attributed to the fecal-borne group. That is, about as many persons per thousand of population die from preventable fecal-borne diseases in China each year as die from all causes in Australia. On the absolute scale of total deaths the appalling significance of these diseases is even more striking—of approximately 15 million deaths per year in China, 4,250,000 are due to the fecal-borne group.

China was at war for eight years, 1937 to 1945, a cruel, bloody war, in which most of her cities crowded with defenseless civilians were bombed repeatedly, in which millions of ill-equipped soldiers were slaughtered in battle. No one knows precisely how many people were killed in these eight years of warfare; probably between 5 and 10 million Chinese died as a direct result of war. And yet from 30 to 35 million Chinese died from fecal-borne diseases during the same period of time. At least three times as many people died from this group of diseases during this eight-year period, or in any other eight-year period, as were killed by the war.

The pattern of relationships that makes the fecal-borne diseases so deadly penetrates the entire web of agricultural and physical life in China. Among this group are four diseases caused by parasitic worms (three of which are found only in the Far East and largely confined to China), and which may be called occupational diseases of the Chinese farmer. They are occupational diseases because their prevalence and transmission are dependent on specific practices carried out in connection with the production of definite crops. They can be controlled only when the cycle of relationships is broken by marked changes in present agricultural methods. They are so important in illustrating the wide range of problems involved in Chinese public health improvement that it will be worth while to consider them in some detail.

The first of the four occupational diseases of the Chinese farmer is hookworm disease. It is caused by two different species of hookworms, *Necator americanus* and *Ancylostoma duodenale*, that live in the small intestine of the human body. These parasites are about half an inch in length, equipped with a strong mouth containing plate or hooklike teeth, and they are popularly called hookworms because the front portions of their bodies are bent to form well-defined hooks. They attach themselves to the walls of their hosts' intestines, and, with special stylets, puncture the intestinal walls and cause blood to flow into their mouths. This blood is prevented from clotting by an anticoagulant present in their saliva. They are voracious feeders, pumping fresh blood from their hosts through their own intestines and absorbing already dissolved food and oxygen without attempting to digest the blood for themselves. Each worm drains about one cubic centimeter of blood from its host each day, and if several hundred worms are present in the intestine of a person they will rob him of about half a pint of blood daily.

Such excessive and continuous loss of blood causes the host to become anemic, and the symptoms of hookworm disease rapidly become apparent, particularly if the host is on a poor diet. If not treated, and if he is subjected to increased numbers of these parasites, the host usually dies. For every death, however, there are dozens of people who survive with lowered energy. Loss due to death is a small part of the total loss a community sustains from hookworm disease.

Fortunately, hookworms, like all parasitic worms, must develop outside the human body. Every day each female worm produces from 6,000 to 10,000 microscopic eggs which are ejected from the host in the fecal discharge. Outside the human body the eggs must develop in a warm, moist environment, such as that provided during hot weather by fecal material mixed with moist earth. Under such advantageous conditions, tiny worms hatch from the eggs in twenty-four to thirty-six hours and live on bacteria in the soil while growing rapidly. The young worms reach the infective stage in about a week under summer conditions, shedding their skins several times and altering in internal structure during this period. They retain the third skin as partial protection against the environment and then cease to feed while awaiting contact with a human body, living the while in films of moisture between soil particles. If they do not come in contact with human skin before they use up the limited supply of energy stored in their bodies they die in about two weeks. But once through the skin of a host, the tiny worms make their way into veins, where the blood stream picks them up and sweeps them along to the heart. From the heart they are pumped to the lungs, where, feeling the stimulus of air, they break through toward the air sacs. The cilia that line the air sacs then sweep them up through the windpipe into the throat, where they are swallowed and pass through the stomach into the intestines. In the intestines they begin to grow rapidly, reaching maturity in about two weeks, laying eggs, and thus completing their life cycle.

Hookworm disease can be prevalent and important only in those places where the human habits make possible the deposit of hookworm eggs on the soil and the contact of bare skin with infected soil in which larvae have already completed their development. In China, where all fecal material is carefully stored and used as fertilizer, these conditions are met in the production of three types of crops.

The primary focus of hookworm disease is associated with the cultivation of silk in the lower Yangtze valley. There it is particularly prevalent among children, girls, and women who work in the mulberry districts near Soochow. In mulberry-hookworm areas, in order that quantities of leaves may be gathered easily to feed silkworms, farmers grow whole fields of small mulberry trees which are kept cut back in order to force new shoots and an abundance of large leaves near the ground. During the spring, just as the weather becomes warm, the trees are heavily fertilized with diluted night soil gathered from the latrines of nearby towns or cities, stimulating both the growth of leaves and the growth of hookworm larvae. Two weeks after the fertilizer is applied in a circular bed around each tree, the ground is swarming with thousands of infective larvae waiting their chance to penetrate skin on the feet or hands of anyone unfortunate enough to come in contact with the soil. The children, girls, and women who have the daily job of snipping enough mulberry leaves to supply thousands of insatiable silkworms must stand for long periods in these culture beds, and since they are either barefooted or wear loose straw sandals, they are exposed day after day to the deadly little worms. It is not uncommon for one person to acquire several hundred or even several thousand worms, with a resultant blood loss too great to sustain. They die, while others less heavily infested, or physically more resistant, live at a reduced level of health and efficiency.

The second type of crop with which hookworm disease is associated has only recently been isolated in the hills of northern Szechuan province by one of my associates, Dr. Chang Kwei, and it is not yet widely known among parasitologists outside of China. Here the disease is transmitted by the fertilization of corn interrowed with sweet potatoes, the most common crop of the area. Sweet potatoes are first sprouted by planting the tubers in well-fertilized culture beds, while the main fields are prepared and planted to corn. As the corn is also fertilized with the customary night soil, those who transplant the sweet-potato sprouts some two weeks later, when the larvae are at their most infective stage, are first exposed to hookworm in the culture bed and again in the cornfield, this work being done with the hands. Wherever these hookworm larvae penetrate the skin there is a strong reaction and swelling known as "ground itch." So frequent is the infection in north Szechuan that workers stop work altogether until the itching and pain in both hands and feet subside. Dr. Chang found that only three or four hundred of these worms will cause an anemia in which the hemoglobin of the patient drops as low as 20 per cent. This low resistance is probably due to the poor local diet consisting mainly of corn and sweet potatoes. Deaths are common, and the strength and energy of the population is much reduced.

Market gardening is a third type of crop to encourage hookworm disease by the use of night-soil nitrogen. Cases of hookworm disease are common among market gardeners in Central and South China, where temperature and moisture conditions are favorable for its development, but in a lighter concentration than among silkgrowers or among the corn and sweet-potato planters because fertilization is less intense and because market gardeners live near cities where much of the fertilizer is derived from uninfected populations.

Lighter infestations of hookworms may be found almost anywhere in China, town and country, traceable to the same source, but in many cases the injury done by the worm is so slight that no actual disease results. The more deadly disease seems to be confined to areas in which the market gardening or the production of silk or corn and sweet potatoes are leading occupations. In other countries where hookworm disease occurs, it affects general populations and is not associated with cultivation of specific crops as in China, largely because most other nations do not use human wastes as fertilizers in the Chinese manner.

The Chinese farmer's second occupational disease, caused by the liver fluke, is not so widespread as hookworm disease. It has an interesting case history in that its existence depends on the methods used to grow fish in artificial ponds and on the eating of a special raw-fish dish much prized in Kwangtung province. The human liver fluke disease is caused by an oblong, leaf-shaped, flat worm about half an inch long and a quarter of an inch wide, a parasite which enjoys the distinguished name of *Clanorchis sinensis* and belongs to a group of parasitic flat worms known commonly as flukes.

The life cycle of the human liver fluke is complicated by the use of three different animal hosts during its various stages of development. The adult worm is found in the small bile ducts in the livers of men, cats, and dogs. There each worm lays large numbers of extremely tiny eggs containing fully formed larvae with cilia on their outer skin. After passing from the host, the eggs do not hatch unless they are eaten by a specific type of snail found throughout the Orient. When an egg is eaten by the proper species of snail, it promptly hatches in the snail's stomach, and the small larva that pops out proceeds to bore its way through the tissues of the snail until it reaches the liver. Here the liver fluke larva elongates itself into a saclike organism which reproduces many more sacs just like itself until the entire liver of the snail is filled with them. In each of these secondary sacs a new type of larva is formed which has a miniature body similar to that of the adult worm with the addition of a long tail with which it can swim through the water.

Six weeks after the snail eats the fluke egg, from a few dozen to several hundred tail-bearing larvae begin to escape from the infected snail each day and swim about in the water hoping to come in contact with a fish. If they are fortunate, they penetrate the flesh of the fish, leaving their tails behind. Inside the fish muscles, they round up and secrete a sturdy cyst that protects them while they await the eating of the fish by a man, cat, or dog. If the fish is cooked, the career of the larva ends, but if the fish is eaten raw or only partly cooked the larvae are digested out of their cysts and proceed to crawl up through the bile duct to the host's liver and set up housekeeping.

The presence of even a small number of these worms in the bile ducts causes thickening and hardening of the ducts, while the pressure of the growing worms slowly destroys the surrounding liver tissue. The body, trying to surround the worms, further destroys liver tissue by increasing the thickening of the bile-duct walls. Sufficiently extensive damage to the liver results in serious disease and death. This disease is the more serious because no effective drug has yet been developed for killing or removing the worms.

Fortunately, human liver fluke disease is generally confined to a relatively small area in Kwangtung province where the much-prized "big-headed fish" is served in a raw-fish salad. The rest of China eats only cooked fish. These Kwangtung delicacies, heavily infected with liver fluke cysts, are raised in shallow artificial ponds that are fertilized in the Chinese manner, usually by having the family privy placed over one corner. Since the fish growers are addicted to the raw-fish dish, the cycle is completed, and the fish are invariably delivered to restaurants completely equipped with flukes. Infection is largely limited to the farmers and the wealthy city people for whom the fish are grown. The world-famous traitor, Wang Ching-wei, who headed the Nanking puppet government under the Japanese, enjoyed the distinction of being infected with liver flukes which, more than likely, helped to hasten his unlamented demise.

The human liver fluke exists also in cats and dogs throughout China, providing a reservoir of hosts which keep many species of fish infected with the cysts. While we were conducting extensive surveys on parasites in Shantung province, we found liver fluke eggs in the stool of one man. Ah, we thought, here is something interesting. Where did this man acquire his liver flukes?

"Have you ever been to Kwangtung?" inquired the investigator.

"No, sir, I have never been there" was the answer.

"Have you ever been outside of Shantung?"

"My entire life has been spent right here in this county."

"Have you ever eaten any raw fish?"

"Yes, I have, once, when I was a young man," he answered instantly.

"How did you happen to do that?"

"Well, about twenty years ago I was sick for many days. so I went to see the local 'doctor.' He felt my pulse. He investigated the state of the *yang* and *yin* principles in the various organs of my body. After long consideration, he finally prescribed for me. He said that my case was serious, and that the balance between the yang and the yin, the heat and the cold, in my body was very badly upset. Only a drastic cure could hope to do me any good. I must prepare many potions according to his directions, and on the second day I must catch two small fish from the village pond and swallow them alive. I carried out his prescriptions to the letter. In a few days I was much better, and I have not been seriously ill since."

The source of the liver flukes was explained, but the number acquired from the two small fish were too few to do serious harm.

The third occupational disease of the Chinese farmer is found in the northern part of Chekiang province between Shanghai and Hangchow. It is caused by a type of fluke that infects the intestine. This worm, known scientifically as *Fasciolopsis buskii*, grows to a maximum length of two and a half to three inches and a breadth of more than half an inch. It causes injury to man both by robbing him of food and by the effects of a strong toxin which it secretes. A few dozen of these worms can cause definite symptoms, and several hundred produce a disease that is frequently fatal.

The life cycle of this intestinal fluke is linked closely to the cultivation of water chestnuts. The worms in the intestine of the host produce thousands of eggs which are completely undeveloped when they pass from the host's body. Before they can hatch they must undergo a two or three weeks' development under special temperature conditions. These special conditions were unknown until they were discovered by Dr. Claude Heman Barlow, the man who first traced the life cycle of the intestinal fluke.

Dr. Barlow came to Chekiang province as a missionary doctor before World War I. His hospital was located in the center of an area where intestinal fluke disease was so common that more of his patients suffered from it than from any other. Drugs effective for the removal of the worms were available, and Dr. Barlow treated many hundreds of people. Although he frequently recovered from several scores to several hundred worms from individual patients, they returned for treatment year after year with newly acquired worms. Dr. Barlow realized that the continued application of treatment alone was futile and that the life cycle of the parasite must be studied in order to prevent the disease before its inception.

Since the parasite was a fluke, Dr. Barlow knew that it would pass part of its life in a snail. He began his search for the culprit by trying to develop eggs so that he could test the penetrating abilities of larvae on different snails and identify the guilty species. It was easy enough to obtain eggs from the stools of patients, but developing them was another matter. Time after time he tried incubating them at high temperatures and at low temperatures, but the eggs remained undeveloped.

As the time approached for his furlough in America, Dr. Barlow sought a means of taking with him a source of eggs which would permit him to continue his research with the aid of specialists at Johns Hopkins University. He could not take an infected Chinese patient with him because American immigration laws are very strict on the subject of diseases. Any eggs he might take would die long before he could reach Baltimore and continue his experiments. The only means of transporting live eggs was to infect himself with the worms and supply his own research material. But how could he infect himself? As yet he did not know the source of the worms that infected so many of his patients. For a while he appeared to be defeated. Only when he noticed that many of the worms passed by patients following treatment were still alive did the idea occur to him that he might acquire an infection by swallowing some. It was a revolting idea, but worth a try, and since he could always treat himself with his drug cures, it appeared to be a safe plan.

Dr. Barlow planned accordingly, treated a patient, selected about thirty-five active, medium-sized worms, washed them several times in sterile salt solution, and then, after taking a huge dose of bicarbonate of soda to neutralize the acid of his stomach, he gulped them down. Since the worms are hermaphroditic, i.e., each worm is both male and female and thus capable of self-fertilization, he knew that he needed to establish only one worm in his own intestine to provide the eggs he would need in the United States.

On the day after swallowing the worms he began to examine each of his stools, and after two or three days he found an egg. Was this one he had swallowed, or was it produced by a worm in his own intestine? The next day he found eggs again. It began to look hopeful. Then for a day or two he found no eggs. Perhaps the experiment had failed? Then they began to appear regularly. He had infected himself and could leave for America with material to continue his experiments.

After five years of separation, a missionary must visit family and friends, but Dr. Barlow reached Baltimore as soon as possible. Again he tried incubating the eggs under various constant conditions, but none developed. Perhaps what was needed was a fluctuating temperature. He washed some eggs clean, put them in a thermos bottle, added warm water until the temperature reached about 80° Fahrenheit. Then he closed up the thermos and set it aside. By the next day, the temperature had dropped to 65°. Again he added warm water and kept the temperature fluctuating between 65° and 80° every twenty-four hours, eagerly examining the eggs at the end of each period. There were indications of development, and in about two weeks some of the eggs began to hatch. He had solved the problem of how to develop *Fasciolopsis buskii* eggs.

Armed with this knowledge, Dr. Barlow tackled the job of tracing the rest of the fluke's life cycle as soon as he was back in China. First, he must ascertain which of the scores of species of snails that inhabit the rice fields, the water-chestnut fields, and the canals that combine to make the district appear a shallow lake, was the particular snail that could serve as intermediate host to the larvae of the intestinal fluke. He incubated eggs and began exposing snails of all kinds to the larvae that hatched. Before long he found that they avidly attacked and bored their way into a certain type of small transparent snail that inhabited all the rice and water-chestnut fields. About six weeks after some of these snails had been infected, an active tail-bearing form began to escape from them. After a few hours of swimming about, the larvae lost their tails, rounded up, and encysted on the sides of the glass dishes in which their snail hosts were kept. Dr. Barlow had the clue to the source of infection.

He began looking for these cysts in the natural environment of the snail species that played host to *Fasciolopsis buskii*, and before long found cysts on the outside skins of water chestnuts. Everything became apparent. First, the parasite had become so thoroughly adapted to conditions in these shallow flooded fields that its eggs would develop only in fluctuating temperatures. Second, people who ate water chestnuts raw were becoming infected when they accidentally scraped parasite cysts off the shells while peeling the nuts with their teeth. To prove his point, Dr. Barlow again infected himself by swallowing some one hundred thirty of these cysts. He developed over one hundred worms and a severe attack of intestinal fluke symptoms, but he had demonstrated that he had discovered the life cycle of the parasite.

In 1925, Dr. Barlow published a monograph describing these experiments and suggesting a series of inexpensive and simple steps to combat the parasite—steps that could be carried out easily by local authorities. In the more than twenty years since then no concerted effort toward control has been made, and the prevalence of fluke disease has diminished very little. Informed and effective local organization capable of dealing with this type of problem has not yet come into existence in this area. Control of fluke disease must await a future day of peace, stability, and organized initiative.

The fourth occupational disease of the Chinese farmer is the most widespread and important of all. This disease, too, is caused by a fluke, commonly known as the Japanese blood fluke, and scientifically entitled *Schistosomum japonicum*. Japanese blood fluke is widely distributed throughout the entire lower Yangtze valley from Ichang to the sea, an area inhabited by about one hundred million people. It is estimated that 10 per cent, or ten million, of them are infected by this parasite.

The injury to its host caused by the Japanese blood fluke is severe and irreparable. The adult worms live in the veins of the hepatic portal system, the group of veins in the abdomen that originate as capillaries in the wall of the intestine and end in capillaries in the liver. This system of veins serves to carry blood, heavily laden with newly digested food, from the intestine to the liver, and it is here that the Japanese blood flukes take refuge to eat and digest blood as well as to soak up predigested food.

The female Japanese blood fluke, which is about half an inch long and the thickness of a coarse thread, is held in a deep groove on the underside of the much thicker and shorter male. When the female is ready to lay eggs, the pair of worms migrates against the flow of the blood stream down to the wall of the intestine. There the female thrusts her body far down into a capillary in the intestinal wall and lays her eggs in the tissues as near to the inner lining of the intestine as she can. She fills one capillary with eggs and then pushes into a neighboring one, depositing from twenty-five to a hundred eggs in a cluster. Eggs are completely undeveloped when deposited, but as they develop they give off a histolytic enzyme which breaks down the surrounding tissue cells and causes the formation of an ulcer in the inner lining of the intestine. The matured eggs fall into the intestine from the ulcer and are passed from the body of the host.

The repeated formation and repair of these ulcers on the

inner surface of the intestine results in one type of irreparable damage these parasites cause to man. Gradually the muscle, glandular and absorptive tissues, on which the intestine depends for its ability to digest food, lose their efficiency and are changed to scar tissue. A progressive decrease in digestive efficiency ensues.

Japanese blood flukes cause another type of permanent injury when the eggs are washed back into the liver by the blood. There, stopped by capillaries in the liver, they force their way out into the body of the liver tissue. Around each egg, partly because it is a foreign body, and partly because it secretes the histolytic enzyme that can dissolve tissue, a tiny area of dead liver tissue is formed. Since these worms are capable of living for years, the number of eggs in the liver steadily increases, and more and more liver tissue is killed. With this continued destruction, the effectiveness of the liver is reduced. This, too, is an irreparable injury.

Gradually, therefore, over a period of ten or more years, patients infected by Japanese blood flukes show increasingly severe symptoms of digestive impairment and liver destruction until they eventually die of starvation, their digestive systems so damaged by the effects of the worms and their eggs that they can no longer digest enough of their food to support life.

Japanese blood fluke disease is associated with the cultivation of rice, although it is also found among canalboatmen. By the time the host passes the eggs the larvae are already developed and, if they fall or are placed in water within two weeks, they soon hatch and swim frantically about seeking for the one species of snail in which they can survive and continue development. These snails, a small amphibious species with long, cornucopia-type shells, usually live on a sloping shore, either a few inches above or a few inches below the waterline where they spend half their time in water and half their time out. When the blood fluke larva approaches it is attracted by chemicals secreted by the snails in much the same manner that land animals exude smells. Six or more weeks after the larva penetrates the snail, forked-tail forms begin to escape each time it enters the water. These tailed forms have a tiny immature body like that of adult flukes plus sets of glands and spines which make it easy for them to penetrate human skin. After leaving the snail, they swim near the surface of the water and wait for a contact which will permit them to enter and develop to maturity in the blood vessels of a dog, cow, rat, or man.

The rice culture beds of the lower Yangtze valley form a most favorable environment for the completion of the Japanese blood fluke life cycle. The snail intermediate hosts are frequently present in the beds themselves and on the banks of the small canals from which the beds are irrigated. When rice seedbeds are first planted, they are heavily fertilized with fecal material containing blood fluke eggs. If the fertilizer is less than two weeks old, larvae hatch from the eggs and infect the snails. By the time rice seedlings are ready for transplanting to large fields, infective fork-tailed larvae begin to emerge from the snails. Since the job of pulling the rice plants from the culture bed frequently is done by bare-footed younger members of the family whose hands and feet are in the water for long periods of time, the fluke larvae have ample opportunity to penetrate and set up infections. As a result, many of the deaths from blood fluke disease are among boys in their late teens or early twenties. The long slow course of the disease sometimes requires ten to fifteen years to reach its climax.

Boatmen also become infected with blood flukes because they frequently have occasion to enter infected canal water. These boatmen, moving from place to place with their cargoes and consistently using the canals as latrines, play a definite part in spreading the disease over wide areas.

All four of the Chinese farmer's occupational diseases—

hookworm, liver fluke, intestinal fluke, and blood fluke—depend on specific farming practices in which human excrement is used as part of an age-old agricultural system. The means by which the Chinese farmer has been able to feed the mouths of China's population has also resulted in the development and maintenance of these important diseases.

There is another worm parasite found in many parts of the world which is common in China and which clearly illustrates other aspects of the problem of fecal-borne diseases. It is the common intestinal round worm, *Ascaris lumbricoides*. The specific name of this worm, *lumbricoides*, means "earthworm like." It is an apt description, for the adult female ascarid is almost a foot long and almost as thick as a lead pencil. The male is two or more inches shorter and about half as thick.

The life cycle of *Ascaris* is simpler than that of the flukes. Daily, each female lays about two hundred thousand eggs enclosed in a two-layered shell that provides a high degree of protection during their stay outside the host. In summer temperatures and in moist places the eggs form infective larvae in about two weeks. The larva remains inside the egg-shell until it is swallowed by a human being. Then it hatches in the small intestine. Instead of remaining there, it penetrates the intestinal wall, enters the blood stream, is swept along to the heart and pumped out to the lung where, like the hookworm larva, it breaks out into the air sacs. The cilia lining the lung sweep it up to the mouth. Only when it is swallowed into the intestine the second time does it grow to maturity. About a month after the infective egg is swallowed, the adult worm begins to lay eggs.

The conditions for the completion of this life cycle are simple. The eggs of the worms, after leaving the host, must find a suitable environment in which to develop to the infective stage. Infective eggs must be eaten in order to infect a person. Since adult worms live for only about a year, the number of worms present in a population group at any one time is the same as the number of infective eggs they have eaten during the preceding twelve months. By means of an egg-counting technique, it is possible to determine not only who has ascarids, but roughly how many worms he harbors. This method has been used quite extensively in a number of places in China. We found, for example, that about 95 per cent of all rural people in Shantung province harbored ascarids, and that the average for the entire population was fourteen worms per person. City dwellers in Shantung were 35 per cent positive, with an average of five worms apiece for the entire population. In Szechuan, in the lower Yangtze valley, and in the area around Canton, 98 per cent of the country people were infected with an average of thirty-five worms per person, while city dwellers in the same areas had an infection rate of more than 50 per cent with about ten worms per person. The comparatively larger numbers of worms in the rice areas are due to a warmer climate, which permits the eggs to survive in greater numbers and to develop to infectivity during a greater portion of the year.

On the basis of these figures, if the conservative assumption is made that each of the 400 million rural people harbors twenty worms, and each of the 100 million city people harbors six worms, we may then arrive at an estimate of 8 billion ascarids now living in the intestines of the people of China. If all these worms were strung together they would form a worm 1,221,000 miles long—long enough to wrap around the equator almost fifty times. In total they would weigh 130,900 tons, or equal in weight about two million adult Chinese. Since about half the worms are females, and since each female produces about 200,000 eggs each day, it may be estimated that there are 860 trillion ascarid eggs being passed into the Chinese environment each day—1,720,000 eggs for every man, woman, and child in China.

Why are these worms present in such astronomical numbers and with such universality among all groups? The principal answer is that the household environment is so universally polluted by children that most of the population is in more or less constant contact with soil in which infective ascarid eggs can be found. To prove this point, we have examined soil samples swept up from the floors, courtyards, and streets in and around more than a thousand city and country homes in Shantung province. We have yet to find a single household in which ascarid eggs could not be found. Most children under five or six years of age wear split pants made so that no adult help is needed for the toilet. As a result, they keep the household environment constantly seeded with ascarid eggs. The worm is most common in children, for, of all ages, theirs has the closest and most continuous contact with the soil.

In addition to the constant pollution of the household environment, unsanitary latrines are a source from which ascarid eggs are spread. Finally, the constant and widespread use of night soil causes a wide distribution of eggs outside the home. Only a hundred fifty years ago this type of environmental pollution was the rule throughout the world.

Fortunately, infection with ascarids is not usually fatal; indeed, in most cases, these worms do no measurable damage to their hosts. But they do cause some deaths and a constant loss of nourishment from food eaten, particularly among small children. The facts about ascarid infection in China have been cited not so much because this parasite in itself is an important menace but in order to underline the extremely poor environmental and sanitation conditions that exist over and above the specialized conditions producing the occupational diseases of the Chinese farmer. Such lack of sanitation opens the way not only for fecal-borne diseases caused by worms but also for the protozoa- and bacteria-caused, fecal-borne diseases.

First there are the dysenteries, amoebic and bacillary. Amoebic dysentery is caused by a species of parasitic amoeba known scientifically as *Endamoeba histolytica*. The infective stage of this parasite is a cyst formed from the whole body of the amoeba just before it is passed out of the body of an infected person. These cysts are able to survive for some days outside the human body and infect a new host when they are eaten with food or swallowed with contaminated water. In the intestine, the cyst breaks open and four small amoebae emerge to attack the wall of the intestine. There they multiply with great rapidity and cause the intestinal wall to ulcerate. It is the reaction of the body to this process that results in the dysentery in which blood appears in frequent, watery stools. In some cases the amoebae enter the blood stream and are carried to the liver, where they cause liver abscess.

Not everyone who carries *Endamoeba histolytica* has amoebic dysentery. Indeed, the records show that only about 10 per cent of those who harbor the parasites have had symptoms that can be ascribed to injuries caused by amoebae. In China, contrary to all expectation, infection with dysentery amoeba and amoebic dysentery is more common in the north than in the south. Why contrary to expectation? One would expect that the amoebae cysts would be able to survive more widely and for a longer time in the humid warm south where liquid fertilizer is used than they would in the cooler, drier north where dried fertilizers are used. Theoretically this supposition is true. But southerners eat cooked rice with chopsticks while it is still hot, while northerners eat cold breads, usually with dirty hands. Flies contaminate the bread with amoeba cysts; dirty hands contaminate the bread. Result: more amoebae in the people of North China.

Bacillary dysentery is more common, more widespread, and the cause of more deaths than any other of the fecal-borne diseases. It is caused by a bacillus that is transmitted from person to person in contaminated food and water and by direct contact. Since it confers little or no immunity, a person can have it repeatedly. It is virulent, and children are particularly susceptible. The same general conditions of ignorance and lack of sanitation that make ascarids so common contribute materially to the prevalence of this deadly disease.

Typhoid fever and the paratyphoids, A and B, are, next to bacillary dysentery, the most deadly of the whole group, and these are fostered by the same conditions that permit bacillary dysentery.

Asiatic cholera is last on the list of deadly bacterial fecal-borne diseases. This disease, caused by a comma-shaped vibrio that secretes a powerful toxin, regularly sweeps through China in epidemics of greater or less severity each summer. The organism finds its way into the human mouth through flies, fingers, food, and water, just as in the cases of bacillary dysentery and typhoid fever. It strikes the individual with great suddenness, and death frequently occurs in a matter of hours after the first sign of illness. If given prompt treatment, principally by continuous injection of saline solution, a high percentage of those attacked can be saved. Without treatment, deaths may run higher than 50 per cent.

As this was written, a cholera epidemic was building toward its climax in Chungking. The first cases appeared early in June, 1945, and, in a matter of a few weeks, were numbered by the hundreds, with deaths by the scores. Most of those attacked were the poor who lived crowded together, although more affluent members of the community were not completely unaffected. Everyone is extremely afraid of cholera, and the city had been swept by rumors and stories about the disease. Soon after the epidemic started almost every house in the city suddenly had crosses made of red paper fastened over the door. The stories that led to the belief that these crosses were a magic protection against cholera illustrate the ideas still held by the great mass of Chinese concerning the causes of disease in general and cholera in particular.

According to one of the stories, three travelers applied for a room in a hotel late one evening early in June. Since they were a young man and his wife, accompanied by an old woman who might have been his mother, and since it was late, the sleepy clerk assigned them all to the last vacant room. Because they were well dressed and respectable looking, the clerk told them they might pay the following morning. During the night people in the rooms next to the three overheard them talking.

"Our work has just started," the old woman was heard to say. "We must work quickly if we are to fulfill our orders."

"But remember," another voice said, "we are not to do any work in homes where there is a red cross above the door."

The people overhearing this conversation thought nothing of it until the next morning when the clerk came to collect from the three travelers. The door to the room was locked and the beds had not been used. The travelers, who could have left by no other route than past the desk, were nowhere to be found. The clerk made a scene, demanding to know where the three travelers had gone, and it was then that the words overheard during the night were repeated. Everyone realized that the travelers were spirits from the nether world come to steal souls.

The point of a second story is the same, but the details are totally different. There was an old Mrs. Wang who lived alone in two rooms opening on a poor alley. Late one night in early June she was wakened by a visitor at her door. An old woman was begging for a place to spend the night.

"I'm a lone woman here," said Mrs. Wang, "and I have no place for guests. Please go away."

"But it is late," replied the traveler. "All the inns are full and I can't spend the night on the street. I'm just an old woman, and I can sleep anywhere."

After much pleading, Mrs. Wang relented and permitted the old woman to sleep across some benches in her front room. During the night the traveler was suddenly taken ill, and before Mrs. Wang could call help, she died. Then, indeed, Mrs. Wang regretted her act of hospitality, for now she would have to bury the woman.

Early next morning Mrs. Wang started out to arrange for a cheap coffin. Once it had been purchased and delivered, the poverty-stricken Mrs. Wang had no money left to have it carried out. She spent the whole afternoon trying to borrow more money from her friends, but when night came the coffin was still sitting in her front room. There was nothing to do but wait until the following day.

Late that evening, Mrs. Wang again heard someone calling at her door. She hesitated, then went reluctantly to see who it was, and again found an old woman begging for a place to spend the night.

"Last night I took in a stranger," whined Mrs. Wang. "In the middle of the night she died and I had to spend my last cent and borrow money to buy a coffin for her. I certainly can't take anyone in tonight."

"I won't die," promised the second traveler. "Besides, aren't you frightened to stay all alone with that dead woman in there? I'll keep you company. I'll watch by the coffin so you can get some sleep."

After much pleading, Mrs. Wang relented and let her in for the night. It was agreed that the traveler would stay in the room with the coffin while Mrs. Wang lay down in her inner room. After these strange events, Mrs. Wang was too restless to sleep, and when she heard a noise from the coffin in the other room she crept to the door and peeped through a crack. There she saw the dead woman sitting up in the coffin talking with the second traveler.

"How are you getting along with your work?" the dead woman asked.

"Oh, all right, I guess, but my work is going to be much

more troublesome. I have just received orders that I am not to work in any houses where there are red crosses above the door."

Mrs. Wang was so frightened that she could do nothing but crawl back into bed and nervously wait for morning. After sleepless hours the room gradually turned light with the new dawn, and people began to move about in the alley. At last Mrs. Wang plucked up courage and went into the outer room. There was no one there. The door was bolted securely on the inside, and the coffin was empty with its lid firmly in place just as she had left it when neighbors helped her to lay the old woman in it.

After these two stories, and no doubt others like them, had been passed from mouth to mouth and from teahouse to teahouse throughout the city the red crosses suddenly appeared above the doors of nearly every home. Red has long been a color that the Chinese believe will ward off evil spirits sent now and then by the chief deity of the nether world to steal souls in extraordinary numbers. So tenacious are the thoughts and emotions of years gone by that the great majority of Chinese, even including some with modern educations, easily integrate the Red Cross symbol of modern medicine and mercy into the old superstitions that still command credence.

A few days after the red crosses appeared, the police had them taken down, and special hospitals for the treatment of cholera were organized. One of the acute problems was the shortage of needles and syringes for injection of cholera vaccine. Another problem was the dearth of stills to produce enough pure distilled water for the huge quantities of saline solution needed for constant injections into each patient. In addition, the crowded and unsanitary conditions of all Chinese cities, aggravated by teeming refugees, made it almost impossible to prevent cases from occurring. This was particularly true in a city like Chungking where most of the excess population was crowded into temporary, mud-plaster shacks built after most of the city had been bombed flat three times, and where even the inadequate water system was outgrown, weakened, and in need of repairs.

It can be positively asserted that cholera epidemics will continue to occur in China for a good many years—until education, expanding medical and public health services, and a rising standard of living make possible the modification of the conditions favoring cholera and the supplying of services for prevention and control.

Popular Health and Medical Ideas

In spite of the fact that modern medicine was introduced into China more than one hundred years ago by the missionary movement, and in spite of the fact that enormous progress has been made in the development of scientific medicine as a result of both missionary and national activity, it must be recognized that the dominating health and medical ideas held by the Chinese people are still prescientific. The persistence of these ideas creates one of the stubborn problems delaying general improvement in the health of the Chinese people.

The roots of notions such as those which made possible the sudden blooming of red crosses as defense against cholera go back for at least three thousand years to two fundamental doctrines. These doctrines were already old when Confucius lived, more than five hundred years before Christ, but they were first recorded at the time of Confucius and given such prestige by his contemporary sages that they have dominated Chinese medicine ever since. The effect was to entrust the study of medicine to visionary philosophers whose scholastic subtleties were so revered by the people that all medical theories and practices have been characterized by a petrified formalism and a pedantic excess of detail.

The first of these doctrines is the Doctrine of the Two

Principles, called *yang* and *yin*. These are fancied philosophical concepts from which everything is believed to have
originated. The yang principle represents the male force
while the yin represents the female. They stand for heaven
and earth, the sun and the moon, day and night, heat and
cold, life and death, positive and negative, strong and weak.
The two principles are represented diagrammatically as a
circle divided into two pear-shaped bodies by a double
curved line. Around this circular symbol usually are drawn
the "eight trigrams" which consist of various combinations of three solid or broken lines that never repeat their
combinations. Each trigram stands for one of the eight
points of the compass and has a special name with a fanci-
ful symbolic meaning. Confucius was greatly enamored of
these figures and said that if he could devote fifty years to
their study he might attain wisdom. Chinese ideas of disease are mostly formed out of this kind of free imaginative
nonsense.

In medicine, everything is classified as yang or yin. The
skin or surface of the human body is yang, the interior yin.
The back is yang, the abdomen yin. The empty organs are
yang, the solid organs are yin. Of the five viscera the heart
and liver are yang organs, and the spleen, lungs, and kidneys
are yin organs. Within the yang there is always something
of yin, and within yin there is likewise something of yang.
Thus, since the back is yang and the lung is yin there is a
yin within a yang. The abdomen is yin, but the liver is yang;
therefore it is a yang within a yin. Again, the back is yang
and the heart is another yang, providing a yang within a
yang. Similarly, since the abdomen is yin and the spleen is
another yin, there is a yin within a yin. A disease is yang
when it is due to external causes and yin when due to internal causes. Thus fever, afflictions of the upper body, respiratory diseases, or those in which the onset is sudden, or
which prevent the patient from bending his body, are yang

diseases. Chills, afflictions of the lower body, circulatory diseases, or those in which the onset is gradual, or which prevent the patient from lying on his back, are yin diseases. A yang pulse is strong, bounding, and large in volume, while a yin pulse is weak and of low tension. When the yin predominates, one suffers from yang disease; when the yang is in excess, a yin disease results. Excessive yang causes fever; excessive yin causes chills. Drugs are divided into the same two classes, stimulants, resolvents, expectorants, pungent substances, and hot decoctions being classified as yang drugs, while astringents, purgatives, hematics, bitter substances, and cold infusions are yin drugs. When treating diseases all these things must be kept in mind.

The second doctrine is the existence of Five Elements—metal, wood, water, fire, and earth. The human frame is supposed to be composed of a harmonious mixture of these primordial substances. So long as the proportions remain proper, health results. If the balance is disturbed, disease follows. The five elements interact on each other to generate or subjugate each other as follows: wood generates fire, fire generates earth, earth generates metal, metal generates water, and water generates wood. Likewise, wood subjugates earth, earth subjugates water, water subjugates fire, fire subjugates metal, and metal subjugates wood. The derivation of these relationships is obvious.

Corresponding with the five elements are the five organs of the body—spleen, liver, heart, lungs, and kidneys. These five organs are further related to a whole group of thirteen different classes of things which fall into fives, such as the five planets, colors, tastes, climates, directions (the fifth direction is center), emotions, and so on. This whole complex of ideas, built essentially on relationships imagined to exist between the names of things without any reference to their real nature, forms the basis of a system of hocus pocus, so massive and so complex that it could swallow whole the best efforts of the astrologers of New York, London, or Paris without visible effect.

There is evidence that before the time of Confucius there was some actual dissection of the human body, but after the sage taught that the body was sacred, all attempts to learn about it by dissection were abandoned. Even today it is almost impossible to gain permission for an autopsy in order to determine cause of death, with the result that Chinese pathologists have a difficult time obtaining material with which to teach students. Ideas concerning anatomy have been generated by guesswork to such an extent that authorities still state that each of the five organs is supposed to communicate with the tongue—the liver with the eyes, the spleen with the mouth, the lungs with the nose, and the kidneys with the ear.

The ordinary man in the street believes that the brain is the abode of the yin principle and that at the base of the brain there is a reservoir of marrow. He believes that the lungs consist of six lobes, or leaves, suspended from the spine, four on one side and two on the other, that sound proceeds from holes in them, and that they rule the various parts of the body. The pit of the stomach is the seat of breath and the source of joy and delight. The heart lies beneath the lungs, is the prince of the body, and the generator of thoughts. The liver is on the right side, has seven lobes, is the residence of the soul and the originator of schemes. The gallbladder, projecting into the liver from below, ascends when its owner becomes angry. Since courage dwells within the gallbladder, the gallbladders of bears or tigers will impart courage when eaten.

Chinese medicine is stylized and has a numbers game all its own. There are, for example, three souls and three germs which reside in the head, in the abdomen, and in the feet. There are four methods of diagnosis—by observation, by auscultation, by interrogation, and by palpation. The number five, however, is far more popular and far more extensively employed. In addition to the five organs, there are five kinds of afflictions (dumb, deaf, lame, deformed, and dwarfed) and five kinds of suffering (birth, senility, illness, death, and parting). Many diseases such as gonorrhea, piles, jaundice, and dyspepsia have five varieties each. Injuries also are of five kinds—overuse of the eyes injures the energy; too much sleep injures the vitality; prolonged sitting injures the muscles; protracted standing injures the bones; and excessive walking injures the tendons. Numbers other than five have special meanings. A girl changes her teeth at seven, menstruates at fourteen, reaches maturity at twenty-one, attains the height of development at twenty-eight, begins to decline at thirty-five, shows signs of decay at forty-two, and the menses stop at forty-nine. A boy experiences similar changes at periods fixed by the number eight and its multiples.

During the course of the centuries, the feeling of the pulse became the most important method of diagnosis. According to an elaborate doctrine, there are three different places on each arm where the pulse must be taken, and since each of these three places has two pulses, external and internal, there are twelve pulses in all—six in each arm. The taking of the pulse is a solemn rite, the most propitious time being at sunrise. The physician uses his right hand for taking the left pulse and his left hand for taking the right pulse, the three fingers, index, middle, and third being used on the appropriate three places just above the wrist joints. The physician must keep cool and collected, making sure that his own breathing is in order since one inhalation and one exhalation constitute one cycle of respiration. The normal pulse is four beats to one respiration.

The list of variations of the pulse is a long one. Not only are the rate, character, rhythm, volumes, tension, etc., carefully observed, but the age, sex, temperament, constitution, weight, and growth of the patient, as well as the time of day, season of the year, and influence of the constellation are taken into careful consideration. These fine distinctions, however, exist only on paper, for no one can give a satisfactory demonstration of them. Each of the twelve pulses is believed to indicate the state of health of one of the organs, but the authorities disagree as to which pulse belongs to which organ. This naturally results in many differing systems of diagnosis, all having little to do with actual causes of illness.

Both Buddhism and Taoism have contributed their quotas of magical ideas to the treatment of disease. The theories and charms involved are too complex and numerous to be recounted in any detail, but they contribute to the confusion of nostrums through which the great majority of Chinese still seek relief and cure of illness.

The Chinese are great believers in medicines, and their writings on materia medica extend as far back as any of their written records. Their greatest work on this subject was written by Li Shi-chen, a city magistrate who lived during the Ming Dynasty. His *The Great Herbal*, written between 1552 and 1578, was submitted to the emperor by Li's son and published in 1595. It is an exhaustive treatise of fifty-two volumes in which the material discussed is arranged in sixty-two orders under sixteen classes. These sixteen classes are: water, fire, earth, metals and minerals, herbs, grains, vegetables, fruits, trees, garments and utensils, insects, fishes, mollusca, birds, beasts, and men. In all, 1,871 different substances are described, and 8,160 recipes are given. Of the drugs mentioned, 1,074 are derived from plants, 443 from animals, and 354 from minerals and other substances.

Among the weird substances listed as having great medicinal value are thirty-five different parts of the human body. It was probably a combination of information from *The Great Herbal* and doctrines of Confucian filial piety that resulted in an interesting medical incident at Chungking some years ago. A young girl was brought into the Methodist Hospital for emergency treatment. She had a gash through her abdominal wall just below the right ribs, exposing her liver, and it was obvious that a piece of the liver had been cut away. The doctor in charge sewed up the wound and then started asking questions.

The girl's mother, it developed, was desperately ill. Somewhere the girl had heard that a piece of human liver removed by its owner was especially effective in the cure of disease. She had heard that the effectiveness of this gruesome medicine was further increased if offered to a parent as an act of filial loyalty by a child. After the family had tried many drugs and many doctors to no avail, the girl slashed open her abdomen and cut out a piece of her liver. With her own hands she cooked it and fed it to her mother. Friends who had heard that the foreign doctors in Chungking were famous for their surgery then loaded the daughter on a boat and brought her to the hospital.

The girl was lucky. Not only had she made a clean cut, but she had severed no large blood vessels. Bleeding from the cut liver was held to a minimum, and, thanks to the hospital treatment, she made a good recovery. Her mother recovered too, and when the story of the great cure became known throughout the city the girl was greatly honored. As a reward for her filial loyalty the magistrate gave her presents, while the merchants and public raised a purse for her. She returned home both wealthy and a heroine.

The story has a sad epilogue. As a predictable sequel to such a dramatic incident, another girl tried to cure her mother a few weeks later by the liver method. She was not lucky. She made her gash too low, cut through intestines and blood vessels, and bled to death.

Inaccurate ideas as to the physiological effects of metals on the human system probably originating from *The Great Herbal* were responsible for another case that appeared recently in a small mission hospital upriver from Chungking. A man came in with a huge abscess on one of his lower ribs. When the doctor made his incision he struck a hard metallic object and pulled out a nine-inch brass tobacco pipe. The patient revealed that he had swallowed the pipe six years before in the belief that brass was poison and would kill him. His suicidal desire thereupon diminished, while the pipe worked its way through the stomach wall, struck a rib, caused part of the bone to break down, and finally produced the swelling and abscess. When the deteriorated bone had been removed the patient made a perfect recovery.

Self-medication is still the rule rather than the exception among the majority, and anyone who can write with a brush and read is considered capable of prescribing. Time and again patients die while neighbors or aged grandmothers ply them with all kinds of noxious preparations. If the drugs are ineffective, magic is invoked, with the grandmother reviling or enjoining the spirits according to her diagnosis. Priests may be called in, or a visit may be made to a temple where a bamboo tally is shaken, with appropriate ceremony, from a section of bamboo filled with tallies. Written on this tally is the lucky number of the prescription supposed to cure. Frequently these prescriptions contain ingredients available only at the temple for a slight fee. Very frequently the "Universal Life Saving Powder" supplied by the priests is nothing but ashes from the incense pot.

Slowly, modern scientific medicine is winning its way through the maze of beliefs and superstitions, but the day when all Chinese will be treated by enlightened methods is still far in the future.

The medical forces that China commands today are pitifully inadequate for the tasks confronting them. Again there are no completely accurate figures, but there are listed some 8,000 or 9,000 so-called modern doctors in China at the present time. Hsia Yi-yung, while doing research for the American Bureau for Medical Aid to China in 1946, estimated that only 1,000 or 1,500 of these modern doctors might be classified as properly trained, and that possibly a few hundred might be considered well qualified by American standards. Even if the figure of 9,000 doctors is accepted, there is only one doctor for every 55,000 people, as compared with one for every 921 people in the United States.

The situation in regard to nurses, pharmacists, and other types of specialized medical personnel is even more acute. At the present time the National Health Administration estimates that there are a few more than 5,000 nurses engaged in their profession in all China. This is the smallest number that China has had for many years, as a result of war and marriage. Because spinsters occupy a low and uncomfortable position in Chinese society, nurses spend relatively few years at their work. China's record of one nurse to every 100,000 people is a contrast to the American ratio of one nurse for every 374 persons.

The shortage of trained dentists, however, is the most severe. There are a few more than 300 registered dentists in all China. This means that there is one dentist for each 1,600,000 people in contrast to America's one dentist for every 1,955 persons. There are, however, many thousands of old-fashioned dental practitioners, among whom are many women who make their living by removing "tooth worms." The "worm remover" goes through an elaborate set of maneuvers, and by sleight of hand produces the worm or worms according to the fee agreed upon. Frequently they relieve the pain in the tooth by placing a lime cement in the cavity, although many times the power of suggestion is an adequate "cure." Then there are old-style "tooth removers" to be found at almost any fair or market, their booths decorated with strings or piles of teeth. For the most part they remove teeth that have already been loosened by chronic or acute inflammatory conditions. "Tooth cleaners" often do a good job, but they may do considerable harm by using a solution of hydrochloric acid which dissolves the outer enamel surface leaving the tooth rough and probably more susceptible to caries and the accumulation of stains. Finally, among the quacks, are the "tooth fitters." They offer to restore lost teeth by full or partial dentures or to cover decayed areas with a more-or-less tooth-shaped cap of gold, brass, or silver. Or, catering to the human desire for adornment, they will cap perfectly good front teeth with glittering metal. It has been estimated that there are at least 5,000 tooth fitters in China. A count made in Chengtu in 1934 revealed thirty-nine shops doing this work. Not only are trained dentists very few in number, but there are now only two qualified colleges of dentistry in the entire country.

The National Health Administration is striving to develop a medical-health organization which can begin to make modern health information and medicine available to the great mass of Chinese people. Most doctors live in large cities where there is enough wealth to make private practice lucrative. Almost nowhere, except in missionary or state-supported organizations, are doctors serving the great rural masses that are too poverty-stricken to support private practitioners. In an effort to alleviate this situation, the National Health Administration of the National Government has planned and is beginning to carry out a nation-wide system of tax-supported medical-health services. The program is called "medical-health" because it includes medical services directed toward the cure of disease and health services directed toward prevention of disease. The program has been continually delayed by war, inflation, lack of trained personnel, drugs, and medical equipment. Nevertheless, it has made some progress in the establishment of clinics, in vaccinations, and in epidemic-prevention work.

The fact that the medical-health program has begun to create a demand for modern medical service among village folk of formerly isolated and backward China was apparent during a trip I made through Szechuan province during World War II. We were traveling from Chungking to Chengtu in an ambulance, and in almost every village we were flagged down by farm folk who expected that we would set up a clinic and treat their boils and their ills just as the medical-health teams did.

No aspect of the national medical-health program of China has traveled wider or gained more acceptance than the work of maternity and child-welfare clinics. Rumor has spread into the most remote corners of China that modern trained doctors and nurses know how to handle obstetrical cases much better and more safely than the old-fashioned midwives. When, during the war, American Army and the Friends Ambulance Unit medical teams penetrated deep into the mountains in western Yünnan, where modern medical services had never been seen before, they were besieged at once by obstetrical cases.

China's health problems are manifold, and the ignorance from which they spring is deep-seated. Many of her most common causes of illness and disease are rooted in the very structure of her overcrowded peasant society. As a nation, she emerges from an eight-year War of Resistance with limited and inadequate forces for coping with her medical and health problems.

Chapter VI

Education

PERHAPS NOWHERE IN THE WORLD IS LEARNING MORE revered than in China, yet there are few places where a larger percentage of the population is without formal education. While almost everyone is trained in some skill or another, whether it be farming or a trade, in no other equally large population is the general level of modern knowledge so low.

In the broad sense of the word "education" it cannot be said that a ricksha man is "uneducated" if he possesses a vast and ready knowledge of his own culture and folklore, can sing the most famous parts of his great operas or repeat long and pertinent passages from the equivalent of Shakespeare or Schiller even if he can't read and write. Yet this type of cultural information is common throughout China.

Education in this broad sense penetrates deep into the life of the Chinese people. The entire culture of the country is based firmly on the writings of the sages who lived five hundred years before Christ and who recorded the knowledge of the previous three thousand years and gave to it the prestige and historical influence it still possesses. The greatest and most influential of these sages was Confucius, a teacher on whose work was built the more than 2,000-year-old Chinese educational philosophy and content.

The focus of Chinese education was the system of imperial civil service examinations, first established more than two thousand years ago by the Western Han dynasty. It was a system which inspired the commendatory writings of many of the first European visitors to China, and which indirectly influenced the pattern of our own civil service. During the time of Addison and Steele, several English writers mentioned the desirability of the Chinese system whereby any citizen might attain high public office by means of knowledge alone.

These examinations, which continued from the year 165 B.C. until they were abolished by imperial edict in 1905, exerted a profound influence not only on education but on the whole social system. Any person who felt himself qualified might take the lowest grade of examination given each year in the local hsien magistrate's *yamen*. If successful, the candidate possessing the equivalent of a primary school education was eligible for the provincial examinations and for appointment to one of the lower ranking positions of government. If the candidate then passed the provincial examination, he assumed a more advanced title and was eligible for the national and highest examination as well as for more responsible government positions. Those successful at the highest examinations became full-fledged scholars and, when appointed, sacrosanct officials, who, under the prevailing family system, raised not only themselves but their entire clan to an enviable social position. Because all examinations were literary in content, Chinese education is literary by tradition, and Chinese officialdom down through the centuries has been composed of the literati.

Since official posts carried with them social prestige and opportunities to accumulate wealth, it was not long until education, wealth, and official position became practically synonymous and the perquisites of a relatively small group. The scholar who had passed an official examination had special immunity before the law. He could not be given corporal punishment, and his person must be respected and kept inviolate. The scholar, with this special position, frequently became the spokesman of the poor and the oppressed of his community. Over and over again it was the scholar who restored integrity to Chinese government after periods of corruption and venality. Even today, nearly fifty years after the abolition of the old-style examinations, the student and scholarly groups in China enjoy a very special position in the community. It is for this reason that student movements play such an important part in China's modern political history, just as they have in centuries past.

Down the generations families have risen to or lost their foothold in this educated class. They have risen because of the ability of a brilliant son, for it has always been possible for a lad with exceptional ability and with an opportunity to study to obtain official position. Many poor families have made great sacrifices to educate their most capable sons because they have known that by success in his scholarly pursuits he could elevate the fortune of the whole clan in a single generation.

The flaw in this system has always been the problem of the opportunity to study, since the type of learning necessary can be acquired only by many years of effort. Even the most brilliant cannot master the complicated and difficult Chinese language and literature in odd moments. The student must have his entire time free from the demands of other work, and he must have both books and teachers. While some poor families in every generation have succeeded in providing these conditions for their sons, most of those who obtained the opportunity to study came from the wealthier families who could afford the books, teachers, and living costs of sons who spent their days at study. In many cases the father and grandfather were the first instructors. Consequently a large proportion of educated officialdom came from already scholarly families.

The old-style education, preparing for the examinations, was entirely classical and literary and was dominated by the elements of Confucian morality (a precept somewhat analogous to the contents of McGuffey's Readers used in American schools since 1836, except that the Chinese classics comprised the sum and total of Chinese education). Dr. Arthur H. Smith, in writing of the limitations of Chinese classics as educational texts, commented in his *Village Life in China:*

> Regarded as the sole text books for a great nation they [the classics] are fatally defective. They are too desultory, and too limited in their range. Epigrammatic moral maxims, scraps of biography, nodules of a sort of political economy, bits of history, rules of etiquette, and a great variety of other subjects, are commingled without plan, symmetry, or progress of thought. The chief defects are the triviality of many of the subjects, the limitation in range, and the inadequacy of treatment.

Nevertheless, the Chinese classics were advanced at the time of their origin, and the system of examinations and officialdom based upon them remained unique until the French Revolution led to a similar civil service system in 1791, exactly 1,956 years after its Chinese origin.

For the successful scholars, education began early in life. It was not uncommon for a child of two or three to begin recognizing characters, and at four or five to study with his father or grandfather, if he was fortunate enough to belong to an educated family. At eight or nine the neophyte began to work with a hired tutor or to attend a small private tutorial school maintained by a retired local scholar or someone who preferred teaching to government service. Almost from the first day of study the child began with the classics, reading the abstruse and profound ideas of Confucius and the other sages, ideas made even more difficult by the highly condensed form of literary writing developed in complicated ideographs. Although the child had little conception of the meaning of the sentences memorized, he was required to hammer away day after day, pounding the classics into his nervous system until he could *pei* them word for word without error. To pei, or "to back," is to turn the back to the teacher and repeat in a high singsong voice the memorized but little understood words of the classic texts.

It was from this historic method of "backing" that the Chinese practice of studying aloud came into being—a system which never fails to arouse the curiosity and interest of foreign visitors, although it is sometimes employed in the teaching of foreign languages in American schools. The practice, still prevalent, is even used in modern Chinese schools. It was brought home to me almost daily by the high singsong voice of my cook's little boy as he sat out of doors repeating in a shrill meaningless monotone, *"Che shih woti fangtze. Woti fangtze shih wo chuti ti fang . . . "* —"This is my house. My house is where I live . . . " and so on through an interesting little modern reader which was certainly not intended to be read in a high monotone.

This classical method of preparation for the imperial examinations produced many thousands of brilliant scholars through the years of China's long history. Among them were men who initiated and maintained numerous periods of great prosperity and cultural achievement, who produced a huge mass of literature and philosophy, and who developed the Chinese language as a medium of expressing and recording rich contributions to human thinking and experience.

On the other hand, the old classical education saddled China with two persistent curses. It has laid the curse of ignorance on the masses, and it has laid the curse of the scholar on the educated.

The curse of ignorance exists because the language structure, the nature, and the teaching methods of classical learning are much too difficult for the average person to grasp in a short time, with the result that the knowledge of the average peasant in China today is severely limited. Most of them spend their entire lives within walking distance of the house in which they were born. Most of them have never seen a map and cannot conceive of anything alien to their immediate experience. One day, for example, a group of Hopei peasant boys who had been conscripted into the Chinese army at the end of the war was watching the loading of a four-motored transport plane bound for Shanghai. I sauntered up to them and opened a conversation.

"It's a big plane, isn't it?" I said.

"You speak Chinese!" they exclaimed. "Where will this plane go?"

"We are going to Shanghai," I replied.

"How long will it take you to go there?" one of the boys asked.

"Between four and five hours."

"Shanghai is in that direction, isn't it?" another asked, pointing in the general direction of the Himalayas.

"No, Shanghai is straight south," corrected another, "and it's more than a thousand li away, too." (A *li* is a third of a mile.)

"Shanghai is off to the southeast in that direction," I said, pointing, "and it is more than two thousand five hundred li from here in a straight line."

These boys had all heard of Shanghai. They knew it was somewhere to the south, but they had no clear idea of how far or precisely where, even though residents of North China are exact about directions in their own areas. Within a few minutes the peasant boys had eagerly accepted my invitation to help load baggage so they might see the inside of the plane.

The same lack of geographical knowledge, coupled with complete ignorance of distance and speed of flight, was the cause of one abortive expedition made by young Chinese recruits who had been flown into India for basic training. After a few days of talking the matter over, several homesick boys went AWOL and started to walk home, following a dusty road eastward across the plains of Central India, still so far from the great mountain ranges separating China from India that they could not see them. After they were intercepted by trucks and returned to camp, they were questioned by officers.

"We were just walking home," explained a spokesman. "We were homesick."

"But don't you know it is too far to walk?"

"It can't be very far," was the reply, "for it only took a few hours to come here from Kunming."

Scores of times, on trains, at country markets, and in villages, I have been engaged in conversations that ran about like this:

"Sir, what is your honorable country?"

"I come from America."

"Does it rain in your country?"

"Yes, it rains in my country. In some parts it is very wet, but in others it is dry. The amount of rain that falls varies from place to place in my country just as it does in China."

"Is it hot in your country?"

"My country is very large, just as China is, so it is hot in the south and cold in the north just as it is here."

"Do you have wheat in your country?"

"Yes, we grow a great deal of wheat."

"Do you have millet in your country?" "Do you have cows in your country?" "What do you make your houses of?" "Are there mules in your country?" And so on endlessly for as long as I would continue to answer. A monstrous ignorance and a mighty curiosity.

Most Chinese peasants are anything but stupid. Their knowledge of their own folklore and folk history is extensive, although it is frequently far from being historically accurate. Usually the history the country person knows has been learned at the opera, and he is frequently unable to say whether a certain character is a real person who lived at a definite time or merely the creation of a dramatist. This confusion is the more frequent because so many of the characters of Chinese drama are patterned after actual people of history.

The curse of the scholar, which lies equally heavily on the educated of China, may be summed up in the proverb: "The scholar can neither shoulder a carrying pole nor lift a basket."

All China accepts the fact that an educated man does not work with his hands. He is considered to be so far above the need for physical effort that nothing would cause him to lose face more completely than to descend to its level. It might be added that the long years of mental labor necessary to master Chinese learning usually undermine the physique of scholars to such an extent that they are unfit for bodily efforts (N.B. the statistics on tuberculosis among students). Because this tradition is held by those who work, as well as by the scholars themselves, many young scientists and engineers returning to China with advanced foreign training, eager to do great things for their country, have their initiative extinguished by community condemnation whenever they engage in shop or laboratory work.

These two great curses of Chinese knowledge, the curse of ignorance and the curse of the scholar, are slowly but surely diminishing. Literacy and the knowledge of things, of people, and of events are slowly spreading. The young men and women of modern China are gradually breaking away from the restrictions imposed on the scholar class.

What of China's education today? If the ability to read a simple book and to write a simple letter is taken as a definition of literacy, what proportion of the Chinese population is literate? I recently put this question to Miss K. S. Kao, lately in charge of the division of Social Education in the Shanghai Municipal Bureau of Education. "We estimate," she said, "that about forty per cent of the people of the city of Shanghai can read and write. Since Shanghai is the largest and most modern city in China we think that our literacy rate is considerably higher than that of the nation as a whole. However, we must be deeply concerned about the sixty per cent of our citizens who cannot read and write."

Peiping education authorities estimate that between 30 and 40 per cent of their population can read and write. Buck found that only a little over 15 per cent of the rural population above seven years of age could pass even the lowest test for literacy. In spite of public education efforts carried on since 1905, 75 or 80 per cent of those over seven years of age are illiterate, although more than a hundred million people can read and write. The largest daily newspaper in China has a circulation of over 100,000, but most newspapers are limited to circulations of less than 10,000.

The possibility of a literate population in China did not exist before the literary revolution that began about thirty years ago. Before that time, only the highly telegraphic classical style of writing was employed, using single literary characters to express key ideas in each sentence, a system of writing so condensed that it is almost unintelligible when read aloud. In order to understand literature at all, the reader had to see the characters, and, worse, he had to recognize many rare characters expressing ideas never used in everyday speech.

The literary revolution came when Dr. Hu Shih, graduate of Cornell and Columbia, and later ambassador to the United States, together with a group of young colleagues began to write with the same word order that is used in speaking. When this was done the number of necessary characters was greatly reduced and, fitted together into conversational sentences, became easier to learn and use. After years of controversy and continued use it was gradually accepted that to write as one speaks is good literary form. Now, while many scholars still use the literary form, most popular works are written in the spoken language or in what is known as "modern Chinese," in reality a cross between the literary form and the pure spoken language form.

As the literary revolution gained ground, the "Thousand Character" movement was initiated by Dr. Y. C. James Yen. A graduate of both Yale and Princeton, he began mass education work among the Chinese labor corps in France during World War I in order that their members might be able to write home and read simple newspapers. His movement, providing a sort of basic Chinese using only thirteen hundred characters, is the foundation for the mass education movement that has long since spread far beyond the organization he first formed.

So successful were Dr. Yen's methods, that the Ministry of Education adopted mass education principles and is conducting classes for adults in the Central People's Schools and the *pao** schools. In each pao, a group of one hundred rural families organized for political, educational, and defense purposes, the Ministry of Education intends to organize one school, with large Central People's Schools in the more populous market towns and cities. Between 1928 and 1943, almost fifty million adults were reported as having made progress toward literacy in these two types of schools and in other special adult classes. In addition, courses were broadened to include instruction in citizenship and some technical knowledge.

One of the remarkable achievements of the Chinese during World War II was the steady growth of literacy education for adults in spite of immense handicaps imposed by war. In 1936–1937, the last year of comparative peace, more than three million adults received instruction in reading and writing. In 1942–1943, during the height of the war, over nine million in unoccupied China received such instruction.

* A pao is an administrative division consisting of from 100 to 150 families that serves as a basic unit of organization in the country.

EDUCATION

It may be inferred from this and other chapters that World War II, which began as the fifth Sino-Japanese War, had an extraordinary effect on education in China and a direct bearing on the rise in the level of literacy. The calculated attempts of the Japanese to destroy educational institutions which were imparting morale, knowledge, and skill for the building of a stronger China, exemplified, for instance, by the systematic blasting of every last vestige of Tientsin's Nankai University, had the unexpected effect of sowing dragon seed. The ultimate effects, when viewed from the safe distance of history, were to unify the Chinese, to give impetus to the development of kuo-yü (Mandarin) as a common spoken language, to create a stronger and more general desire for education, to acquaint large numbers of remote people with modern ideas of health and education, and to create a more general awareness of and interest in the ultimate purpose of government.

Much was gained merely by the shifting of populations, distributing new ideas and materials, breeding modern attitudes and methods. Thousands of foreigners trekked through the most remote reaches of China, and thousands of Chinese were introduced to new and better ways of living through periods of military or industrial training in India and the United States. Among the most important causes of the broadening of thought was the overland exodus of seventy-seven colleges and universities from the enemy-occupied coast toward the hills of free China. Carrying with them almost fanatical devotion to education, they left behind, when they returned in 1946 and 1947 to their former campuses, not only a new appreciation for education itself and for better ways of living and thinking but also a new series of educational institutions spawned in areas which would have remained long untouched if left to normal educational development.

Literacy in China is extremely low, but there is no doubt

that World War II reduced ignorance, even as World War I gave birth to the Mass Education Movement that has made this improvement possible. But what of the general education system?

China's system of modern education may be said to date from the edict of September 1, 1905, which abolished the imperial civil service examinations. Continual loss of wars and territories had suggested to the occupants of the Dragon Throne that something more than classics, humanities, discipline, and contemplation was needed in Chinese education, and that additional educational facilities were necessary. Prior to that time, education was largely private, and girls usually were not considered worth educating. By 1905 there were a number of Chinese who had studied abroad who helped prod the Dragon Throne out of its traditional and antiquated conservatism, and who further influenced the trend of educational organization, curricula, and methods. To assist them there existed a nucleus of foreign mission schools and colleges exemplary of modern education already adapted to Chinese needs.

It may be observed here that in 1932 a group of European-trained educators representing the League of Nations was invited by the Chinese government to inspect the budding Chinese system of education. Among many valuable suggestions, the commission reported that the whole system was much too American. The honorable members were right.

Although the system itself dates from 1905, modern education in China goes back nearly one hundred years more to 1807 when Robert Morrison, an American Protestant missionary, arrived in South China.

The arrival of Morrison to set up a school in South China, at a time when students had to be paid to attend or recruited from an ample supply of street waifs, marked more than the beginning of a long exodus of Chinese students for study abroad. The first such student, one who originally had been coaxed to attend the Morrison school, was Yung Wing. Actually there were two others, but one of these suffered from homesickness and returned to China with all convenient speed; the other was sponsored by a Scotsman who insisted that he study in Scotland. Yung Wing not only finished his formal education at Yale College, but he returned to China as the first native proponent of modern education in China and of study abroad.

In the one hundred years that followed Morrison's arrival, literally hundreds of hospitals and schools were established in China by American private interests, and millions of American citizens acquired a very real interest in Chinese health and education. The oldest of China's modern universities, founded by American missionaries in 1864 with a student body of eight, later developed into Cheeloo University at Tsinan, Shantung province. Gradually fifteen foreign-supported colleges and universities developed. Fu Jen University at Peiping and Aurora University at Shanghai were Roman Catholic institutions, partially sponsored by American funds but staffed by Chinese and Europeans. The other thirteen were developed as Protestant ventures in international co-operation, with a large percentage of support and manpower coming from the United States. Two of them, Ginling and Hwa Nan, were the first colleges for Chinese women. Some of the thirteen institutions were chartered under the Regents of the State of New York, and all have held consistently high practical standards, equal to the best in the United States. From these American-supported institutions have come many of the men and women who now hold posts in China's educational system and in governmental and private agencies of primary importance.

In addition, the United States Government has recognized the importance of education in the establishment and maintenance of a modern, democratic China. The last empress of China, Tz'u-hsi, a recalcitrant observer of modern encroachment on her traditional domains, making a last powerful endeavor, in 1900, to drive the hated Westerners into the sea, lost to a combined army representing many nations with interests and nationals in China and was assessed an ample indemnity. When the United States Government had settled private claims for damages sustained during the Boxer Rebellion, more than $12 million remained. In 1908, during the administration of Theodore Roosevelt, the United States took the initiative in returning the surplus funds to China to be used for educational purposes (followed by Austria, Belgium, France, Germany, Great Britain, and the Netherlands, all of whom had considerably lesser claims).

With these funds, Tsing Hua College was founded in 1912 at Peking, Enjoying the nickname "Indemnity College," it later became Tsing Hua University. The purpose of this institution was to train men for further study abroad, a privilege which was extended later to successful competitors from other Chinese universities. Until inflation drastically reduced invested funds in and after 1945, each year several hundred Chinese pursued graduate study in the United States under this arrangement. In 1924, the American government having returned more indemnity funds, the Chinese and American committee (ten Chinese, five Americans) established the China Foundation for the Promotion of Education and Culture. The China Foundation in turn founded and supported scientific research institutes and libraries in China, fostered graduate research abroad, and was responsible for the founding in 1926 of the China Institute in America at New York. Since the suspension of the indemnity payments by the Chinese government at the end of 1938, both the China Foundation and the Tsing Hua Foundation have been maintained largely by dwindling endowments and other sporadic, inadequate income.

When the new national government had begun to build

the educational system of China under the republic, Professor Paul Monroe of Columbia University was called in as adviser on education. His influence was both direct and indirect, since many Chinese who were sent to study at Columbia Teachers College under pragmatist John Dewey returned imbued with modern American methods of education.

In 1921–1922 a group of American educators under the direction of Professor Ernest Burton of the University of Chicago visited China, studied Chinese educational organization and needs in conjunction with a group of Chinese educators, and issued a report containing suggestions to the Ministry of Education.

When World War II prevented free movement between China and the rest of the world from 1942 to 1945, the United States channeled into China by air a constant flow of educational material, ranging from instructions for the maintenance of typewriters to vaccines and scientific journals. In addition, many American experts in agriculture, engineering, and public health went to China during the war years at the request of the Chinese government. Released for such work by American commercial and industrial organizations, universities, and even by the armed forces and American governmental agencies, their salaries were paid or supplemented by these agencies or by the government. At the same time over five hundred Chinese students stranded in the United States for four years were permitted to continue or complete their education with American government support. Private sources also rallied to the needs of stranded Chinese students, with many state and private institutions providing scholarships and fellowships ranging from a single endowment to free tuition for all Chinese. Among other commercial benefactors, the International Harvester Company established a half million dollar program in agricultural engineering, bringing students from

China for study and maintaining chairs in the subject at two Chinese universities.

Although probably the largest number of Chinese to study abroad until World War II were Japanese-educated and many have studied in Europe, Americans have done a great deal directly and indirectly to shape the education of China. The report issued by the League of Nations commission was quite correct in its charge. During the years when the Chinese government was setting the pattern for an education system, American-trained Chinese and American-operated institutions in China provided a ready-made pattern on the spot.

In spite of all her efforts to develop primary education China still has no free compulsory education, as Westerners understand that term. Not more than 30 per cent of the children of primary school age are in school. To remedy this situation the Ministry of Education intends to set up a four-year course of study in its pao country schools and a six-year course in its Central People's Schools. Just before the last Sino-Japanese War, there were in all China 320,000 primary schools with a reported total enrollment of over 18 million. In 1942–1943 there were 258,000 primary schools in unoccupied China alone, with a reported enrollment of over 17,500,000.

The war years also saw an expansion of secondary schools, called middle schools in China. In 1936–1937 there were 3,264 middle schools registered with the Ministry of Education with a reported total of 627,246 students. By 1942–1943, in spite of war, in unoccupied China alone, and not including the "more advanced areas," there were 3,455 registered middle schools with a reported enrollment of 1,101,087. Normal schools and vocational schools at the middle school level are included in the total.

In spite of the amazing educational efforts that brought

about unprecedented expansion during the war years, the quality of education declined. The hasty moving of schools resulted in heavy losses of books, materials, and equipment. Living, teaching, and health conditions deteriorated in crowded wartime quarters. Many British and American teachers were forced out of China, impairing the quality of English teaching, an effect almost immediately discernible among graduate students arriving for further study in the United States after the war. A further aggravation has been the lack of good textbooks even though efforts were made to produce enough texts with the limited supply of fourth-rate paper available in unoccupied China.

Middle schools in Japanese-occupied territory also had difficulties, although books were more plentiful and better made. English studies were reduced to the number of hours required in Japanese schools; Japanese language was added to the curricula; and textbook contents were modified, especially in regard to civics, history, and social studies generally. Students in occupied China, always aware of and active in national crises, continued to go to school, but developed a resistance to learning. Since it was patriotic to avoid learning the Japanese language, students competed for the lowest grades. However, the resistance to learning conscientiously developed over a period of eight years eventually backfired. Postwar teachers found that these students had difficulty in learning when they wanted to.

Postwar graduates from all middle schools far outnumber prewar graduates but are much less well prepared to enter college or even to hold employment.

Although middle school education, even during the war years, has been largely conventional, there have been some significant attempts at experimentation. One of the most successful and interesting of these experiments was inaugurated by Dr. Tao Heng-chih, a returned student who obtained his progressive ideas of education from the University of Illi-

nois and from John Dewey at Columbia and applied them at
Yu Tsai school, or the "school for talent." Most of the students in this unusual school are orphans, and all are of exceptional ability. The aim of the school is to provide a broad,
socially centered education, with emphasis on fine arts, including music, dancing, and drama, while supplying training in science and shopwork. Its philosophy decrees that
children learn to use their hands in conjunction with their
brains and to associate dignity with labor. Perhaps the most
significant feature of the school, however, is its emphasis on
service to the community. The late Dr. Tao was the originator of the "little teacher" movement by which school children go out to teach other children and adults. The Yu Tsai
school practices this doctrine with great success.

Another significant experiment in education is conducted by the Chinese Industrial Co-operative Movement in
the Baillie schools. These schools are basically technical
schools, but of a strikingly new type. Since their purpose is to
train effective community leaders as well as to provide
technicians for the industrial co-operatives, the curriculum is
flexible, permitting development according to the aptitude
of the individual. Each of the several Baillie schools consists
of a small group of instructors and a number of boys selected
from among the sons of members of the industrial co-operatives, plus some orphans, all living together as a common
work and study group with emphasis on the management
of their own affairs by the students. Into these schools come
flea-ridden young boys with little education and limited
opportunities, and out of them go clean young men who have
learned how to live and work in a group, who know a great
deal about the world, even though their information is
necessarily secondhand, and who have the capacity to develop into effective leaders.

A third type of experiment has been the expansion of
conventional types of technical middle schools modeled after

Western technical high schools. They are experimental only in the sense that they are relatively new to the Chinese educational system. Some of the best have been developed in southeastern China. None is well equipped, nor do they provide as thorough or varied a training as they should, but their future development can provide a badly needed group of skilled technicians.

Higher education in China more than doubled in volume during and in spite of the war, although it too has had to accept lowered standards. When the last imperial dynasty was overthrown in 1911, the college scene was drab indeed, with a few Chinese colleges enrolling only a few thousand students. By 1936–1937, in all China, 108 colleges, universities, and technical schools of college grade were registered with the Ministry of Education. In the academic year of 1936–1937, 41,922 college students were enrolled and 9,154 were graduated. In 1944–1945 there were 145 institutions of higher learning in unoccupied China alone, with 73,669 students enrolled and 10,514 graduating. The rehabilitation of institutions after the war has brought the total number of colleges and universities to 182 and the total number of students enrolled to approximately 110,000. These figures do not include the twenty-seven research institutes and graduate schools above college grade.

With the rate of college graduations exceeding 10,000 a year the total number of college-trained people in China is still probably not more than 250,000, including those who have studied abroad. This total number, which includes a number of people retired from private life or approaching retirement age, is less than half the number graduating from college *each year* in the United States.

The supply of modern trained leadership that China now possesses is totally inadequate to modernize her society. The scarcity of medical and health personnel is an example. In 1943–1944 there were 8,329 students graduated from academic colleges and universities as distinct from technical colleges. If all these students were to enter medical training, and if all were to graduate, it would require thirteen years to supply the number of doctors China needs.

Similarly, China has only about 10,000 engineers of all types in her brain barrel. In America, during World War II, 202,400 people, highly trained in the engineering fields, were registered by the National Roster of Scientific and Specialized Personnel, a ratio of one engineer to each 650 of our population. In order to equal this ratio, China would have to train 778,461 engineers.

From top to bottom, China's education structure is far too small to provide the level of literacy and technical development she urgently needs.

It was the realization that China needed modern technology that resulted in the decree of 1905, which removed the classical examinations. The general shift from humanities to technology has not diminished since that time.

Most Chinese colleges and universities provide what might be called a liberal arts course. However, specialization starts not only with a first-year separation of arts from science courses, but also includes a further division into departments from the very beginning. A student taking an entrance examination for the freshman arts curriculum must state whether he wishes to enter the Chinese Language and Literature Department, the Economics Department, the Sociology Department, or some other department, the subjects required and the subjects elected being determined by his choice of department. The tendency has been toward too early and too thorough specialization. For example, the required curriculum in biology a few years ago was so concentrated in biological subjects that students majoring in biology had more courses in the field during their undergraduate years than I had taken after completing my Sc.D. in biology in the United States. This overspecialization is now in the process of being modified.

Even with its weaknesses and lack of balance, the curriculum of the modern Chinese university is a far cry from the scholarly studies of years gone by—and many times more useful.

What of the quality of the average Chinese college student? How does he compare with the average American student?

Students in China, like students anywhere, range from the very brilliant to the relatively stupid. On the average their intellectual abilities match those of students in any American college of high academic standing. In terms of application to work and effort to learn, they average considerably better than American students. American teachers who have taught both Americans and Chinese rate the Chinese as a group somewhat better students than the Americans, and those who have studied in the United States have made consistently better records than any other national group. They are influenced by the long tradition of extreme diligence and discipline imposed by the difficulties of the old classical education and held as the proper qualities of a scholar. In addition they are impelled to great effort by the realization that they are members of a small and highly privileged group with opportunities rare and enviable in China. The paucity of college-trained men in China in relation to a plethora of manpower caused the Chinese government to request that students refrain from active participation in the last Sino-Japanese War. Their potential value as leaders was considered far in excess of their actual value as officers and soldiers.

The change, within forty years, from an educational system that was a veneer of highly refined, almost superficial, philosophical contemplation, possessed of no more than a few institutions of college grade into a network of comparatively modern public schools and colleges numbering at least 510,000 units and bringing some degree of enlightenment to at least 75,000,000 common people, is a stride worthy of historical note. There remains, however, a herculean and expensive task to bring China to the educational level of a modern nation.

Chapter VII

Language

IT IS IMPOSSIBLE TO UNDERSTAND FULLY THE CULTURE and psychology of a people without a thorough knowledge of their language. Lacking the opportunity to master the Chinese language, Westerners may learn at least something of its nature.

The Chinese language employs a system of writing different in principle from that of any other living language, including Japanese, which has borrowed extensively from it. For Westerners, accustomed to thinking in terms of a phonetic alphabet, it is difficult to conceive of a language that has none. Yet that is precisely the difference between Chinese and all other living languages. Although there have been a number of recent attempts to develop such an alphabet, and there exist numerous systems for writing Chinese sounds with the Roman alphabet, none of them have been completely successful. The entire vast structure of the Chinese written language, with its capacity for expressing every human emotion and thought, is based on the use of ideographs or characters originally developed from picture writing.

An ideograph is a symbol, figure, or hieroglyph not naming an object but suggesting an idea. In the Chinese language there are more than forty thousand of these ideographs, and the way in which they have been developed constitutes one of the greatest achievements of the human mind. Indeed, the only other fields of annotation evolved by mankind equal to the Chinese language in complexity, volume, range, intricacy, and creative effort are the entire field of mathematics, the whole of music, or all of modern organic chemistry. The complexities of the Chinese system of recording ideas make the difficulties of learning to spell English words seem insignificant.

In contrast to the complexity and excessive richness of China's written language is an oversimplicity in phonetic structure which, since any written language that is to be spoken and understood must have a flexible phonetic structure, amounts to downright poverty. In other words, ideas are expressed vocally by a series of sounds linked together to form words and sentences, ordinarily meaning the same to the eye when they are read as they do to the ear when heard. Chinese is phonetically poor because the sounds used in the entire language can be written with only about four hundred Romanized syllables, while almost that many syllables in English have been used since the beginning of this chapter.

Because four hundred syllables are not enough phonetic building blocks for the construction of a rich spoken language, the Chinese have increased the number, not by adding more syllables, but by applying various modulations or tonal changes to basic syllables. The result is a total of fifteen hundred distinguishable sound combinations.

It is the necessity of distinguishing and forming these numerous shades of tone that makes learning the Chinese spoken language difficult. In the College of Chinese Studies in Peiping, where many missionaries, diplomats, military and commercial people learn Chinese, the matter of mastering tones is considered so important that hundreds, even thousands, of hours are spent in tonal drill. When we started our language study at the college in 1932, the first two weeks were spent entirely in listening—listening for seven hours each day to what could be said with only sixteen

Chinese words. These words had been carefully selected to represent all four tones and to be easily demonstrated by the actions of the teacher without the use of another language.

The scene was a large lecture room filled with seventy young Britons and Americans plus a sprinkling of representatives from half a dozen European countries, all graduates of Western colleges, many with advanced degrees, but all eager to possess the essential language tool necessary for efficient work in the school, church, hospital, consulate, or commercial house for which they had trained during the past eight or ten years.

The foreign director of the college entered, welcomed the group, and made a few announcements. Among them was the instruction that no student should attempt to write down the sounds heard until three months had elapsed. Full attention must be given the teacher in order to learn to hear correctly, and, in any case, he added, letters of the Roman alphabet, as used in English, do not accurately represent Chinese sounds. Then he went on to say that our instruction was to be given by a group of Chinese who spoke no English; deference would require that we rise, in the approved Chinese fashion, when the teacher entered the room. We were to bow when the teacher reached the center and remain standing until the bow had been returned.

Whereupon Mr. Wang, the head teacher, entered the room, dressed in a long, blue silk gown which almost touched the floor. We rose and bowed, were introduced, and it was noted among us that this was the gentleman who had merited the nickname "Dearest" for the past dozen years. With a smile, Dearest turned to us and started the long task of teaching us Chinese by pointing to himself and saying *"Wo, wo."* He drew the word out with first a falling then slightly rising intonation, and we recognized that he was saying, "I, I."

Then he pointed toward us and said, *"Ni, ni,"* the inflection starting slightly higher on the tonal scale and ascending in a rapidly climbing glide. By repetition we gathered that the meaning was "you, you."

Then Dearest pointed off in the direction of a third person and repeated *"Ta, ta,"* the tone pitched high, level, and clear without a shadow of a glide, and meaning "he, he." After several weeks we found out that *ta* could mean either "he," "she," or "it." We had learned our first three Chinese words, each representing a different tone.

Then by showing us a piece of money, a piece of paper, or by acting out a simple motion such as sitting down, our vocabulary was built up to eight different words before the bell rang at the end of the first hour. Dearest bowed to us, we returned the bow, and he went out. Then for each half hour we had a different teacher, drilling over and over again the sounds of those first words—I say *they* drilled because we were not yet permitted to say them ourselves.

On the second day, Dearest added a second group of eight words, and for two solid weeks we sat and listened to those sixteen words as they were repeated over and over again in every possible combination. Gradually our ears became attuned to the differences of inflection in those four basic tones, but it was not until weeks later that the tones were analyzed and explained to us. By that time we could identify them distinctly but were still having difficulty in saying them. It was pointed out that a tonal scale of one to five notes might be imagined, the first note low and the fifth note high. *Ta*, a first-tone word, would then be highest on the scale with no variation. *Ni*, a second-tone word, would start at three and climb to five. *Wo*, a third-tone word, would start at two, drop to one, and then climb to four. In some respects, third-tone words are the easiest to say, just because they have the most exaggerated tonal change. *Tso*, meaning "to sit," is a fourth-tone word which begins on five and drops sharply to one, like a camel's hoof coming down on the sand, spreading a bit, and then stopping suddenly.

Several different systems of writing the basic four hundred syllables of the Chinese language in the Roman alphabet have been devised. The one taught at the College of Chinese Studies was developed by Wade, a British official who worked in China in the nineteenth century. In the Wade system there are syllables such as *an*, *ang*, *cha* (ja), *ch'a* (cha), *chang*, *chiang* (gee-ang, the Generalissimo's name), *fu* (foo), *ha*, *han*, *hang*, *li*, *shen*, *sheng*, *shu*, etc. Each of these sounds has the four tonal variations. In order to distinguish between the four tones for each syllable, the Wade system employs numerals inserted after the Romanized word, fu^1, fu^2, fu^3, and fu^4.

As may be imagined, Chinese, with forty thousand ideographs and only fifteen hundred different shades of sound, has more homonyms than any other language. (It may be added that the educated man normally uses only some five to seven thousand ideographs.) In English, we have relatively few homonyms—to, too, two being one of the most extensive examples. The Chinese language carries this kind of thing infinitely further.

To take an example or two, in Fenn's Five Thousand Dictionary, containing the five thousand most commonly used characters listed by tones, there is a total of seventy-seven ideographs listed under the syllabic sound *li*. Four are first tone, twenty-two are second tone, fourteen are third tone, and thirty-seven are fourth tone. Thirty-seven different characters have, therefore, exactly the same pronunciation! The meanings of li^4 include 利, meaning sharp, clever, interest (on money), through; 痢 meaning dysentery; 力 meaning strength, force; 立 meaning to set up, stand; 厲 meaning severe, oppress; 例 meaning law, precedent, regulations; 麗 meaning elegant, beautiful; 詈 meaning to revile, curse, scold; and several others.

Another example is the character Romanized *fu*. In Fenn's dictionary there are forty-eight characters listed under this sound—five are first tone, twenty-one are second tone, thirteen are third tone, and nineteen are fourth tone. Among the twenty-one fu^2 characters are the meanings to uphold, support, help; a scroll, hem, or border; a square cloth, wrapper; tally, charm; to tie, bind; and to go back.

As a result of this plethora of homonyms, it is frequently necessary to identify or even write out characters in the course of daily conversations to make sure of exact meanings. A good illustration of this confusion of characters is the experience I have had with my Chinese name. It is a very good name, given to me by Lau Shaw, the author of *Rickshaw Boy*, just after I arrived at Cheeloo University where Lau Shaw was then a professor. It is, of course, made up of the usual three characters approximating the sound of my English surname, Winfield. The first of the three characters is one of the regularly accepted "Hundred Names" (actually nearer four hundred) which are the relatively few family names for all of China's millions. The second and third characters are the given name, hyphenated to distinguish them from the family name. Romanized, the three characters of my name are *Wen Fu-li*. The confusion of which I speak has occurred many thousands of times when I have met or been introduced to a Chinese who spoke no English.

"Sir, what is your illustrious family name?" the stranger asks.

"My humble family name is Wen^1," I say, exaggerating the first tone in order to avoid the inevitable. But nine times out of ten the next remark is, "Is your name the Wen^2 meaning 'literary'?" Two of China's family names may be Romanized *wen*, one being first tone, the other second tone, and the latter, meaning "literary," is the more common; besides, is it not likely that a professor would be literary?

"No," I patiently reply, "my name is the wen^1 character

written with the three-dot water radical that forms a part of the spoken expression *wen nuan*, meaning 'warm.' " Again I emphasize the tone and give the word a common context, but to complete my verbal identification I hurry on to say, "My given name is *Fu-li*—the *fu* of *fu-chi* meaning 'good fortune,' the *li* as used in the expression *chan-li* meaning 'to stand at attention.' "

Although the phonetic poverty of the Chinese language is such that it requires links like those above to connect spoken thoughts with the superabundance of ideographs, it is the medium by which the everyday affairs of one quarter of the human race are carried on. This is possible because monosyllabic characters are grouped into combinations that amount to the formation of words with two or more syllables. Such polysyllabic terms are formed usually by linking two characters with different pronunciations but similar meanings to form a word that is always clearly recognized by the ear alone. Eventually the spoken language will be put into phonetic writing that will be easy to read and write.

While for many purposes this overabundance of different meanings marked phonetically by the same sound causes difficulties, it is turned to advantage in both Chinese poetry and humor. Punning is easy and popular. One of the most popular types of entertainment offered at fairs, markets, tearooms, and theaters is a dialogue carried on between two wits who speak in metered lines. The essential feature of this vaudevillian poesy is that the first syllable of each line has the same sound as the last syllable of the previous line, but, of course, with a vastly different meaning which permits double, triple, or even quadruple implications.

Such multiple meanings are also convenient for reviling or cursing in Chinese. Since the name of a deity does not enter the picture as in English swearing, people in China are content to imply that the obnoxious character is an animal or to cast aspersions on the nature or morality of ancestors. In such a process, double meanings greatly enhance the range and type of calumny. Indeed, most foreigners, even after years of experience with the Chinese language, are still in some danger of having innocent remarks turn out to be first-class slander.

Phonetic poverty has had other effects, including limitations in grammatical construction. Since it is not possible to vary verb endings by the addition of a syllable or two, there is no such thing as tense, number, or agreement between verbs and other parts of speech. The verb remains the same.

> Today I go to town
> In a few minutes I go to town
> Yesterday I go to town
> Last year I go to town
> Now I go to town
> In the past I go to town many times
> Tomorrow I go to town
> Next year I go to town.

Similarly, the problems of gender and number disappear in Chinese:

> Today I are here
> Today we are here
> Today, she, or he, or it, are here.

Nor is there any plural form for nouns, the idea being expressed by:

> One piece apple
> Five piece apple
> Many piece apple.

In order to facilitate use of plurals, there are classifiers similar to those used in English when reference is made to so many "head" of cattle or "sheets" of paper. Some commonly used Chinese classifiers are:

"Piece," applied to many types of objects, including men
"Lump," applied to money, coal, stones, and other lumpy objects

"Sheet," applied to paper, tables, faces, or other objects with surface

"Head," applied to cattle and other animals

"Mouth," applied to men

"Length," applied to fish, string, rope, and dogs.

Once one has seen the lean and emaciated dogs that inhabit the streets of many villages, it seems quite logical to speak of a *length* of dog.

Singular pronouns become plural by adding a character pronounced "mun," but Romanized *men*. For example, *wo* (I) becomes *wo-men* to make "we"; *ni* (you) becomes *ni-men* in the plural; *ta* (he, she, or it) becomes *ta-men* to make "they."

In spite of all these complexities, the greatest difficulty faced by foreigners studying Chinese is the correct usage of tones! Innumerable comic and some almost tragic situations have arisen because of the misuse of tones by a foreigner.

The story is told of two Chinese men who emerged from a small village deep in the mountains of Shantung to engage in trading at the market town. Neither had met missionaries or even Chinese Christians, but they had heard sordid tales common in the countryside about the holy sacraments. Since there is no way in Chinese to distinguish between flesh and meat, the "eating of flesh" and "drinking of blood" has been misinterpreted, especially during the Boxer Rebellion of 1900 when deliberate attempts to play up the cannibalism of the sacrament were made by those who opposed the presence of foreigners.

When they had finished their shopping, the two mountaineers strolled around the streets taking in all the rare sights, and finally came upon a Christian chapel where a foreigner was conducting services. The singing of hymns aroused their curiosity, and they finally gathered enough courage to slip into a rear pew to watch. It was difficult to follow the strange music, but when the foreigner began to preach in a queer accent about some very strange ideas it was still more difficult to understand. However, it all seemed harmless enough, and the men were content to sit back and relax while the foreigner waxed eloquent. Suddenly he stopped, raised his hands to heaven, and said, in a very solemn and impressive voice, "Now let us sharpen our knives."

The two on the back seat bolted for the door and fled down the street toward the safety of the hills.

The minister had made a slight error in tones. Instead of saying, "Now let us have silent prayer" ($mo^4\ tao^3$), he had said, "Now let us sharpen our knives" ($mo^2\ tao^1$), which amply confirmed the suspicions of the hillfolk.

To what extent Chinese phonetic limitations and the resulting invention of tones are the cause of the development of ideographs as a means of writing, and to what extent these phonetic limitations are the effect of ideographs, is a moot problem. It is possible that the phonetic range may have been limited before the first characters were invented. On the other hand, it is also possible that the use of characters prevented expansion of the phonetic language base to the extent that would have been possible with a phonetic alphabet. No matter which is the hen or which the egg, these two aspects of the Chinese language have combined to produce an extremely intricate language.

The very oldest Chinese characters of which we know are those carved on oracle bones. A study of the first of these bones, excavated from the central and lower reaches of the Yellow River valley about fifty years ago, corroborated many theories concerning early Chinese history and led to new evidence relevant to the origin and development of characters. Indeed, these bones have supplied so much authentic information that the limits of confirmed knowledge of Chinese history has been pushed back by many hundreds of years.

LANGUAGE

Oracle bones were used by the ancients as a means of divination. If a king of one of the small states wished to go hunting, he would seek the prognostications of his court wisemen in order to find out whether or not the time was auspicious for his trip and to ascertain the outcome. With a jade stylus the wiseman would carve the question on a flat piece of bone from a turtle, deer, or other animal. Then, on the same side of the bone, the wiseman would make a deep scratch, and underneath it on the other side a hole. With proper ceremony and incantation, a live coal was placed in the hole, and, as the bone was burned and dried out, cracks would appear. From the pattern of these cracks, particularly in relation to the scratch, the wiseman read the answers and interpreted them to the king. Since the wisemen frequently scratched the answers on the bone, scholars studying them thirty-five hundred years later have gained new insight, not only concerning the etiquette of hunting expeditions, but also concerning important historical activities and language development.

The characters appearing on the bones were hieroglyphs forming clear indications of the ideas they recorded. Even then, however, by more or less logical association and extensions, abstract ideas could be represented by these simple pictorial symbols. From these pictorial beginnings the written language slowly evolved. It is possible to trace many modern characters to their hieroglyph origins. Others have metamorphosed beyond clue.

After the bones as writing material came strips of bamboo into which the characters were carved with a knife. As long as characters were carved with stylus or knife they retained curving lines and much of their original pictographic character. However, the invention of the writing brush, over two thousand years ago, caused a radical change in the formation of characters. Since it was no longer possible to inscribe curved lines easily, characters were squared up and adapted to nine basic brush strokes. The arrival of the brush, with its variety of delicate shadings and vigorous strokes, also marked the beginning of the art of calligraphy that since the early days of Chinese character writing has been a fine art ranking with landscape painting and portraiture. In fact, most Chinese painting is done with the same nine fundamental brush strokes. Addiction to beauty in writing may partially explain the tenacity with which the Chinese have held to their ideographs in a phonetic world.

The early, simple hieroglyphs, such as those appearing on the oracle bones, have undergone a vast and complicated development which has led to the contemporary language of more than forty thousand stylized characters. In the course of their development, characters divided into two classes. First are the simple pictographs, numbering a few dozen, which developed almost directly. Second is the vast majority of present-day compounded characters that evolved from various combinations of simple pictographs.

This array of compounded characters is built up by combinations of 214 radicals and 888 phonetics. Both radicals and phonetics are characters themselves of either simple or compound types. In general, radicals classify meanings into broad categories, while the phonetics indicate pronunciation, but there are so many exceptions that it is only fair to say that radicals merely aid in remembering meanings, while phonetics are merely aids in remembering pronunciations. Then, too, most radicals are also phonetics.

Radicals include most of the simple characters of which other characters are compounded. Among these simple radicals are many that retain enough of their pictographic origins to make their development obvious. For example:

人　　is the radical for "man." Through centuries of simplification only man's two legs remain to represent him. It is the 9th radical and the 429th phonetic.

刀 is the "knife" radical. In it can be seen the heavy chopping blade of the Chinese cleaver. It is the 18th radical and 219th phonetic.

力 is the radical meaning "strength." It differs from the "knife" only in that the left-hand stroke extends above the horizontal; differences this slight are frequent. It is the 19th radical and the 223rd phonetic.

口 is the "mouth" radical, the picture of a puckered-up mouth. It is the 30th radical and the 694th phonetic.

子 is the "child" or "son" radical, with the head of the child projecting above the horizontal line representing the covers, the feet and body below. It is the 39th radical and 112th phonetic.

日 is the "sun" radical, the squared-up circle that represented the sun in primitive writing. The single dash within it may represent the light it gives off, but it is more likely that the sun, occupying the heavens alone, contributed the "lone" or "single" idea. It is the 72nd radical and the 792nd phonetic.

月 is the now highly stylized picture of the "new moon." It is the 74th radical and the 621st phonetic.

木 is the "wood" radical. It shows roots under the ground and a trunk and branches above the ground. It is the 75th radical and the 474th phonetic.

田 is the radical for "field," the picture of a field divided into four parts. It is the 102nd radical and the 809th phonetic.

Within the radicals themselves are many compound characters, built as follows:

口 *k'ou*, the "mouth" radical, has been introduced above. If a single dash is added within the mouth, a new radical,

日   meaning "to say," is created. It is the 73rd radical and is broader and shorter than the 72nd radical, 日, for "sun," given previously.

舌   If the mouth radical has three strokes written above it, the new character means "tongue," for the tongue comes out of the mouth. The "tongue" radical is the 135th.

言   Then, if four strokes are written above a mouth, the 149th radical meaning "words" is created. Thus on the mouth radical are built three other radicals meaning "to say," "tongue," and "words."

Many compound characters contain logic in their formation. For example, the pictographs meaning "strength," 力, and for "a field," 田, where crops are grown combine to form the character for "man," 男 as distinguished from "woman," for in agricultural China it is indeed the man who uses his strength in the fields.

Another interesting example is the word for "east." When one can see the sun 日 through the trees 木, then you have 東 meaning "east."

As has been stated, radicals indicate broad classes of meaning. For example, in the Five Thousand Dictionary there are 268 different characters based on the "mouth" radical. These characters tend to deal with things which are in, about, or associated with the mouth. When fifteen of these 268 characters were taken at random and checked for meaning, nine were found to deal with speech or eating, including such definitions as "to call," "to scold," "rhyme," "to bite," "to swallow," and "to howl." However, among the six others were meanings as divergent as "a march," "ancient," "to permit," and "wise."

Similarly, of twenty characters picked at random from the 252 which are built on the "wood" radical, fourteen had to do with wood and wooden objects, including such definitions as "cherry," "coffin," "a post," "root," "plum," and others. But again there were words not directly associated in meaning with the wood radical root such as "sullen," "urgent," "style," and "plain." These two illustrations serve to show that a radical gives only a lead toward the meaning of a character, and that characters have been borrowed, from time to time, to express abstract ideas. Ultimately, learning the meanings of Chinese characters is a matter of sheer memory.

Most characters are made by combining radical and phonetic, the former giving some clue to meaning, and the latter a hint to pronunciation. A typical phonetic illustrating how sound and meaning change when combined with various radicals is written 青, pronounced *ch'ing*[1], meaning "color of nature"—green, blue, or black. (In the Wade system of Romanization an apostrophe means an explosive exhalation. Therefore, *ching* would be pronounced "ging," with the "ch" like the "g" in "George," while *ch'ing* would be pronounced as it is spelled, with the "ch" as in "change.") A series of meanings is given for this character, which, used in context, may mean a number of things. When used with the character for "years," for example, the combination becomes "youth," or, literally, "green years."

When the phonetic 青 *ch'ing*[1] is combined with the water radical 氵, we get 清, which is pronounced *ch'ing*[1] also, just as the phonetic alone is pronounced. The meaning is "pure," "clean," "ringing," since blue or green water in nature is pure.

When the phonetic 青, *ch'ing*[1], is combined with the heart radical 忄 to make the character 情, pronounced *ch'ing*[2], it means, with the tonal change, "feelings," "emotions," "affections," "facts." Since the Chinese consider the heart to be the seat of both emotions and thoughts, the logic of this derivation is apparent.

When 青, *ch'ing*[1], is combined with the sun radical 日 it becomes part of the character 晴, pronounced *ch'ing*[2], meaning "clear," "blue sky." Used in a two-character combination with "heaven" or "sky," it becomes the term for "clear weather."

When 青, *ch'ing*[1], is written with the radical for "words" 言, the resulting character 請, pronounced *ch'ing*[3], another tonal change, means "to request," "invite," "please."

When 青, *ch'ing*[1], is written with the eye radical 目 it becomes the character 睛 pronounced *ching*[1], a more complete change in pronunciation. While still a first-tone word, the character has changed a "ch" sound to a soft "g," and the meaning becomes "iris," "eye," or "pupil of the eye."

When 青, *ch'ing*[1], is written with the radical for "rice grain" 米 it becomes 精, pronounced *ching*[1], and means "essence," "spirit."

When 青, *ch'ing*[1], is combined with the insect radical 虫 the resulting character is 蜻, pronounced *ching*[1], meaning "dragonfly."

When 青, *ch'ing*[1], is combined with the radical meaning "upright" 立, it forms 靖 and is pronounced *ching*[4], meaning "quite."

When 青, *ch'ing*[1], is combined with the radical for a pig 犭 the result is 猜. Here the phonetic connection jumps the track; it is pronounced *ts'ai*[2], and means "to guess."

From these examples it becomes apparent that there is some logic in the way radicals guide meanings and phonetics guide sound. Also it becomes apparent that only because there is so much logic in the formation of characters is it possible to learn Chinese at all. Mental leaps from combination to combination, reflecting cultural development and poetic meaning, make the study of Chinese characters fascinating. At the same time, the number of exceptions and irregularities makes the study of Chinese a great effort of memory.

Considered as a tool of culture and everyday communication, the Chinese language has both advantages and disadvantages.

The written language based on ideographs has bound together the people of China politically for many thousands of years because it permits a common recorded culture independent of spoken dialects. People in different parts of China who cannot understand each other in conversation can, if they are educated, carry on a completely intelligible correspondence that reflects a common background of thought and experience in a literature common to all. Without this unifying element, China today might be a continent of small states speaking different languages and holding different traditions and emotional loyalties very like Europe, where cultural unity of language disappeared when Latin ceased to be the medium of scholarship.

As a tool of literary expression, the Chinese language is superb. The very extent and richness of its literature is sufficient proof of the effectiveness of the language as a medium for poetry, drama, philosophy, and historical writings. One cannot overemphasize the poetic quality, intrinsically and phonetically, of Chinese writing, nor the art potential in its calligraphy.

Yet the very nature of the Chinese language creates a number of serious and basic human problems. The overwhelming mass of illiteracy that now crushes the Chinese people and slows their march of progress is seriously increased by the difficulties of learning their own language. A Chinese child must put in several times as many hours of work to master his language as does a British or American child to gain an equal command of English. Most Chinese do not have the leisure necessary to gain the mastery of language as a tool in the activities of society, even though more simple methods of teaching and using the language are being developed.

Complexity and phonetic poverty also are deterrents to

full and current participation in a modern world. It is impossible to send Chinese characters directly by telegraph. They must be encoded from a directory, sent as four-digit numbers by wire, and then decoded. Press dispatches must be handled the same way. Recently a new machine operating on new electrical principles for the selection of the desired character has been developed. This machine is too cumbersome and expensive to serve as a personal typewriter but it can be used in business houses and as a teletype for the transmission of messages in directly readable characters. With further improvements and adaptations it may also serve the purpose of a linotype machine and so greatly speed the setting of type. It is not unreasonable to expect continued advances in machines for handling the Chinese language but by the very nature of the language itself these machines will always be more costly and less efficient than those used by phonetic-language peoples.

Chinese is a cultural barrier between the Chinese people and the rest of the world. Altogether, there are no more than a few hundred Westerners who can read and write Chinese with sufficient facility to contribute to Chinese literature. In China there are several hundred thousand people who can read at least one foreign language and tens of thousands who have complete mastery of some non-Chinese language, usually English, but, even so, foreign writings must be translated into Chinese if they are to reach the majority of Chinese people who can read. During the past century much Western literature has been translated into Chinese, but only a small percentage of Chinese literature has been translated into other languages. The one-way flow of literature has been so marked that China never has felt the need of entering into any of the international copyright agreements that protect writers in most countries.

It is, however, in the field of modern science that the language barrier is of greatest significance. No field of science exists in which one could be trained solely from Chinese source material. While much basic science material has been translated into Chinese, it would take the full time of all China's comparatively few scientists to keep up with the production of the world's current scientific literature if all of it were to be translated into Chinese for the relatively few people interested, and the cost of publishing these specialized materials would be far beyond China's ability to bear. There seems to be no solution other than the teaching of a Western language to hundreds of thousands of students in order to produce the few thousands of capable scientists needed constantly and the two or three ranking scientists needed in each generation. Cognizance of this problem has resulted in the teaching of English as a second language in Chinese secondary schools and colleges.

Another aspect of the science problem is the need for the translation and presentation of basic concepts in Chinese in a manner so simple that all the people may learn the fundamentals of sanitation, cause and transmission of disease, and all the principles of modern life by which the welfare of the common people may be improved.

The structure of the Chinese language has been a factor in glorifying the scholar, in creating and maintaining a conservative traditionalism which China is struggling to cast off, in shaping the old imperial bureaucracy that is still obstructing modern efficiency in government. In spite of the fact that, through the literary revolution, modern Chinese is considerably more adapted to progress than was the old classical writing, the complex and difficult structure of Chinese characters, aggravated by a phonetic poverty in the spoken language, which makes it difficult to abandon ideographs, constitutes one more burden that China must carry in her obstacle race to become a modern nation.

Chapter VIII

Local Government

As in any nation, the progress of the change and adaptation of China's language, education, agriculture, public health, and industry is heavily dependent on her government. Since a constant flow of books and periodic reports cannot keep pace with the rapid fluctuations of her current political situation, it serves the purpose of this book to examine the form of her local government and its background.

Held firmly in the historic cultural pattern that has dominated all her institutions, China's government is deeply rooted in the past. In spite of the 1911 revolution that overthrew the Ching dynasty, political philosophy is still influenced by two ancient Confucian tenets.

The first tenet prescribes the relationship between individuals in society in the order of importance ordained by Confucius: emperor and subject; father and son; husband and wife; teacher and pupil; friend and friend.

As in European medieval thinking and practice, the relationship between emperor and subject is that of superior to inferior. The Chinese believed the emperor to be the representative of heaven, and, as such, he was due respect and honor as the father head of the national family. The very word for nation or state in Chinese is "nation-family"— *kuo-chia*.

The emperor-subject relationship was closely akin to the second of the five relationships, father-son, or, more broadly, parents and children. In Confucian thought and in Chinese practice this is the key relationship in life. It is the source from which the emperor-subject relation evolved and on which the whole structure of filiality is based. The father is in the position of a superior, older being with absolute authority over the son, while the son looks up to and honors the father with unquestioning loyalty and obedience. Although in practice there may be a great deal of warmth in the relationship, it is based on an austere fundamental attitude serving to bind the younger generation to the domination of the older.

I shall never forget the astonishment of my students when I made the remark that my father and I were good friends. This seemed almost incomprehensible to them, for the relationship between son and father, with its awe and obedience on one side and its benevolent superiority and authority on the other, was a much higher relationship than the equalitarian give-and-take between friends. They could not conceive of anyone being the friend of his father because the relation of friend to friend is fifth and last among the five relations.

The whole mood of Chinese government down the centuries has been based on the father-son, emperor-subject thinking and feeling. It placed the emperor and his representatives in an exalted position of power and importance, provided powerful sanctions for teaching the beliefs that supported that exalted position, and obligated the subject to obey and honor the emperor and his representatives. From it has grown a government that is firmly based on an hierarchy ruling from the top down.

The absolutism of this hierarchy of rule is modified, however, by the second of the major Confucian tenets concerning government—the belief that people are by nature essentially good and that the greatest function of the emperor as supreme ruler is to provide an example of character and justice. In practice these ends were served by the meticulous carrying out of "rites" and "ceremonies," by the following of etiquette, by the rewarding of virtue and the punishing of wrongdoing among the officials. According to Confucius, the influence of this good example was expected to be reflected in the ministries, where each minister would then conduct his departmental affairs according to the precepts of virtue, in turn setting standards which would pass the substance of good government down the ladder to the provinces, the districts, and the local magistrates. Finally, all fathers would become virtuous as a result of this exemplary influence and would rule their families with a high virtue equal to that of the emperor.

The moral obligation to rule by precepts of virtue was reinforced by the public right to revolt when the emperor ceased to do so, a privilege that has resulted in more than twenty dynasties of emperors in the course of Chinese history. This right to revolt against the emperor marks the chief difference in the political histories of China and Japan, for Japan, while basically Confucian in its attitude toward the emperor's position, did not maintain the right to revolt. The result has been that Japan has had only one dynasty, and has developed a highly centralized national power in the name of the emperor and the technique of the shogunate, or rule by strong groups using the emperor as a puppet when his shortcomings necessitated a new accession of vigor.

The first unit in the Chinese line of authority was the imperial court made up of the emperor and his ministers, each minister being responsible for one of the many functions of government, such as finance, examinations, war, censors (a sort of imperial inspectorate), rites, etc.

Next in importance below the court was the provincial government (roughly corresponding to the American state), controlled by a governor appointed by the emperor. Throughout her history China has been divided into provinces according to a number of patterns. In general, however, there usually have been eighteen provinces south of the Great Wall, an area still commonly called "the Eighteen Provinces." Each province was divided into sub-areas headed by a special commissioner, and then into hsien (counties) headed by a magistrate. Commissioners and magistrates were appointed by the throne, although the provincial governors had a good deal to say about the appointment of officials who served under them and could greatly influence their promotion. Each official was largely responsible for the organization and the functioning of the unit under his direct control.

Officials were appointed only after they had passed examinations appropriate to the rank of office. Furthermore, in order to discourage nepotism, a practice to which the Confucian concept of filiality is conducive, officials were never permitted to serve in their home province.

Actual functions carried out at the various levels of government were not so numerous as those performed by modern governments, consisting for the most part in maintaining the peace, security, and government through the prosecution of criminals, the collection of taxes, and the conscription of men and materials for both the imperial armies and for the great work gangs that constructed and maintained such public works as the Great Wall, the Grand Canal, and the river dikes.

The "law" under which all these levels of government functioned was general in character and frequently vague in its statements. In practice this ambiguity produced a government guided by tradition and precedent rather than by statutory law. In the light of current legal practice the decisions and penalties handed down by magistrates and other officials were severe, a theory of judgment devised to discourage people from going to court with their civil disputes and to encourage the growth of a system of village government by the people themselves to take care of most local conflicts. Except in taking from the people through taxes or levy and in prosecuting serious criminal offenses, the official government had little contact with the individual citizen.

The conduct of village affairs is still carried out by a council of elders, usually consisting of two or three of the most scholarly and elderly men of the community. On the one hand they represent the village in dealing with the official government, and on the other they interpret the government and its wishes to the people. The council assists the government in levying and collecting taxes, and, by virtue of superior knowledge, its members become the "lawyers" who defend the interests of the villagers. In case a member of the village is accused of a serious crime, the council is held responsible and tries to have the case placed in its own hands for judgment and punishment. It supervises the transfer of property and adjudicates all disputes arising in the village. Since there is no fixed court or written code, actual judgment is made by public opinion and, in practice, by consultation between the council and the head of every interested group.

Following the same pattern, the designated head of the household is responsible for the actions of all its members. This representative of a family group is usually the oldest male who is still under seventy years of age. The position is passed down, not from father to son, but from the oldest to the next oldest in the clan, modified, of course, by the candidate's qualities as to prestige and judgment. If the head of a clan dies or passes his seventieth birthday and no longer possesses the vigor necessary to conduct clan affairs, the clan members consider likely candidates among those in their late fifties or early sixties and choose by consultation and eventual agreement, usually without voting, the one most likely to serve the clan's best interests. He may not be the oldest candidate, but he usually possesses the most scholarship, experience, and tact. Other qualities being equal, age is decisive.

This, then, is the pattern of government built up in China through the centuries, with the village level the most democratic but based on the family rather than the individual. Although this pattern is now in the process of being modified extensively, it is still the basis for government hierarchy under the republic, the Central Government taking the place of the imperial court. However, the structure of the Central Government itself has been altered and is much more modern in its functions than was the old court.

At the provincial level, some provinces have been divided into a larger number of political units, while other provinces, such as Szechuan with an area of 166,485 square miles (nearly equivalent to the area of France), may be divided in the future. The subdivision of large provinces has aided the Central Government by reducing the inefficiency inevitable in local governments forced to control large areas with slow and inadequate communication systems and by decreasing the power of local warlords rooted in the provincial structure.

Provincial governments are now set up as "committees" under a Central Government appointee known as "chairman" rather than "governor." In addition to the chairman there is frequently a provincial military commander appointed as a "pacification commander," although in some provinces the same man holds both jobs. A series of provincial bureaus carry on administrative functions analogous to the Central Government ministries, among them bureaus for finance, construction and public works, education, health, justice, social affairs, etc. The actual work of these various bureaus is carried on in each province under the joint supervision of the provincial government and the appropriate ministry in the Central Government.

In addition, the municipal governments of the larger cities are directly responsible to the Central Government and are not under provincial direction. The governments of these special municipalities are organized in much the same manner as the provincial governments and are considered to be of equal importance. Smaller cities and county seats come under the provincial authorities.

Most numerous and active of the local governments in China are those of the 2,019 hsien, each with populations ranging from 50,000 to well over 200,000 presided over by magistrates appointed by the Central Government on the advice of the provincial government concerned. If, in America, local governments frequently are inefficient and corrupt, in China, where the local magistrate has great power unrestricted by direct popular appeal or power, both inefficiency and corruption are able to flourish that much more easily. In addition, now that government in China is attempting to supply many new functions that were not a part of the traditional pattern, there is an acute shortage of personnel adequately trained to administer such functions as modern education and public health.

Genuine efforts have been made to modernize and improve the quality of local government by training officials, but reform is slow and difficult against the resistance to change characteristic of inbred traditionalism and vested interests. Each year a government school for magistrates trains promising young college men to become administrators of model hsien which have been established throughout the country as centers for the testing and exhibition of improved managerial methods. A number of these model hsien already have been influential in raising the standards and efficiency of local governments.

LOCAL GOVERNMENT

I visited a model hsien near Chungking with a population of about 125,000. Its hsien city of Peipei, a bandit stronghold only twenty-five years before, was now a cultural center of the area. Each one hundred families were organized into a *pao*, or ward, according to the *pao chia* system, with an elected chief and vice-chief, an elementary school with one teacher, and a home defense organization under a militia commander for protection during the war. The school taught illiterate adults as well as children, using visual education media including movies where electricity was available. Plans existed for the purchase of radios to be used in schools and other village centers and for a small broadcasting station to supply music and information. A hsien-wide health organization had been organized with first-aid agents in the villages and a graded series of clinics feeding into a well-equipped but small hospital in the hsien city. A well-organized and active agricultural department was busy helping farmers improve their crops, and, on the day of my visit, the results of a corn-improvement contest were announced with prizes awarded to winning farmers.

Early in 1947 the first prefecture of Szechuan consisting of ten hsien, including Peipei, was designated a model experimental prefecture, and was placed under the guidance of the Mass Education Movement. Mr. L. C. Sun, one of China's best-known rural reconstruction leaders and an able administrator, was named commissioner of the prefecture. Already rapid progress has been made in reforming the tax system, in reducing illiteracy through the well-tried techniques of the Mass Education Movement, and in building up grass-roots democracy. It is the most hopeful postwar development in the field of local government.

Not all model hsien do as well as the one at Peipei which, during the war, was host to several refugee colleges that helped raise the general cultural level. In many of the model hsien the young magistrates have difficulty in surmounting local resistance to change, and in others the magistrates do not have the necessary ability. Nevertheless, some progress is being made in spite of the fact that there are too few model hsien and that there are too many nonmodel hsien operating as they have for many decades past.

With all its limitations and many evils, the existing pattern of local government in China is capable of real accomplishments. I had an opportunity to see proof of this when, in the spring of 1944, near Chengtu, a system of gigantic airfields was constructed from which the first B-29 raids on Japan were launched. The U.S. Army engineer in charge praised the whole effort as an outstanding achievement.

"We could not have built these nine fields, four of them with nine-thousand-foot runways for B-29s, in this short period of time even if we had been in the United States with unlimited supplies and machinery. Altogether I have had only fourteen Americans on the job, and all they have done is to make sure that the finished runways and hard standings would support the loads of the new giant bombers. The real job of construction has been done by the Chinese in ninety days, with no trucks, no steam shovels, no concrete. Just sixty days after the first rice field on the site for the north field was drained a B-29 actually landed on the strip."

There were several small airfields already in existence when the larger airfields became essential, but it was necessary to enlarge them and to construct several new ones from swampy paddy fields. The irrigated Chengtu plain (described in Chapter II) was the only flat country available. When the decision was finally made, about January 1, 1944, the Generalissimo's headquarters instructed Governor Chang Chün of Szechuan province to provide 450,000 workmen, to be recruited and moved to the fields by January 15, together with tools and food for ninety days' work. Mat sheds were to be erected for sleeping quarters and a health organization set up to supply clean water, sanitation, and general health protection.

The Chinese local governments swung into immediate action, and orders went out to twenty-two hsien governments telling them of the project and requesting quotas of men and rice. In proportion to their population, each hsien was to supply from 10,000 to 30,000 workers, organized by pao. Within a few days the first groups began to arrive with tools, rice, and materials for mat sheds, moving on foot and carrying their equipment or pushing it in the thousands of wheelbarrows that were later used for the hauling of stone. By January 15 the gangs, distributed by the 40,000, 60,000 or 100,000 to each field, were ready for work.

In the meantime, Chinese engineers, working with the fourteen American engineers assigned to the job, had surveyed and staked out the work to be done. There were long discussions of how best to organize the workers, the Americans wanting to organize and train the gangs by trades, American style. The Chinese vetoed that plan.

"You do not understand the psychology of handling our people," the Chinese said. "We can't mix up people from different hsien in any such fashion as your plan would require. We would lose track of them and there would be too many quarrels and fights among those from different districts. No, the best way is to give each hsien a section of the field right straight across. With this plan we can keep track of our people; they will work more effectively, and as each gang finishes its part of the field it can go home."

Thousands of men and boys were set to work with wicker baskets and shoulder poles, clearing off the rich soil of paddy fields that for three thousand years had grown the rice of a hundred generations. Now, because of the demands of a little-understood war, peasants whose ancestors had nursed the topsoil down the centuries carried it away. In many places it was necessary to dig out the subsoil as well, to a depth of many feet. The runways had to be level and safe for the heavily loaded planes that would roar down them for ticklish take-offs under full bomb loads. The hard subsoil was rolled flat by huge concrete rollers pulled back and forth by hundreds of laborers. Stones were hauled from the beds of nearby streams by lines of wheelbarrows miles long, moving continuously back and forth, to and from every part of the giant fields. The foundation layer of the runway was made of cobblestones the size of a man's head, hand fitted, stone by stone, so that they could not roll and cause layers above to shift and weaken the surface. Then the topsoil and subsoil were hauled back, mixed with water to make a thin slurry used to bind succeeding layers of cracked rock laid on the cobblestone base. For weeks, tens of thousands of women and girls did their part by sitting and cracking stones with small hammers. As the runways became thicker and thicker, each new layer of cracked stone and mud slurry was packed down by the heavy, man-drawn, concrete rollers.

As one approached the construction area, the earth seemed to swarm with human beings, and from a distance it seemed scarcely possible that there was room to work or that there was any order in the teeming confusion. Yet in the mass of working men and women, boys and girls, there was order. The men in floppy-brimmed hats carrying pennants on which were marked the name and number of each gang were the headmen of the villages, guiding the work of their own townspeople. Each foreman took his orders from a group commander who in turn received them from one of the dozens of Chinese engineers, while back and forth across the field rode two or three American engineers, each in his own jeep, accompanied by an interpreter. When some detail of the work was not being done quite according to specifications, the jeep would come to a halt, the Chinese engineer responsible for the area was found, the gang foremen called together, and by repeated statements, gestures with the hands, drawings on the ground, and now and then a demonstration, the desired changes were indicated.

At mealtime cooks for each gang shuffled on the field with shoulder poles, carrying bushel-sized wooden buckets of steaming rice and smaller buckets with a few cooked vegetables. Now and then, not more than once a week, there would be a little meat, and twice a week there was bean curd. In still other buckets were boiling hot water, crude earthenware bowls, and chopsticks. Each gang squatted down on haunches, devoured meals, and returned for additional bowls of rice. In empty rice bowls each man dipped up steaming water and sipped it until his thirst was quenched. Cooks gathered up empty buckets, bowls, and chopsticks and trailed away to nearby mat-shed kitchens, and after a brief rest the gangs returned to work.

Day after day they swarmed over the giant airfields like locusts devouring a field of young wheat. After a few weeks came Chinese New Year, when these peasant workers ordinarily would have had the only real rest and holiday of the year. But driven by the dual necessity of finishing the fields for urgent operations and of returning home for their spring harvest and rice transplanting, they took no rest and increased their efforts through the fifteen days of the festival period.

Gradually the great fields took shape. In addition to the workers who built the runways and hard standings, thousands of carpenters, masons, and helpers were brought in to build the buildings necessary to house the airmen and machines to come.

All this was not accomplished without running into problems and difficulties. Early on the job there was an epidemic of dysentery which might have incapacitated thousands of the workers and resulted in at least some deaths had not the provincial health authorities been ready to purify water and halt the dysentery before it became serious. Some cases of smallpox broke out, and at once the health teams were on the job vaccinating the entire group—no small task, vaccinating nearly half a million people at a moment's notice.

Japanese agents also were at work in the area, and ancient superstitions added their share of difficulties. On a visit to one of the fields where it was my job to inquire into some disturbances, we found that one of the local soothsayers had dreamed that a baby was to be born in the district who would someday restore the empire and become the founder of a new dynasty. The dream and the talk about it were seized upon by enemy agents, who used handbills and a whispering campaign to proclaim the royal birth and inspire revolt against the Central Government. Within a few days this farfetched story had gained hundreds of supporters. Groups began to discuss the great wealth and prestige possible if they were to rise up and place this babe on the throne, and instances of how new dynasties had risen from just such beginnings were cited as local feeling became intense. The local authorities had to step in, stop the meetings, and arrest a few of the leaders before the incident quieted down.

Because of language barriers and vast differences in background, problems between Chinese and Americans were by no means absent. One day I went to call on the commissioner in charge of seven of the hsien contributing labor to the project. He had moved his headquarters into the vicinity in order to give personal attention to his heavy responsibilities and to keep things going as smoothly as possible. His local office was protected by fences and guards, and I was ushered past them into a thatch-roofed reception pergola newly built under the trees in one corner of the garden. I had met the commissioner, an elderly gentleman of many years' experience in Szechuan's local government, two years before when I was participating in the public health program in his home city of Wenchiang and knew him to be conscientious and thoroughly loyal to the Central Government. He was a medium-sized man in his late fifties or early sixties, with a pleasant, round face punctuated by long thin mustachios, a beard, and two shaggy eyebrows that overhung piercing black eyes full of intelligence and humor. Because of our personal acquaintance and because I was an American official to whom he could talk in Chinese, he unloaded his troubles for more than two hours, with particular attention to the American engineers.

Much of the conversation concerned an incident that had occurred ten days before on the most southerly field, where most of the work was nearing completion. Each of the work gangs was driving hard to finish its assigned section as soon as possible in order to be home for the spring harvest and rice transplanting on which livelihood for the coming year depended. Near the south end of the main runway, in the middle of the section being built by 10,000 workers from the commissioner's home hsien, were two springs that had been plugged to a depth of twenty feet before the runway was built over them. When the runway was completed and the work gang was almost ready to go home, two days of rain left a huge wet spot over the springs where the water had seeped up through the completed runway surface.

With the engineers watching carefully, the telltale spot over the springs remained after the rest of the surface had dried. The American engineers knew that a spongy spot would be dangerous for the landings of heavy-laden aircraft, and the Chinese were ordered to tear out the old work, dig down thirty to thirty-five feet, and replug the springs.

The Chinese have a habit of seeking a compromise when opinions differ, and they are willing to accept a "good enough" solution. Faced with restive gangs, the leaders, who understood little of technical engineering problems and considered the job completed, sent word that they thought the springs had not really broken through but that water from the recent rains had merely remained on this spot. The Americans retorted that the water came from the springs, and insisted that the commissioner and his subordinates arrange immediately for the necessary repairs.

For a day or two the work gang ignored the orders and continued to finish odds and ends preliminary to their departure, while the American engineers met polite evasion. Finally, it was agreed that the hsien magistrate in charge of the 10,000 workers should meet on the field with the American engineers to decide what should be done. Present were my acquaintance, the commissioner, most of the Chinese engineers, and a large number of the village headmen from the hsien involved. Since the hsien magistrate could speak a little English, the parley started out in the middle of the wet runway with the magistrate sometimes using English, sometimes interpreters. The American engineer, a young lieutenant from Texas with much experience in airfield construction, arrived at the parley provoked because the springs had not already been recapped and the field completed. The old commissioner himself had had much experience with construction of public works by Chinese methods and he was convinced that his workers should not be required to dig out and recap those springs. With that backing the hsien magistrate took the position that the dampness on the runway did not come from the springs but from the rain that had fallen three or four days earlier. So the argument went, keenly followed by several hundred witnesses, the American insisting that the water came from the springs and the Chinese insisting that it did not. Finally, the young American began to lose patience. Thrusting out his chin, he looked the hsien magistrate straight in the eye and said very slowly and carefully, "Do you mean to say that the water there on the runway did not come from those springs?"

"Yes," said the magistrate.

"Well, I say that it did come from the springs," insisted

the American. "Do you mean to call me a liar?"

"Yes," replied the magistrate, completely innocent of the fighting nature of the words.

The young Texan boiled over. With one movement he grabbed the hsien magistrate by the collar of his long blue cotton gown and thrust his face into the mud of the runway.

"See that water there?" the lieutenant shouted. "See it? That water came from those springs. Do you hear me? I said that water came from those springs. You've got to dig them out and plug them again! Do you hear me?"

The poor magistrate could do nothing. No humiliation could begin to equal the loss of face he was suffering and an instant flash of anger went over the crowd of Chinese present. It was as if the long-respected county judge of an American court were to be manhandled by some impudent young foreigner and humiliated in the presence of all the county commissioners and the lieutenant governor of the state. The old commissioner stepped in and helped to pull the young American off the magistrate, and then turned with dignity to his men and told them that they would have to do as the American had suggested. That night the commissioner had difficulty in dissuading the whole 10,000 men from open revolt, from chastising the American, and from returning home, but by the use of all his authority, influence, and persuasion, he managed to induce the village headmen to see that the job was finished as the Americans wanted it. Within a few days the job was done.

The old commissioner poured the whole story out to me and begged that I try to make the Americans more reasonable. He still was not convinced that the springs needed replugging. "Why," he remarked, "I have been supervising public works here in Szechuan for more than forty years, and I know all about our Chinese earth and what you can and can't do with it. How is it that this young American who has never seen Chinese earth before knows so much about it?"

Even though he possessed no understanding of the universality of scientific knowledge, the commissioner had done his job well. The springs were repaired and the fields finished. Giant B-29 planes flew in supplies from India immediately, and early in June the first big raid on Japan's steel industry at Yawata took place. Chinese local government had done a magnificent job of organization and execution in a completely Chinese way.

If China is to be rebuilt, her whole structure of local government must be reorganized. The ancient pattern still dominating local government is not flexible enough to permit the drastic and extensive changes required if China is to become a modern nation or if the Chinese people are to enjoy the advantages available in a world of progress.

As the Chinese grope toward a more workable system of local government it is natural that they should be heavily influenced by the basic ideas that have dominated their past. Since government in China has been based on ideological control and has stemmed from the conceptions of Confucius as inculcated through a system of education that gave these ideas power by teaching them as comprising the greater portion of reliable knowledge, it is not surprising that the leaders of present-day China should seek to found their government on a new sacred book.

The book that the Nationalist Government, under Kuomintang party tutelage, has chosen as a guide and has been canonizing for the past twenty years is the *San Min Chu I*, or *Three Principles of the People*, of Dr. Sun Yat-sen. Dr. Sun, born near Macao of peasant family and many years an exile in the United States, England, and Japan, was a political observer, dreamer, theorist, and revolutionist who adopted foreign ideas as a basis for a Chinese revolution and republic. The *San Min Chu I* is a collection of his lectures in which he sets forth his ideas about patriotism, citizenship, government, international relations, economics, and general community and social outlook.

Since the death of Dr. Sun in 1925, the *San Min Chu I* has been used by the Kuomintang party as the bible of China's political life and has influenced the thinking of a whole generation of Chinese to such a degree that even the Chinese Communists and other opposition groups have accepted the Three Principles as the gospel and the median law and now attack the Kuomintang for failing to carry out Dr. Sun's real intent.

It is safe to say that no document in American history has ever been ground into the consciousness of the American people the way the *Three Principles of the People* has been ground into the Chinese people during the past twenty years. Every Monday morning since 1929, in that great majority of China's schools which are under the control of the Kuomintang party, a memorial service in honor of Dr. Sun has been held. During this service the Kuomintang National Anthem, *San Min Chu I*, is sung, there are three bows from the waist before the portrait of Dr. Sun and the Kuomintang national colors, Dr. Sun's will (in which he enjoined his followers to carry out the purposes for which he struggled for forty years) is recited by chairman and audience, three minutes of silence are observed, there is a recitation of Dr. Sun's teaching, and the ceremony is ended by the recitation of the Kuomintang Creed.

Every school child studies the *San Min Chu I* in every school and college year of his career. Every speech that Generalissimo Chiang has made has been based on the Three Principles. The ideas of the *San Min Chu I* are woven into every paper and magazine and every textbook on history or civics or international affairs published in China.

The basic ideas of this document, which Dr. Sun, in his

introduction, frankly acknowledges were written primarily for use as propaganda, were expressed hastily under trying circumstances and, therefore, are much in need of revision and improvement. They play an important part in shaping both local and national government in China, but are they adequate to support such a structure? Could a government founded on them competently serve China's need as she tries to rebuild herself? What, then, are the basic ideas of the *San Min Chu I?*

The three principles themselves are Nationalism, Democracy, and People's Livelihood. As they are set forth by Dr. Sun, all three have a strong collectivist emphasis:

By *nationalism* is meant the unification of China and, primarily, the throwing off of the yoke of foreign peoples as embodied in the unequal treaties. When, in 1943, these treaties were at last revoked, the leaders of China proudly pointed to the fact that they had achieved an important goal set by Dr. Sun's will. It cannot be denied that the principle of Nationalism has played an important part in the achievement of such unity as China has attained. Yet much of the specific material presented by Dr. Sun is now outdated and erroneous. For example, Dr. Sun says that Japan is "now the strongest nation in the East, on a par with the nations of Europe and America." He goes on to say that "Japan could destroy her [China] within ten days . . . If we want China to become strong, Japan is an excellent model for us." These ideas are understandable in terms of forty or more years ago when they developed in Dr. Sun's mind, but they become erroneous and positively dangerous when taken as they are today, for it is in the nature of gospel that the Chinese, at least outwardly, regard the writings of Dr. Sun.

Dr. Sun's definitions of *democracy* are also of some value in their general directives, but they include many contradictions which may well make difficult the building of a workable system if followed literally. For example, Dr. Sun insists that democracy in China must, by its very nature, exercise the three functions of initiative, referendum, and recall, while branding as frauds the "democracies" of the West because the people cannot issue orders to their governments through these devices. These three functions have been written into the new constitution of China.

Under the principle of *people's livelihood*, Dr. Sun, while professing a desire to interest foreign capital in helping Chinese development, defines the principle itself as aiming at "the destruction of the capitalistic system." Dr. Sun insists that it is the responsibility of the state to provide the necessities of food, clothing, shelter, and means of travel and that "anyone should be able to call the state to task if it does not provide enough of each." Much present-day thinking about economics in China is warped by trying to follow Dr. Sun's advice and reasoning while grappling with problems that have undergone extensive changes since his day.

Although Dr. Sun's leadership and ideas have played an important part in the shaping of recent history of China, it may be tragic if his writings and thinking are followed too literally while local government is being organized to meet the variety of new problems confronting China today. After talking with many Chinese leaders one has the distinct feeling that their thinking is too limited and too bound by Dr. Sun's reasoning. Many observers who have felt these limitations at work in the Kuomintang party have been led to turn to the Communists as offering the greater hope for the solution of local government problems. Yet the rigidity of the doctrinaire approach of the Communists also presents many weaknesses.

Both the Kuomintang and the Communists profess to want forms of local government that permit the people to have a real voice in their own affairs, yet both groups actually operate on the old pattern of passing all major decisions down from the top. In local situations both groups allow a limited scope for the expression of the will of the people, but in neither group is there much democracy as it is known in America.

It would be highly unrealistic to expect an American-type democracy to develop rapidly in China. The ingrained habits of centuries make difficult the introduction of the American kind of open political struggle in which the voter is the ultimate arbiter and the judge to whom contending candidates carry their differing programs and platforms. The whole manner of conducting human relations in China makes our method of public attack on contending candidates seem inapplicable. Nor is there anything in Chinese culture that would permit or lead a man to stand up before his constituents and praise his own policies as being superior to those of his opponent—although I have yet to meet many Chinese who, like most Americans, are not pretty sure that their own opinions are correct. Likewise, there is nothing that would make it possible for two candidates to take sharply different and critical attitudes toward each other unless there was bad blood between them personally. The very nature of a political attack in which one person opposes another openly is considered a complete breach of personal relations. The fact that Mr. Roosevelt could ask his former opponent, Mr. Willkie, to be his personal representative on a world-wide mission was a matter of great marvel to the Chinese. Because of this attitude toward opposition, decisions are usually made in Chinese circles without the use of formal voting.

Dr. John Earl Baker, who has spent many years with Famine Relief and other private and public agencies working closely with the Chinese government and who has participated in hundreds of meetings with Chinese officials, once told me, "In all my years in China I have never but once participated in group meetings in which a vote was taken on an important decision. Always the pattern is like this: the chairman, and in many, many conferences the chairman was the Generalissimo, carefully observes reactions of the different members as the problems involved are discussed, and the decision is thereupon announced without vote.

"I remember one meeting in which an important decision was being made involving China's international relations. An existing ministry wanted to carry on activities for which a new international organization was being proposed. The minister himself was very eloquent as to why the job should be given to his ministry rather than to the new international organization. He even went so far as to say that in the international organization the Chinese would be nothing more than running dogs for foreigners. During his speech the Generalissimo watched the expressions of other group members. When the long tirade was finished and a brief time had been given for others to express opinion in which very little was said to support the international organization, the Generalissimo ruled that it was the decision of the body that it be set up. The Generalissimo had gathered accurately from changes of expression and from the few words spoken that most of those present supported the idea of setting up the international organization rather than turning the function over to the existing ministry.

"That is the way the Chinese work—they simply do not force people to take clear-cut stands against ideas supported by individuals who would consider a vote against their idea a personal insult."

While the American pattern of democratic procedure may not come into immediate favor in China, it is probable that through their own methods the people of China will develop more and more ways to express their will and to determine how their government will function at both national and local levels. In both Communist and Kuomintang areas the trend in this direction is at work. Since there will be many years of struggle before China finally develops adequate local government, and since it is efficient government at the local level that actually implements enlightened policy and agencies, the processes by which China must rebuild herself will evolve slowly and painfully.

Chapter IX

War and the People of China

THIS WAS THE SCENE WHEN KUANG TI, GOD OF WAR, descended again upon China: A China essentially agricultural, with 80 per cent of its humanity directly dependent on the land. A China overpopulated and desperately poor, with much too little arable land for the millions depending on its production. A China of periodic famines with only 12,000 miles of railway to carry food over $1\frac{1}{3}$ million square miles. A China moving nearly all its production by wind, water, and the muscle of man. A China in which education was still the special privilege of the few, all too frequently producing scholar-officials unproductive of good for either community or nation. A China badly disunited after revolution, counterrevolution, another revolution, a split within the revolutionary party, ten years of civil war between those factions, and the remnants of a quarter century of local warlordism. Kuang Ti had not been idle, but his past efforts were merely practice.

War came gradually at first, with the Manchurian "incident" in 1931 when the Japanese moved into Manchuria and set up the puppet state of Manchoukuo; in the spring of 1932, with the first attack on Shanghai that laid waste a large section of that city; in the spring of 1933, with the occupation of Jehol and East Hopei; and then with four years of economic attack in which Japan sought to undermine China's national economy by the deliberate and wholesale smuggling of sugar, cotton goods, and other commodities through occupied areas.

WAR AND THE PEOPLE OF CHINA

War came with a rush after the clash at Peiping's Marco Polo bridge on July 7, 1937. In the first few days it engulfed Tientsin while Chinese police tried to fight the Imperial Army of Japan, and Nankai University, one of China's finest private institutions of learning, went up in smoke under Japanese bombs and shells. Then there was a lull for negotiations while the situation teetered in the balance for several weeks. Early in August it appeared that fighting might be limited to the north and that some sort of compromise might be worked out. But the demands of the Japanese were too heavy. A wave of popular demand for resistance swept China, and on August 13, 1937, clashes occurred in Shanghai in which 40,000 civilians died.

Then war broke out in full fury. Weeks of heavy fighting in Shanghai destroyed a large part of the city and decimated most of China's well-trained and well-equipped troops. When the Japanese landed through Hangchow Bay, the Chinese lines were outflanked and broken and the defeated armies streamed back toward bomb-shattered Nanking. By December, less than six months after the Marco Polo incident, China's capital had been occupied and looted, its women raped by the thousands, its young men machine-gunned or tied together, soaked in gasoline, and set afire; China's air force was all but destroyed; most of her good troops were killed or wounded; her government had fled up the Yangtze to Hankow under a rain of bombs; and all but one of her main ports were lost. The League of Nations was powerless to lend more than a polite ear to China's appeals. Not a single friendly nation was willing to do more than stand safely on the sidelines, as America did, and scold the Japanese for being naughty-naughty, while continuing to sell the Japanese all the scrap iron and petroleum products they wanted.

Yet China did not give up. After a few weeks' breathing spell she rallied new forces, won a victory at Taierchwang in Shantung during the spring of 1938, but lost the campaign to keep the Japanese from uniting their northern and southern forces in the Yellow River valley. Millions of acres of cultivated land were flooded when the Yellow River was cut loose to stop the united Japanese forces from driving westward. Canton fell with little resistance. Early in 1939 Hankow lost her stubborn struggle and the government evacuated again, this time to the hilly city of Chungking in Szechuan.

Less than two years after hostilities began at Peiping, more than 80 per cent of the normal sources of public income were lost to the enemy and China was completely blockaded except for the little narrow-gauge railway that wound its way through scores of tunnels and over hundreds of bridges down through the mountains to Indo-China. However, Japanese pressure on the French reduced this line to a negligible source of supply. So China, hacking her way out the rear with bare hands, built the Burma Road through the gorges, peaks, and jungles of the world's most rugged mountains.

Again and again constant merciless pounding pushed the Chinese people and the Chinese government beyond their depth, and time after time the ragged and stunned millions clawed at debris and death to clear a way to survival. Yet, in spite of superhuman efforts without tools—prodigious feats like the construction of the Burma Road, the building of huge airfields, the marching of whole armies hundreds of miles, the carrying of thousands of tons of machine tools inland, and the hacking of bombproof arsenals deep into solid rock—the great mass of Chinese people never really understood the full meaning of the war. To the majority of Chinese the wrath of Kuang Ti came ravaging like flood or famine or cholera and struck as inexplicably, to be borne in silence and patience without reasoning. The peasants and city dwellers of Szechuan were not prepared for such things as the bombers that pounded and harassed them in the summer of 1939, nor did they ever comprehend the seasonal visitors from the heavens that dropped death from April through September for three years.

With thousands trapped inside the city gates of Chengtu and slaughtered by the first bombing raids, the menace of Kuang Ti was understood well enough to speed the widening of city gates to permit quick evacuation of the city. Yet the mysterious ways of modern warfare were so bewildering that Chengtu regulations required complete silence while planes were overhead lest the planes hear the noise and be guided in the bombing and strafing. People crouched silently under the bamboo clumps that shade the farmhouses across the plain. Military and civilians lived in such constant dread that someone would signal planes with white articles that a white shirt was a direct invitation for a bullet from any one of the thousands of patrolling military. Once I watched a policeman brave the overhead planes for fifteen minutes in order to drive three white geese from a pond on the West China Union University campus.

Nor were such misconceptions of bombers limited to the illiterate masses. Soon after the United States had been attacked and had struck back, an article appeared in one of the well-known Chungking newspapers concerning the Flying Fortresses then being turned out in quantities. The learned but literal author, reasoning from the root meanings of the four Chinese characters into which Flying Fortresses had been translated, flatly asserted that these "forts in the air" were so powerful that "just three of them hung at each of the three corners of Chungking could prevent all Japanese bombing." He was correct about the three corners, for Chungking is built on a triangular tongue of land at the confluence of two rivers, but the American Office of War Information had to combat this misconception of the Flying Fortress for many months and never was sure that it had been entirely corrected.

WAR AND THE PEOPLE OF CHINA

In spite of being caught unprepared for the lethal panoply of Kuang Ti, in spite of not understanding the nature of the weapons hurled at them, in spite of all the limitations of possible defense, the adaptable people of China adjusted themselves to the conditions of war, and the nation survived.

Thousands died and most of the city was burned during the first raids that caught Chungking unprepared. Yet by the third bombing season, 1941, the whole city was able to go underground smoothly and unhurriedly. One of the best air-raid warning nets in the world kept Chungking informed of Japanese preparations a day in advance of raids. When enemy planes on Japanese fields at Hankow began to warm up, and again when they took off, the news would be flashed to the war-time capital. The warning system informed authorities of the number and location of attacking planes with such accuracy and consistency that hours before the first planes approached the city the population was warned, and a good half hour before raiders were overhead people would be off the streets and in the shelters, with only police and fire wardens aboveground.

Historians will spend many hours in years to come in evaluating China's contributions to the winning of World War II. They will have to point to many failings and shortcomings, and there will undoubtedly be those who will heavily discount China's contributions, and some may even argue that China was a military liability. Yet, in spite of the fact that China lacked able administrators to operate her army and her economy with efficiency, and in spite of the fact that many individuals and families, some high in government circles, profiteered in goods and made fortunes in the controlling of money and transportation, the Chinese people and the overwhelming majority of officials made great sacrifices which contributed materially to the successful prosecution of the war. Determination and privation kept unaided China in the war, sapping enemy strength, matériel, and manpower for years, contributing as she could with methods essentially Chinese.

Many of the people of China exhibited courage and showed loyalty to China's allies that is unsurpassed anywhere anytime. Once on the central front, an American fighter plane, while strafing Japanese positions, received a hit in its cooling system. The pilot had only a few minutes before his engine froze, forcing him to bail out, still in full view of the Japanese. He had scarcely landed when Chinese villagers, without waiting for explanations, hustled him into the hills overlooking the village and hid him in a cave. In a few hours a battalion of Japanese soldiers came hunting him. They seized the villagers, lined them up, and demanded to know where the American was. Not one of the villagers, from small children to graybeards, would tell. The Japanese made a search. Again they returned and demanded to know where the flier was. No response.

"If you don't tell us where he is we will burn your village," they threatened. Still no one knew anything about the American. The Japanese put the torch to the village. The villagers stood under the cover of machine guns and watched their meager, hard-earned goods, clothing, houses, harvested crops, tools, and seed grain go up in smoke. No one spoke.

"Now if you don't tell us where he is we'll really get tough with you," the Japanese snarled. Again great pressure was exerted to force the villagers to lead the way to the pilot's hideout. No one cracked. The Japanese lined up the two or three hundred people of the village. Down the line they went, shooting every fifth person, man, woman, or child. Still the hiding place of the pilot was safe.

The expedients of brute force were exhausted. The frustrated Japanese marched away. After many hours the villagers came for the young American and guided him by devious trails to safety.

As illustration of the contributions of the Chinese people

to the international war, the construction feats of the Burma Road, the airfields, and underground arsenals have already been mentioned. To these may be added the story of a purely Chinese accomplishment, the transporting of two hundred thousand tons of machinery to unoccupied territory in the summer of 1939.

As city after city fell to the enemy during 1938 and 1939, the Chinese retreated into the mountains of the interior, taking with them as much war and educational equipment as could be lifted by human backs. Whole arsenals were moved upriver, from Nanking, Canton, and Hankow, spinning mills from Wusih, Kukiang, Nanking, and Hankow, machine shops from Shanghai, Wusih, Soochow, and Nanking. Dozens of types of machinery and equipment from a dozen other fallen cities were stripped from factories and shipped out under the Japanese guns like the oxygen and acetylene plants of Mr. Lee. They poured into Hankow by rail from the south, and by river boats, steamers, junks, and even sampans, glutting the godowns of the upriver city. As it became obvious that Hankow was next in the list of cities to be occupied, shipload after shipload of valuable war potential once more began to move up the winding, sluggish river to the city of Ichang where the Yangtze changes from a slow-moving river of the plains to a mighty mountain giant plunging out of gorges. Since most of the ships lacked the power to force themselves against currents running nine knots in smooth places and twelve or thirteen knots in the rapids, all they could do was unload the precious cargo at Ichang and return to Hankow for more.

By the late spring of 1939 more than two hundred thousand tons of machinery had accumulated in Ichang. Hankow had already fallen. The Japanese were advancing overland toward Ichang, sending bombers ahead to harass the city. Few of the accumulated machines had been moved to safety beyond the gorges because the normal low-water period of the spring made it impossible for the large, specially designed steamers to navigate the gorges. With the situation growing desperate, the Chinese government called on Mr. Lu Tso-fu, head of the Ming Sung Industrial Company and at that time also vice-minister of communications. The Ming Sung Company, built from scratch in fifteen years by Mr. Lu, owned and operated the largest fleet of ships designed to navigate the swift waters of the upper Yangtze.

When Mr. Lu accepted his assignment the normal late spring rise was just beginning. He knew he would have to move the machinery in a race against both the Japanese Army and time. He had to move it during the limited period of high water when he could use his steamers to best advantage. High water, however, meant that he could not use man-towed junks as extensively as he could in low water.

Mr. Lu boarded the 1,300-ton flagship of the Ming Sung fleet and radioed all available ships to report to him at Ichang. There he was almost swamped by people who had machinery or other goods piled in warehouses or in the open. He was offered all varieties of bribes and found himself unable to work because of the host of "expediters" who swarmed to his office. He banned all such time-wasting activities and organized a priorities system. Mr. Lu set to work getting the goods flowing smoothly to ships kept working day and night. Lacking trucks and with a limited number of cranes to handle loads of as much as twenty to thirty tons, coolie work gangs were organized to handle loading and unloading.

The Chinese are masters at carrying huge loads by manpower. The heavier pieces were placed on skids and hauled along hastily built wooden tracks by hand winches. Loads of four to six tons were carried in huge rigs designed so that more than one hundred men could lift and carry at the same time. Day and night the chant of the work gangs rang against the Ichang hills. Smaller machines, and boxes and bales of parts and supplies were carried aboard by the tens of thousands to the rhythmic swaying of elastic carrying poles on the shoulders of two, four, or six men, surefooted as mountain goats, who bore them down slippery banks and across narrow plank gangways.

Day and night Mr. Lu kept in touch with each of his ships, driving them to the limit of their capacity, even urging them again and again to take chances in order to make way through rough water in the last remaining light before night forced them to tie up. Through the sweltering, muggy summer heat, through rainstorms and repeated Japanese air raids the shore gangs at Ichang sweated and chanted as they loaded ships. Day after day the steamers fought the rapids and tied up at upriver ports to unload precious cargo. The backed-up piles of machines at Ichang grew smaller and smaller as steamers pulled away and junks started up through the gorges in spite of the added risks of high water. Forty-two days after Mr. Lu arrived the last machine was loaded. The tools that were to play an important part in keeping China in the war were saved. A few weeks later, when the Japanese marched in, they found the Ichang dumps empty.

Moving valuable machine tools was only one of many contributions Mr. Lu and the Ming Sung Company made to the effort of war. They transported millions of soldiers up and down the waterways of the upper Yangtze. The engineering works of the company, with meager supplies and limited equipment, most of which came up through the gorges during those forty-two days in 1939, played a major part in keeping shipping in operation on the upper Yangtze. They salvaged and rebuilt five large ships. A typical example was the conversion of a diesel-engined ship to steam power when fuel-oil supplies were gone. Because she was too short to permit the installation of a steam engine and boilers, the ship was hauled on shore with skids and hand winches, cut apart amidships, and lengthened by forty feet of built-in steel hull. A boiler was reclaimed from a bombed and sunken ship and supplemented by another built from limited supplies of plate and tubing; new steam engines were constructed and installed, and the ship thereafter operated on coal.

In addition, the Ming Sung Company built four steel-hulled and thirteen wooden-hulled ships, the machinery required for all of them, plus machine tools of many types, two locomotive boilers, and water turbines. Also, the company converted a large electric motor into a generator and built a water turbine to drive it. Compared to production in other parts of the world, the list of Ming Sung accomplishments is not impressive, but all these ingenious feats were done in a series of caves excavated from the solid rock of the riverbank, using materials reclaimed from war losses or squeezed from tiny supplies. With less than two hundred powered ships available on the upper Yangtze, the building of seventeen new ones by Ming Sung stands out in truer perspective.

Many aspects of the war in China were fantastic and probably could not have existed in any other country. The story of the Chinese Post Office, for example, would provide material for a fascinating thriller. Throughout the war it was possible to send letters from almost anywhere in "free China" to most places in "occupied China" simply by addressing them and dropping them in the nearest postbox. Postal service was maintained in spite of incredible difficulties met by postmasters who packed up their stamps and seals for a brief stay in the hills while fighting swept back and forth over their districts, after which they would emerge from hiding to inquire who was holding the town at the moment and to resume the handling of mail. Links between

Japanese-controlled and free areas were maintained at hundreds of points by carriers moving on foot, junks, or carts, keeping a huge flow of mail in transit.

During the last winter before Pearl Harbor, the Christian Literature Society found itself confined in occupied Shanghai with quantities of Bibles and tracts while clients in unoccupied China clamored for religious literature. Since the time when the Chinese had cut the dikes and loosed the floodwaters of the Yellow River on the Japanese hordes in Honan province, there remained several villages west of the flooded area that were listed by the Japanese as under their control but were actually in free China. When Myron E. Terry of the Christian Literature Society discovered that great quantities of goods were moving into free China from occupied Kaifeng, he went there and called on the Italian postal inspector whom the Japanese had retained in office. The inspector spotted one of the villages west of the flood to which he could forward mail. Thereafter, quantities of literature, ordered by Terry from his Shanghai office, were forwarded to him in free China. For weeks the packages came daily on carts that waited at the boat landing to pick them up. The several thousands of packages delivered to free China played a part in keeping the Christian community of the interior supplied with literature during the long years between Pearl Harbor and V-J day.

War has cost the Chinese people an enormous price in suffering and retrogression. Many people in the West are aware that every Chinese city of 25,000 population and over suffered from bombing. Most people know that as many as fifteen or twenty million people were forced from their homes for varying periods or migrated into the interior to escape Japanese rule. But misery in the aggregate is sometimes too much for comprehension. Tragedy in the singular is more impressive.

After the fearful bomb-shelter accident that occurred at

Chungking in the summer of 1941, when five or ten thousand people smothered to death, dozens of shops in downtown Chungking never opened again. No one came to claim the property, for whole families had been snuffed out together.

When war broke, Mr. Shen left Shanghai. Well known in China as a playwright and movie director, he retreated to the interior with the Central Motion Picture Studios in order to continue production of educational and war propaganda films, but he left his wife and two small children at home in Shanghai rather than risk the trip to bomb-gutted Chungking. After seven years of living under Japanese rule, Mrs. Shen, with the children and some relatives, set out on the long, circuitous route leading to free China and Chungking to rejoin Mr. Shen. As soon as they reached a point in free China a telegram was sent to Mr. Shen, who was overjoyed at the prospect of seeing his family—especially the baby, who must by now be a sizable son. By telegram he followed their tedious progress by bus, train, and foot across South China toward Chungking, and the day of their arrival found Mr. Shen elaborately prepared for the family reunion. But the war-weary bus carrying the family overturned on the steep mountain road leading to Chungking. Clouds of dust arose and settled on the Shen family as they lay in the valley below, a short way from town.

With us in the American Office of War Information was Shu Tsung-chiao, who edited our *United Pictorial*, a highly successful picture journal dedicated to the presentation of the American war effort. Mr. Shu was with us for three years, but he had been away from his Nanking home and family for more than eight, receiving occasional news from his parents and younger brother through the clandestine mail route. After V-J day we flew down to liberated Nanking, over the Yangtze gorges, the plains of the central Yangtze valley, and bomb-shattered Hankow. We were thrilled to catch the first view of Nanking's Purple Mountain rising in molded contours from the plains beside the ancient city, with the world-famous tomb of Sun Yat-sen on its eastern slope. Before continuing to Shanghai, Mr. Shu left the plane for a brief visit with his family. The home lay wrecked, his mother dead, mashed by American bombs during the last days of the war.

All China was war weary. The millions of refugees in free China overwhelmed all remaining means of transportation in an effort to return to their liberated coastal homes. I watched Mr. Lu's flagship, the largest of the steamers to ply the rapids through the gorges, as it docked in Shanghai one day. It was one of the first loads of repatriates to arrive home. Three thousand of them were jammed into a tiny river steamer for sixteen days—so crowded that three children were accidentally pushed overboard and lost.

Yet perhaps more tragic than any one or all of the personal losses of millions of Chinese is the atrophy of the nation as a whole, the destruction and retrogression of budding progress in an ancient land.

When Kuang Ti swept the invading hordes over China, a national health program was beginning to spread, directed from new and well-equipped buildings of the Field Health Station of the National Health Administration at Nanking. Administratively and experimentally, a modern system was gradually proving its value. The Bureau of Vital Statistics collected accurate information on incidence of illness and death, causes of death, and reportable diseases for the planning and implementing of a sound health program. A first-class chemical laboratory had begun the enormous task of maintaining and enforcing standards of native and foreign drugs in order to protect the public from thousands of useless nostrums. A sanitary section was making progress in improving water supplies and general rural and urban sanitation. Sections dealing with health education, maternity and child welfare, hospital services, and the training of health workers, were steadily increasing the number of local medical-health programs scattered over the nation. Then war came.

Two years after the evacuation from Nanking the National Health Administration found itself leaving Chungking under bombing and strafing. When the organization finally settled in a secluded valley, fifteen miles from Chungking, workmen were recruited to construct new wartime quarters. But malaria broke out, and 60 per cent of the workmen were stricken. Building proceeded slowly. Health work slackened as members of the administration, one after the other, came down with malaria before they discovered that they had moved from the lair of Kuang Ti into the very center of one of the worst malaria areas in Szechuan province. In the spring of 1941, when I visited this village of Hsinchiao, the work of the administration was again under way. Malaria had been brought under partial control marked by occasional relapses among staff members, and, in spite of primitive conditions and loss of equipment, the administration was creating an excellent record. Yet the national health program has been retarded by decades.

Although the number of students attending schools at every level has increased, the progress of education has fallen far short of prewar expectations. The greatest losses in education, however, are the lowered standards of academic work and teaching caused by isolation and inflation.

China's tiny corps of teachers has been deprived of recourse to contemporary thinking and progress; it has been deprived of sufficient food, clothing, and equipment; and it has been overloaded with students and work. Teachers, scientists, and professional people are years behind world developments in their fields, and the students, reflecting this privation, are poorly equipped to take their places in teaching. Yet scores of young scientists continued research and teaching under formidable war conditions and have made some real advances in their fields. For example, Dr. Chang Kwei, biologist of Cheeloo University, returned from Iowa to China and the Tsinan campus just in time to flee with the rest of Cheeloo to the interior, where the Biology Department eventually reassembled under his direction. Almost at once he began field studies on the distribution of human parasites in Szechuan province, using methods we had applied in Shantung province before the war. For three years he gave special attention to hookworm disease. Co-operating with the Provincial Bureau of Health and supported by grants from the Rockefeller Foundation, he gathered a great deal of new knowledge about the distribution and epidemiology of this important disease.

Teachers, too few for the numbers seeking instruction, also suffered physically from inflation and its effect. The cost-of-living index increased approximately four thousand times during the war, while salaries for teachers increased only about five hundred times. In effect it reduced their purchasing power to less than one-fifth of its prewar level, a condition prevailing for six of the war years and then growing steadily worse during the years following the war. This meant that many of China's best brains have been forced to live and work under conditions that sapped vitality, health, and teaching ability. In order to continue their teaching, supplemental incomes were necessary, and teachers began with the sale of personal belongings and continued by holding two or three jobs simultaneously in order to raise salaries to subsistence levels. Holding multiple jobs, some teachers have taught as many as forty hours a week, exclusive of time for preparation and necessary travel. Many with families to support eventually were forced to abandon teaching and enter business, thus reducing the teaching corps still further. Yet thousands of valiant teachers have stuck to their jobs, largely because of loyalty to the ideals of education.

The physical destruction of China's educational institutions and equipment amounted to millions of American dollars. Libraries, museums, colleges, universities, and laboratory equipment must be rebuilt or replaced. In Shanghai, in 1947, for example, thirty-three colleges, universities, and technical schools still had only the American Information Library of three thousand volumes to offer a contemporary picture of the outside world and its experiences, and the existence of that and other small American libraries seemed doomed by Congressional economy measures in Washington.

The destruction of Nankai University and its library was the most complete single loss among damages ranging from thorough razing to the surprise that welcomed Fuhtan professors and students back to their Shanghai campus in 1946. There the Japanese had removed the heavy, sweeping roofs of tile, demolished the top stories of each building, and then replaced the same roofs, so that larger planes might safely use the adjoining Kiangwan airport. The Japanese also left a well-equipped village built at the airport on Fuhtan property. Thus one of China's largest universities has inherited street after street of attractive houses and public buildings left in fair condition by hurriedly departing Japanese. Most institutions, however, faced sordid destruction and loss rather than such playful quirks, and the thirteen Christian colleges, with prewar plants valued at $11 million American and war losses of $6 million, suffered fates more typical of all Chinese institutions. It will require many years for higher education to re-equip and to re-establish its standards.

Although the war forced development in some of the interior provinces, modern agricultural progress in China has been retarded by many years. Like the Health Administration activities, the sound agricultural work of the Nanking Government was interrupted, and years of experimental work in plant breeding to produce new disease-resistant and better-yielding strains of seeds and plants were lost to the people of China. However, some agricultural work was carried on under Japanese sponsorship. When I returned to North China after the Japanese surrender I was impressed by the availability of improved fruit derived from previous Chinese experiments supplemented by strains from Japan.

The Ministry of Agriculture and Forestry will need many years to recover from budgetary limitations and to re-establish agricultural administration and experimentation at the level of 1937, even though interior provinces have been exposed to unexpected advances during the war years, and even though China has had unexcelled research assistance from America through the services, advice, and planning of potato breeder Clarence Dykstra, animal husbandrymen Ralph Phillips and Ray G. Johnson, and many other agriculturists flown to China by the United States Government during and after the war.

China's wartime transportation losses have been dramatic and terrible. The forces of Kuang Ti destroyed precious rails, rolling stock, bridges, and highways and ran the remaining facilities into obsolescence. In spite of losses in existing rail mileage, the roads hauled 21,582,000 troops and 4,433,000 tons of military supplies during the first five and a half years of the war, much to the gratification of Chang Kia-ngau, then minister of communications, who proudly claimed "an achievement unprecedented in China's history." Most poignant loss to Chinese railway builders was the Chientang Bridge near Hangchow, blown up one month after this most beautiful of modern Chinese bridges had been completed. After constant demolition by Americans,

Communists, Japanese, and Nationalists, the end of the war found China's railway system in very poor condition indeed.

Highway transportation, while making considerable gains in terms of new highways constructed, also suffered heavily, and some of the new roads essential to the war, impractical for peacetime use, are now washed out and overgrown. During the last months of 1944, in all free China there were less than five thousand trucks, most of which had been converted to burn charcoal or other substitute fuels and were so worn and patched that twenty to thirty miles was an average day's run. Although motor vehicles in occupied territory were more numerous and in better condition, a postwar accounting would reflect a motley array of decrepit jallopies bouncing over the potholes of run-down roads and carrying sturdy planks for use as makeshift bridges over ditches. Only in Shanghai, chief port of entry, are the shiny new vehicles of Europe and America to be seen, driving on the right now instead of the left—a changeover effected on January 1, 1946, with remarkable efficiency.

With the wholesale destruction and deterioration of transportation facilities, the Chinese have fallen back more and more on the old, slow, and expensive types of transportation that depend on wind, water, and muscle.

But of all the losses that history may lament, the world will probably miss most those gifts to its culture which once came from China's craftsmen. Many of the skills that produced treasured expressions of Chinese culture—ceramics, lacquers, rugs, glass, pewter, textiles—have been lost or severely limited by the war. In China, birthplace and zenith of fine porcelain, the thermochemical art reached legendary perfection in more than one famous center. It was the product of skilled co-ordination between consecutive generations of artists and artisans. Each step of the creative processes was carried out by a different man, with a division of labor so extreme that the man who fired the kiln knew this job alone, while another damped the fire to control the temperature and kiln conditions. The porcelain body was shaped by the potter and glazed by the glazier, while still another knew the tricks of mixing and aging the clay. The finished product was the work of a score of men, each contributing some specialized skill handed down, perhaps for centuries, as a carefully guarded trade secret of the family. Now war has scattered those teams of families whose combined work alone could produce certain types of fine porcelain. When I visited the home of a lacquer worker outside Peiping's Chien Men gate, I was told that all of his skilled workers had gone to seek other employment because they could not make a living at lacquer carving. Death, damage, inflation, lack of transportation, loss of markets, equipment, and men have wiped out many vestiges of a golden age. Some of these special skills and the secrets on which they were based may well be lost forever, snatched by Kuang Ti as a tribute to war.

Kuang Ti has levied a heavy toll on every phase of China's development. While there have been some gains as a direct result of war, they have been bought at a terrible cost. Sheer destruction of physical wealth is incalculable. Thousands of villages were laid waste when fighting swept through them, were burned punitively by Japanese for harboring guerrillas or American airmen, or by Chinese guerrillas for co-operating with the Japanese.

The people suffered, for only as the people produce does the nation acquire the wealth to wage war, and only as production is destroyed is resistance weakened. War destruction added to the already heavy burdens of the people and upset their limited capacity to produce and survive. Millions lost the gamble to Kuang Ti.

So the people of China have died. Under the wreckage of their homes, suffocated in air-raid shelters, seared in flames of villages and cities ablaze with war, drowned by walls of water, frozen while fleeing along drifted mountain trails, starved in drought when armies consumed stored grain. They died for lack of rice when money from overseas relatives stopped coming; they died alone as orphans, widows, aged, and infirm, unable to survive a struggle that taxed even the young and healthy. They died as underfed recruits forced to march for hundreds of miles and loaded like beasts. They died as soldiers from the slightest infections, from lack of medical care, or from care worse than none. Forced building of roads, railroads, and airfields left a trail of dead from dysentery and cholera. Yet China survived, and after eight years of debacle was still on her feet, dazed but fighting back.

However, the balance of China's biologically centered economy was destroyed. Everywhere in China man's relation to his environment is so intimate and the environment is utilized so thoroughly that a precise balance exists between production and consumption. For ten years Kuang Ti ravaged that balanced economy like a voracious giant salamander suddenly let loose in a small aquarium. Its ravages have been most terrible in the countryside.

Rich Hunan province, the heart of China's rice bowl, and scene of Japan's last thrust down the southern corridor, was such an area. Here, in the center of a region normally blessed with plenty, famine stalked during the first winter after the end of war.

Western Honan was another such devastated region. After traveling through the province, Dr. Raymond Moyer of the United States Department of Agriculture wrote the following description:*

"Honan was one of the provinces of North China invaded by the Japanese early in the war. Of its 35,000,000 inhabitants, approximately 12,000,000 lived in regions damaged seriously, and at least 2,000,000 were on starvation rations

* Far Eastern Survey, July 17, 1946.

last winter. Epidemics ravaged badly disrupted communities—malaria, dysentery, typhoid, typhus, smallpox, relapsing fever, diphtheria—and, unhappily, conditions in Honan are typical of conditions in a number of wartorn provinces of interior China.

"A visitor to China seeing only Shanghai, Tientsin, or Canton might conclude that China has suffered very little, an incorrect conclusion, for coastal cities [1932 and 1937 rubble already cleared away] were recovered to a large extent intact, but there have been destruction and serious loss in the interior of China. The writer's tour of investigation took him through seriously affected portions of western and central Honan where the streets of village after village were bordered with gutted dwellings, smoke-blackened mud walls still standing.

"In two *hsien* where frontal fighting was most severe, between two and three hundred thousand persons left their homes and belongings to flee into the mountains . . . before the harvest of the wheat crop, which was lost. When the refugees returned, their fertile soil was producing only weeds . . . a disaster of great magnitude to the majority of the refugees . . . who had in sight no further supply of food before the next wheat harvest, eight months in the future . . . most of them had lost their work animals and implements and they had no wheat seed for planting. In ruthless retaliation of the unexpected show of resistance, Japanese troops had deliberately burned tens of thousands of homes, and, to make matters worse, epidemics of disease had been induced by malnutrition, exposure, and unsanitary conditions . . . in some districts ten or fifteen per cent of the whole population died between return to their homes and mid-November. In home after home the same story was told, 'The wheat was not harvested, and the summer crops were not planted; we have nothing to eat or wear, and nobody wants our labor.' "

Of eastern Honan, where the Chinese had cut the Yellow River dikes and stopped a united Japanese drive early in the war, Spencer Coxe, an American, of the Friends Ambulance Unit, wrote:

"During the past eight years, an acreage comparable to that of Connecticut has been flooded at one time or another and thousands have been rendered homeless and hungry. Some of the land has been reclaimed [spring, 1946] but large tracts remain utterly desolate, for farmers dare not go back for fear of a recurrence of floods. In addition, what meagre capital they possessed in the form of houses, plow animals, and tools, has in most cases been destroyed.

"Statistics furnished by provincial authorities indicate that in the *hsien* of Sihwa, with a normal population of well over 100,000 and an area of about five hundred square miles, three-quarters of the land has been flooded and is almost unproductive. Three-fourths of the draft animals have disappeared, three-fourths of the houses have been destroyed, and about two-thirds of the farm tools are gone. Most of this *hsien* which I visited recently is an utter desolation of brown earth stretching flat and unrelieved to the horizon. The river left a deposit of some ten feet of mud over the land, now dried to earth. All housetops and most trees protruding above the deposit were either washed away, or have been removed as firewood. Now there is scarcely a landmark left, not a road, and not a living creature to be seen except crows and an occasional wayfarer.

"Refugees from such *hsien*, many of whom have gone to distant provinces, will be unable to resume farming until the Yellow river is definitely controlled and the depleted livestock of the region is partly replaced. Meanwhile, non-productivity has reduced an untold number of Honanese to semi-starvation. I have seen old women grubbing about in the fields for grass, herbs, and roots to make soup. Little children have followed me along the country roads begging for food or money. One particular ten-mile stretch of road is a nightmare for the traveler, for it is lined with scores of beggars who run along behind one's cart, crying for help, until exhausted they sit down and wait for the next passerby. The Chinese Government and private agencies have established a few feeding centers in the most afflicted localities, but the need is immense, and can be met only by restoration of productivity."

Death, destruction, and dispersal across the face of a continent were not all of the price the Chinese people had to pay Kuang Ti. They had to pay the price of inflation. It might have been possible for the Chinese Government to finance the war by some other means but it is doubtful. Eighty per cent of the sources of national income already had been lost by November, 1938, when the government began its gradual move to the Chungking area. There warlords had collected land taxes for years in advance and business was so organized that the levying and collection of income taxes was impossible.

Most of the trade of Szechuan is still carried on without ledgers from which income can be established, and most businesses are said to keep three sets of books—one for the tax collector, one for the family and partners, and one in code for the manager's eyes alone. It is also the practice to close big deals with no written records.

For instance, Mr. Chang has a large quantity of paper that he wants to sell. Mr. Li hears of it, finds out about the quantity and quality of it and invites Mr. Chang to a teahouse. They sit down at one of the small tables as the teaboy pours two huge cups of tea, steeping it directly in the cup so that hot water may be added again and again. A big dish of watermelon seed and another of shelled roasted peanuts are put between them. The two men sip their tea, crack watermelon seeds between their teeth, and chat about the health of their families, the weather, and about everything imaginable including a little about war, but nothing of politics, for one is never sure who may be listening in a public place. Apparently they are completely disinterested in buying or selling as each maintains the strongest possible position for the bargaining that will come later.

Hours pass before some oblique reference is made to the matter that has been uppermost in their minds all afternoon, and finally they are ready to get down to serious bargaining. Mr. Li slyly slips his hand into Mr. Chang's ample sleeve and his finger taps out a code on Mr. Chang's wrist. At the same time Mr. Chang's hand, concealed in Mr. Li's sleeve, makes reply. Then they fall silent. At last, after repeated tapped changes in offer and price, the bargain is silently agreed upon and only the two men know what was agreed. Documents prepared later certainly will not reflect all the details of the transaction and will be of little use to a government tax collector.

The government, therefore, paid for the war by importing paper bills and running its printing presses. By the end of 1940 the buying power of money began to sag. By 1942 prices were rising steadily. When V-J day arrived, the cost-of-living index had hit nearly four thousand times its prewar figure. Two years after V-J day it was still climbing, particularly in the liberated coastal cities, and had passed the staggering figure of twenty thousand times prewar.

A few people made fortunes. Those able to convert profits to goods or real property have made more profits, but the effect on the majority has been that of a collapse in the value of savings, insurance, and working capital. For years the salaried middle class, teachers, and government employees have been living at decreasing levels. Everything they owned is gone, sucked up to finance the war. That most government officials are in the same fix is illustrated by the fact that the supreme court judges once struck for higher wages.

When I was in Peiping after V-J day I frequently traveled in dilapidated public rickshaws drawn by men who had been skilled artisans. Once I was pulled by a master rugmaker, a man who had designed exquisite rugs for which China is famous, and he had been well paid for it. He told me of his daily struggle to make enough by pulling a rickshaw to keep himself and his family alive. Another time my puller was a former maker of cloisonné.

Farmers have not suffered so much under inflation as have the formerly better-off salaried middle classes, because they have produced their own necessities of life and maintained higher prices for produce sold. Moreover, since their taxes advanced less rapidly than prices even when farmers paid them in kind, their relative position improved and many were able to increase their holdings. I know of one tenant farmer who rented land from the College of Rural Reconstruction and earned more than the professors.

The total effect of the long siege of war-born ills was a mass war weariness, especially marked among people of the middle classes who for years lived on incomes insufficient to provide mere subsistence. And the end of the war, though greeted with high hope, brought not relief but disillusionment, increased by discouraging turns in political events.

The inflation picture was further complicated by the complex monetary situation that existed in the first months of "peace," for Kuang Ti was not content to kill and destroy and take. There were five different kinds of currency in circulation. First and most important was the legal tender of the national government, called Chinese National Currency, and written CNC$, or just CN$, eventually inflated to a point beyond CNC$6,000,000 to one American dollar.

In the formerly occupied sections of China, "controlled" by three puppet regimes, there were three separate currencies. The first, known as CRB$, was issued by Nanking puppets through the Central Reserve Bank. Just before the war ended they had run wild, appropriating printing machines ordinarily used for printing cigarette package labels and altering them to turn out millions of 100- and 500-dollar bills. They lost count of issues and made no effort to imprint serial numbers, with the result that no one knows the total value of CRB issues, much less the National Government which fell heir to the economic situation and finally agreed to accept 200 CRB for one CN. One well-informed source estimated that there was CRB$400 trillion in existence. Another currency, FRB$, was issued by the Federal Reserve Bank of the North China (Peiping) puppet government. It was not so badly inflated as CRB$ when the war ended because the Japanese had a much firmer and earlier grip on North China than on Nanking and had done more to control economic conditions. The national government agreed to exchange these notes at five FRB to one CN.

The third puppet currency was that used in the northeastern provinces and issued by the Manchoukuo government. Although it was less inflated and presented a relatively minor problem in itself, the situation in Manchuria was further complicated by Russian invasion currency, and the fact that the Central Government did not gain control of all Manchuria.

And then there was a fifth currency issued by the border government of the Chinese Communists, more strictly controlled than any of the others and the least inflated.

The untangling of war currencies and the establishment of a buying power of a single national currency adjusted and held to the buying power of foreign currencies presents a tremendous task.

Kuang Ti had indeed done a thorough job. In addition to her physical and financial disruption China came out of the international war a nation divided. The split came between the Nationalists and the Communists in an all-out struggle

for power, and the course of events since the Japanese surrender can be understood only if one grasps the fact that
there are two groups organized essentially on totalitarian
lines contending for control over the Chinese people, both
heavily influenced in organization and organizational methods by the Russian pattern. Neither the voices of the more
articulate educated group nor the mute longings of the unin-
formed masses can bring peace and security as long as the
real talismans of political power are rifles and men to use
them. The two groups have jockeyed for position in a gigantic chess game, both too much aware of the wholesale desire for peace and unity to make the first move and accept the
blame for an all-out civil war.

The first great prize to be captured was the Japanese matériel that surrender made available. Although much of it
was held by Japanese units scattered over a broad area, its
heaviest concentrations were in the large centers of Central
and North China. While the Central Government and the
Russians argued over the right to accept the Japanese surrender in North China, the frustrated Chinese Communists
retaliated by wrecking North China railroads. Finally, the
Central Government, as a recognized member of the United
Nations, received Lend-Lease equipment and military aid
from the United States in order to transport troops to the
major centers where the Japanese surrender was received.
Thus the Nationalists acquired most of the Japanese arms
south of the Great Wall. The Soviets maneuvered with closed
eyes so that the Chinese Communists might gather up Japanese arms in Manchuria. Both sides thus replenished, the
civil war continued. But even though the activities of the
Communists and the Nationalists merit most headline space,
there are other political and ideological forces at work without benefit of armaments or headlines.

During the past decade, as both Kuomintang and Communist parties have been accused of displaying more interest

in partisanship than in the welfare of the Chinese people, several liberal parties have developed which now assume some size and potentiality. These liberal political parties are composed largely of those Chinese whose educational backgrounds permit of some comparison between the practice of democratic government in China and the practices of democratic governments in the West. Their memberships are largest in coastal cities where there has been most contact with Western civilization. The active membership of the Democratic League, the National Socialists (no connection with non-Chinese groups of the same name), the Young China party, and others is composed largely of Chinese authors, playwrights, artists, professors, and others of China's literati.

Early in 1947, the single-party Kuomintang Government opened its doors, at least nominally, to participation by other parties meeting certain demands, but the liberal element has, for the most part, held out for further reform and more equal privileges before taking part in the National Government as it exists today.

While the members of these parties constitute a well-informed section of the Chinese population, there is but little group co-operation, comparatively little political leadership, and no militant leadership with which to implement their liberal views and tenets. Furthermore, the only two political parties in China possessing persuading armies and police are the Kuomintang and the Communists, while the liberals frequently find themselves harassed by one or both contestants.

The liberal parties probably will assume a share of influence in the future development of China in a world community of democratic peoples.

But China is not divided only by political mistrust and maneuvering. It is split also between those who went to free China and those who stayed in occupied territory. This cleavage is made more subtle and complicated by the fact that it involves the problem of quislings and collaborators. Those coastal residents who abandoned everything to trek inland, who have survived and are now returned to their coastal homes, consider themselves the true patriots, while those who remained (many times to keep Chinese institutions functioning in the national and public interest) feel that years of furtive and loyal endeavor under enemy domination merit some sympathy and understanding.

As we jogged along by the golden imperial city of the ancient capital, shortly after Peiping was liberated, we passed some Japanese moving by truck to repatriation camps. "We Chinese are too tolerant," my rickshaw man growled as he saw them. "Have you ever heard of *hun ho mien*?"

"No," I replied. "What is hun ho mien?"

"Hun ho mien was the flour that the Jap devils made us eat during the winters of 1942 and 1943. It is called hun ho mien [mixed flour] because it was made by grinding together more than twenty kinds of waste materials—dirt and husks and rotten grain, mixed with bran and the husks off soybeans. They added stuff that animals wouldn't eat and sold it to us at prices five times as high as their own people here in Peiping were paying for the best quality white flour. It's all we could get to eat, and almost everyone in the city came down with diarrhea immediately. We couldn't work, but we had to go on eating the stuff. Now just look at those fat, healthy Japs there. They've been whipped, but they are still perfectly safe—no one has really tried to get even with them. I tell you we Chinese are just too tolerant!"

Those who suffered under the Japanese felt like martyrs; so did those who had survived hostilities in the interior, but there was a tendency for those from the interior to consider everyone who stayed behind as a traitor.

The new China, split asunder with suspicion and confusion, came into sudden possession of cities, towns, commerce, industry and finance, once Japanese operated but now left totally without organization. Carpetbaggers and inflation reigned. The Chinese found themselves unprepared heirs not only to cities formerly Chinese, but also to the former extra-territorial areas that had been built up and operated by nationals of at least twenty-five advanced Western nations. Included was one of the world's largest cities, completely disrupted politically, socially, economically, and morally, crowded with foreign troops, dilapidated, and lacking in food, housing, and supplies. As time went on, the victory seemed more empty, for the vision of China as a great nation reflected only inefficiency, avarice, inflation, civil war, starvation, disease, and more foreign encroachment, while China's traditional bully seemed to be rapidly becoming united, democratic, and organized in the rebuilding of government, economy, and society. A Chinese student orating at a Shanghai university assembly declared, "Our enemy, guided by Western principles and powers, can now achieve in a few years what we have been fighting for through the past thirty years, because she is organized, willing to learn, and at peace. When Japan is strong again, we shall be as weak as usual!"

Those who were weary of being refugees were also disillusioned with the difficulties of going home and with the fact that their economic lot had continued to deteriorate since the war ended. Those who were in occupied territory were disgruntled by the ineffectiveness of the government they had hoped their own people would set up. And they were disappointed with the Communists too, because they knew that the continuation of inflation and soaring prices and insecurity was much affected by them, partly by Communist persistence in disrupting and destroying communications.

Through all the chaos and babel of Kuang Ti there remains the keenest struggle for survival, for China has survived these many ages because family units have survived —a doctrine that is the very core of Confucian morality. With filiality as its highest loyalty, Confucian morality is also the root of nepotism and graft, for Chinese society not only condones the use of public office to take care of the family economic needs, but actually respects and honors the man who does it. In periods of economic stress, in flood, famine, or war, the families of China close their ranks, and anything is justified for the survival and benefit of the family. Result: public morality takes a nose dive. And that is exactly what is happening to China now.

The China that we see today—China as she is—is the product of many forces, with roots buried deep in history. Her problems are linked to the invention of irrigation and the development of a vegetarian diet, for out of these factors has grown the huge population dominating the Chinese scene, its very size a prime factor in her present difficulties. They are compounded by an ideographic language and a complex code of customs and ideas about man and nature embedded in and expressed by that language. Confucian ideas of government and human relations are overlaid with Taoist superstitions, for in Taoism humanism revolts against intellectualism, and it is in Taoism that the Chinese seek to manipulate the forces of nature and the netherworld spirits in order to mitigate disaster or generate good luck.

One of the most impressive displays of such Chinese superstition I have encountered occurred during my second summer in Shantung when I was directing a survey of the parasites harbored by the people of a rural area. It was a drought year, and after an exceptionally dry winter the usual June rains had failed to fall. As the hot dry days continued, the village folk began to take appropriate action to summon the water dragon who controls the rains and to call his attention to the severity of the drought. First they broke off willow branches and stuck them in jars of dry sand outside the door of each village household, showing the dragon that even the marshland willows were beginning to wither. Then each household made sacrifices to its ancestors and sent responsible members of the family to the market town temple where the patron god of the village was enshrined. Still no rain. The individual efforts of the separate families were apparently not enough, hence the whole community must unite in the "begging for rain" ceremonies.

In each village dotted closely across the plain, the elders met to plan the solemn undertaking, choosing first the chief actor for the propitiation ceremony. Called a *ma-tze*, the leading character plays a dramatic and complicated role in the proceedings; in one sense he is the scapegoat, representing all the sins of the community at large that may have displeased the water dragon; in another he is the good citizen who, driven frantic by the drought, is determined to slay the water dragon for not bringing rain. There are many risks of reprisal by the water dragon involved in acting the part of the ma-tze, so it is necessary to pay a large sum of money to some young fellow who is willing to assume the role.

All the families of the village paid their quotas, and the ma-tze was selected. On the day of the chief ceremony, he was equipped with a huge sword with which to kill the dragon. Before him went a procession of men and boys shooting off firecrackers and carrying dried stalks of kaoliang, ten or twelve of them equipped with staves with which to defend the water dragon from the crazed ma-tze. Behind the ma-tze came all the older men of the village, with young boys bringing up the rear. Far out in front of this weird procession went male runners to warn all women and girls that the procession was coming, for if by chance a menstruating woman happened to observe the ceremony the magic would have been destroyed. Hence no women or girls were permitted to witness the proceedings.

First the procession wended its way to the Taoist temple where the portable village god sat in his small shrine. With proper ceremony, but not too much gentleness, he and his shrine were taken out of the temple and carried along to witness the wild actions of the ma-tze, while the participants went through pantomimes appealing to every possible emotion to which the village god and the dragon might be susceptible. Their sympathies were solicited. The seriousness of the drought was called to their attention by carrying the village god and his little shrine over dry kaoliang stalks laid across the road so that he would hear the dry and rustling sound of prancing feet on withered vegetation.

With the ma-tze preceding, the village god was carried to the nearest spring or river where the water dragon was believed to live and as his home was approached the crackle of firecrackers increased while the ma-tze began a wild dance of anger at the niggardly dragon. He brandished his sword while the other villagers made strenuous mock efforts to stave off the blows, but the ma-tze cut the water again and again with his sword, his thrusts and parries designed to appeal to the dragon's sense of fear while the mock efforts might arouse his sense of obligation. After all these attempts to appease, frighten, cajole, and wheedle the water dragon, the village god was carried back to the village to sit in a place of lessened respect until he saw fit to make it rain.

When the rains came there was another procession, and with many offerings of food and thanks the village god was carried back to his honored place in the market town temple.

In every aspect of Chinese life there are similar Taoist ceremonies weaving an endless amount of superstition into the basically Confucian fabric of Chinese life as a means of affecting the course of nature. In addition, China is colored by Buddhist mysticism, and when drought comes Buddhists are sure to petition the authorities that the killing of animals be stopped. During droughts it is often impossible to obtain pork or beef until the rains come.

All these forces—historical, cultural, ethical, religious—created from the events and developments of Asia during the past hundred centuries have been wedded and welded and woven together in a familyistic society to create a juggernaut moving forward with an irresistible force too great for even Kuang Ti.

This is the picture of China emerging from war. This is China as she is.

Part Two

REBUILDING CHINA

Winfield

The Chinese farm laborer wears the garments of poverty with dignity and unfailing good humor. In the common people lie the deep roots of China's future.

The dry North—in early spring carefully hoarded fertilizer is hauled to the fields.

The wet South—population pressure has driven paddy fields up each water course and forced the cultivation of every square foot of hilltop soil.

On the semiarid Shantung plain the winter wheat, brought to maturity by hand irrigation, is pulled by the roots to provide a maximum of stalk for fuel. The Shantungese are sturdy and independent.

Winfield

Final, careful winnowing completes the laborious harvesting of winter wheat. In agricultural China, grain is the truest measure of wealth.

Winfield

The fish head designed by Li Ping, 250 B.C., still divides the waters into the outer (left) and inner feeder channels that irrigate the Chengtu plain.

"Rock sausages" protect the bank and guide the water.

Miles away on the plain the irrigation waters flood newly plowed fields to receive transplanted rice, and (below) bring the grain to muturity for fall threshing.

The hill paddies in the "valley of ten thousand mirrors" store the fall rains and must be plowed while flooded.

Guillumette

Most production is still carried on in small family shops by hand methods. These coppersmiths hammer out the utensils for everyday living.

The beautiful things for which China is famous are the product of manual skills handed down from father to son.

Guillumette

Guillumette

Junks and sanpans by the tens of thousands play a vital part in transportation on scores of lakes and along hundreds of miles of canals.

Through the centuries tow gangs have pulled junks through the rapids of the upper Yangtze.

At every stop along the railroads women and children dig through the ashes for bits of coke and coal.

Masterly skill and ingenuity made possible the wartime repair of ships in the Ming Sung Shipyards.

New timbers were fitted to bomb-damaged wooden hulls.

Guillumette

Simple but effective drills drove holes for screws and bolts.

Metal parts were turned out in bomb-proof machine shops.

Guillumette

Winfield

Education continued throughout the war. Here, a modern primary school operated in an ancient temple.

Refugee universities doubled up in a limited number of laboratories.

Guillumette

Guillumette

Industrialization and modern construction are a growing part of the Chinese scene—but billions of dollars worth of new plants must be built before general standards of living can improve.

Guillumette

Scores of experiments have demonstrated that composting can turn farm wastes, including human excreta, into harmless organic fertilizer and return most of the nitrogen to the soil.

Scientific methods applied to biotechnological problems in agriculture can play a significant part in expanding production.

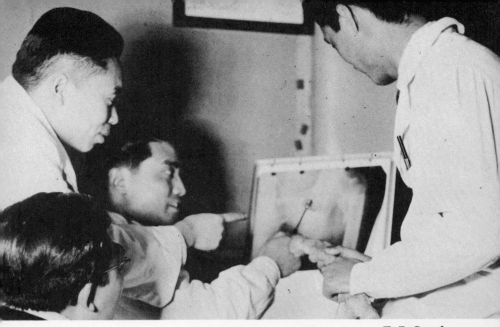

E. B. Struthers

Medical education is one of many professional fields that must be expanded to provide the leadership for rebuilding.

The special skills of nurse, dietitian, social worker, and doctor are required in the pediatric program which must play a significant part in population control.

E. B. Struthers

Rebuilding China must start with the farmer, and if it is to be other than a mockery it must end by making possible a higher standard of life for him and for all the millions who comprise every group and class.

Chapter X

Can China Be Rebuilt?

CAUGHT IN AN INGROWN PATTERN OF LIFE, WITH HER social structure, her culture, language, industrial and agricultural methods, her basic processes and perspectives of thought bound by ancient dicta and mired in centuries of philosophic inbreeding, China is poorly prepared to take her place in a new world of closely knit, mutually responsible nations.

In its greatness and its weakness the inflexible tradition of her antiquity has kept China, in terms of population, the greatest nation on earth, the most intellectually isolated. Relative to the standards of the modern world, she is backward. That many of her leaders recognize this fact is the beginning of change.

"Being a backward and weak nation is a bitter thing," Mr. Lu Tso-fu, head of the Ming Sung Industrial Company, once said. "There is too much poverty and hunger, too much ignorance and superstition, too much inability to cope efficiently with even relatively simple problems tied up with this business of being backward. There is too much danger of being swallowed up or used for ends which you don't want to be used for in this business of being weak. Yes, being part of a backward and weak nation is a bitter thing."

China must be rebuilt. Yet even the word "rebuilt" is inadequate. Although in her national and civil wars she has suffered enormous destruction of material things which must be rebuilt, her essential need is the construction of an entire new pattern of existence. In a sharply real sense China, as a modern nation, as a technological economy, as an integrated community, and as a national society, must be built for the first time.

As she builds, what will be her goal? Will it be the attainment of military might for protection and perhaps for aggression? Will she modernize primarily for the enrichment of a favored class in her society? Or will she build for the basically simple purpose of raising the standard of life of all her people?

The answer must be the latter. Only by building toward a better life for all her people can China take her place in a world in which there is but one paramount demand—the demand that all mankind direct the power of every mental, moral, and physical resource toward the creation of a global community of abundance, freedom, and peace, a community in which the bitterness of backwardness and weakness can be lifted from men everywhere.

Raising the standard of *life* of a people involves much more than merely raising its standard of living. Yet a high level of physical welfare is fundamental to a better life. The necessities of such a level are, therefore, basic to China's problems.

The people, all the people, must have food—not only to supply belly-filling bulk but to provide nutrition. They must have a diet that supplies them with energy and with proteins that will permit successive generations to grow successively stronger bodies. They must have the extensive array of chemicals required in minute quantities to keep their physiological machines working smoothly and to protect them from deficiency diseases and toxic organisms.

The people, all the people, need clean, well-ventilated houses—houses that provide not only the minimum requisites of shelter but also the beauty and protection that mean the difference between a home and a hovel. They must have houses with floors that can be kept clean, rooms that can be kept warm, kitchens that can be kept free of fumes and soot. They need furnishings that provide comfort, lights that make the evening hours a pleasure, rooms in sufficient numbers to provide occasional periods of individual quiet and privacy, and enough cubic space to reduce the risk of contagion from sustained human contacts.

All the people must be able to live in communities and homesteads that are basically sanitary. They need the techniques required to collect and dispose of all human and household wastes in such a way as to destroy the pathogenic organisms or flies that may exist or breed in those wastes. And they need an adequate source of pure water.

The people, all the people, must be well clothed, not merely for protection from winter cold and summer sun, but adequately for neatness, cleanliness, and comfort, and with enough variety to permit the expression of individuality.

The people need access to the whole panoply of knowledge and skill amassed by modern medicine to prevent disease, cure illness, and aid the normal biological processes of human life. Childbirth must take place with the aid of skilled attendants able to protect mothers from bleeding to death, and from the living poison that clings to dirty hands. Babies must be protected from the spasms that pull their spines into a bow of death at nine days. Children must be guarded from contagion and permitted to grow to productive adulthood. Medical care and health education must be provided for the adult so that the growing hazards of an industrial civilization can be met and controlled.

Working conditions must be improved. Bright, well-ventilated factories and shops must replace half-lighted holes. Industrial hazards must be minimized by special training and modern safety devices for workers. Technological methods must be introduced in order to increase production, decrease hours of work, and create leisure time for recreation and individual interests. There must be parks, playgrounds, and all the requisites of relaxation and relief from crowded city quarters.

China as she builds must work for a high level of national physical welfare, a society with the indices of good health: a low morbidity rate, low general mortality, and low infant mortality—a society in which a low death rate is matched by a low birth rate and good health is reflected in a long life expectancy, a society in which good mental health abounds and in which people are protected from excessive pain when pain is inevitable.

But this kind of physical well-being cannot come into existence in and of itself. It must be paid for. Therefore China must work toward a higher degree of economic productivity and security. She must produce and distribute the wealth essential to establish and maintain the necessities of basic physical well-being. To accomplish this she faces gigantic tasks.

1. Production per acre must be at least doubled.

2. Production per farmer must be at least quadrupled, and half the agricultural manpower must be shifted to other types of productive activity.

3. Fisheries must be vastly expanded to bring from the sea many times the tonnage of fish now used for food and industrial production.

4. Mineral output must be increased from ten to one thousand times the present rate to provide industrial raw material and energy.

5. Transportation facilities must be multiplied to ensure quick and inexpensive movement of goods throughout China's vast territory.

6. The output of China's industry must be increased to hundreds of times its present volume, and in that industry millions of men must be put to work.

7. The number of people engaged in modern personal

services must be increased to provide adequate facilities in the fields of medicine, dentistry, nursing, teaching, writing, productive art, scientific research, and legal practice.

8. With expanded production and its concomitant expanded capacity to consume, she must build an economic structure capable of providing security during the incredibly involved process of transition from the old pattern to the new and capable of maintaining stability once the transition period is past.

In the drive toward higher standards of living, all the people must share and benefit. Its success depends on a thoroughly democratic organization in the state, the community, and in personal life, a democracy in which the informed opinion and will of every normal adult determines all social policies.

The processes of the entire system of democratic organization must be limited by a bill of rights protecting the civil liberties of all citizens—rights so thoroughly applied that any individual may exercise his political franchise without fear of recrimination or retaliation. Such a system must be carefully developed and constantly guarded so that basic and fundamental liberties are brought into existence and protected, especially during the period of transition when multitudes of changes are being made in the social structure. Particularly must it maintain freedom of speech, of the press, of assembly, and of their end product, the habit of valid discussion and argumentation. Democracy must be grounded in the intelligence, courage, integrity, impartiality, co-operation, and moral character of its citizens, each prepared to accept responsibility for personal and community actions. Called by any name, the principles and practices embodied in our conception of democracy are essential to the rebuilding of China.

Fundamental to this democratic organization is a government squarely and firmly based on law, a law which protects the rights and interests of all groups in Chinese society, a law which can be altered only by the people it governs. The democratic practice of formulating plans and resolving conflicts must be exercised at all levels of government—community, county, province, and nation; it must be applied to the forming and operating of all community enterprises—to political, economic, and social associations, to co-operatives, to religious groups, and to all the units that together create a complex modern society. People must have voting control over assessment, collection, and expenditure of all local taxes and they must be able to protect themselves from injustice and from the graft of officials ministering to their interests.

However, physical well-being, a high degree of economic productivity and security, and a thoroughly democratic organization of political and social units cannot come into being or stand without the development and maintenance of supporting cultural values.

Cultural values are a product of education in its broadest sense. The foundation of cultural development is a universal primary education that provides the tools of learning for the use of the entire population. The people, all the people, must share directly in the cultural heritage of their own nation by being able to read its history and to understand something of the forces that have shaped it. To balance this knowledge of China and her culture, her people must also have a general knowledge of the world of which China is necessarily a part—of its history and expanse, its contemporary problems and how it seeks to solve them, its social triumphs and its failures. They must be able to think in terms of China's relations with other peoples and other ideas. The entire experience of mankind must be available for comparison of ideas and formulation of rational judgments. The people must become acquainted with the great mass of scientific knowledge that affords understanding and mastery of nature, of their own bodies, of the soil and its produce, and of the forces that can provide energy for productive activity. From unabridged knowledge the people must learn to lay aside bias and prejudice and to make detached evaluation of social facts, and discerningly adapt from the experiences of all men those principles and practices best fitted to raise the cultural and physical standards of Chinese society. Only through the dissemination of knowledge among them will China's majority gradually shed the fears and superstitions that hamper its progress.

On such a broad foundation of education for all the people there must be erected a system which makes possible the development of special abilities in order to elicit and utilize the genius of each generation essential to the growth of culture. For China, in order to rebuild and create, must train a great mass of people in every phase of the complex culture on which a modern nation depends—bodies of competent scientists, technologists, technicians, writers, artists, educators, musicians, statesmen, administrators, religious leaders, farmers, doctors, lawyers, and all the thousands of specialists needed to create and operate a modern society. She must grasp and assimilate the world culture now in the process of synthesis, and she must add her share to the creation of that world culture.

But even the development in her people of an appreciation of cultural values—her own, those of other peoples, and those of the new world culture that is building—is not enough in itself. In the final analysis the rebuilding of China, indeed the rebuilding of the life of the world, comes down to a basic problem: can men develop the moral stature to create and hold a high standard of life?

Progress can exist only as the people of the world, as individuals and as groups, realize that productive and truly realistic self-interest demands a mental and moral stature, a wide-angled and long-range vision capable of seeing every problem, no matter how seemingly local or individual, in its perspective with the world, its facts, its future, and all its people. Only as man gives himself to values that are true, as he is able to discover truth, for all times and all places in his world can he build realistically.

China, no less than every division of the world, must rebuild herself according to human values and material needs necessary to the functioning of the world as a whole. For a nation which has existed according to a pattern basically unchanged and insulated from the rest of the world for thousands of years, such a revolution in viewpoint will be a long and difficult process. Yet any attempt to build or rebuild China beyond the perspective of the world in which it is to exist must fail. The level of life of her people cannot be raised without commerce in ideas and materials with the rest of the world.

Can it be done? Can China create physical well-being, develop a high degree of economic productivity and security, achieve effective democratic organization, attain a national and individual appreciation of cultural values, and maintain through all her activities a deep regard for human values and relationships? In concrete terms, how and with what must she begin, and what are the difficulties she will encounter?

No man knows enough to answer all these questions. The following chapters are an attempt to sketch in broad strokes a picture of at least some of the problems that will have to be solved and some of the approaches available for their solution.

Chapter XI

Starting with Sanitation

THE NUMBER, DEPTH, AND MAGNITUDE OF CHINA'S problems are indicated by the fact that her rebuilding program can logically begin with the fundamental issue of her health. If any program is to succeed, her people must be mentally and physically able to conceive and undertake the drastic reforms and expansions of activities necessary throughout the nation—from national institutions to the family unit. Conversely, any program that does not begin with an improvement in general living standards, of which health is a major factor, would cause fatal popular resentment against a cause so all-inclusive as to require overwhelming popular support.

China's number one health problem is sanitation, the key to fecal-borne disease control. Aside from millions of nonfatal or unreported cases of dysentery, cholera, diarrhea, and typhoid fever, the annual toll of death from fecal-borne diseases is as high as four million—one-fourth the total number of deaths from all causes each year. The astronomical number of parasitic worms inhabiting the Chinese people are the direct result of bad environmental sanitation.

When I first went to China in 1932 I tackled the problem of controlling this group of diseases. We used the prevalence of ascarid worms in the intestines of people and the distribution of *Ascaris* eggs in the surroundings as our index of environmental pollution. Our studies, added to those of others, provided the data from which the numbers of worms to be found in China* were calculated. It was quite clear that if we could develop methods that would reduce the number of worms in the population we could reduce the prevalence of all the fecal-borne diseases. The beginning of our search for effective ways of stopping the spread of parasitic worms, a seemingly simple goal, led inevitably to interrelated problems that must be solved if standards of living are to be raised. Starting with sanitation, a picture of these problems can be constructed.

The great prevalence of deadly fecal-borne diseases in China is the result of a series of factors. First among them is the fact that almost all human wastes are carefully saved and returned to the soil as fertilizer. The actual processes by which these wastes are conserved and used differ considerably from place to place. In general, there are two major variations, the dry method of the north and the wet method of the south, each an adaptation to the regional climate.

Heavy rainfall and a network of canals providing inexpensive transportation of bulky materials account for the southern system of using diluted human wastes. The common practice is to store all family excreta in huge vats, to supplement them with additional supplies purchased from a nearby city, dilute them, and haul them to the fields several times during the year. As yet only a small percentage of the inhabitants of a few larger cities (Shanghai is an example) are served by water-borne sewage. The great majority still depend on scavenger coolies who make their living by contracting for the collection and sale of wastes. Among the poorer classes in the cities, scavengers even make small payments for the privilege of collecting the highly salable night soil. Normally, the night soil, both home produced and bought, is accumulated and stored in the farmer's vats for several months. If it is held for six months or longer, most of the pathogenic organisms and worm eggs present die as a

* Chapter V.

result of overgrowth of other bacteria and from lack of oxygen. There is some reduction in the number of dangerous germs during shorter periods of storage. However, millions of worm eggs, billions of protozoan cysts, and trillions of pathogenic bacteria survive and are transported to the fields, frequently splashing around the courtyards and streets of villages along the way.

The North China farm family handles its household wastes in a totally different manner. Human and animal manure, stove ashes, and other household wastes are mixed with large quantities of field soil to form a compost in the pits of the pigpen-latrine that is a fixture of most farm households. The mixture of material thus accumulated during six months or a year is dug out, hauled to the fields, dried, spread, and plowed in. Detailed studies made of this "soil compost" on thirty-two farms of western Shantung province indicated that the nitrogen present in them was not much greater than that in ordinary medium-rich American farm soil, and the organic matter present was less than that of rich American garden soil.

In northern cities only solid fecal material is collected, the urine being discarded. It is carried to the edge of the city and dried into thin cakes containing a considerable amount of nitrogen. It is interesting to note that the amount of nitrogen present in these feces cakes is in direct ratio to the richness of diet of the people producing the night soil. In Peiping the empirically determined price of cakes varies in almost exact proportion to the amount of nitrogen present. Cakes from the wealthier sections of the city command a premium price. In such cities the night-soil business is often worth a million dollars a year, American money equivalent.

All the present methods of collecting and utilizing human wastes in China are far below even minimum standards of sanitation. Our studies of the distribution of ascarid eggs in the North China environment showed clearly that city latrines, country pigpen-pits, and the methods of transportation everywhere were sowing millions of ascarid eggs in all household and village environments, to say nothing of the pollution of the fields. Where ascarid eggs exist there also abound protozoan cysts and pathogenic bacteria, while in the cases of the occupational diseases of the Chinese farmer, hookworm disease, intestinal fluke, liver fluke, and blood fluke diseases, the use of night soil as fertilizer is an integral step in the transmission of disease.

Yet from a sanitary point of view the practice of using human excreta in agriculture has a negative advantage. The preservation of fecal material and urine for use as fertilizer probably does not cause so serious a pollution of the general environment as would occur if the dense rural and urban populations directly polluted the ground as is done in countries like India that do not use human excreta as fertilizer. Of course this is only the advantage possessed by a bad practice over the worst.

A second factor in the spread of the fecal-borne diseases is the habit, particularly of the smaller children, of direct pollution of the environment. It should be remembered that the practice of small children's defecating freely about the household and village is one which until relatively recently was common to all parts of the world and still extends much more widely than most Americans realize, particularly among rural folk. Yet even this practice is probably more prevalent in China as a result of the economic necessity of keeping human wastes for use as fertilizer. A by-product of the conservation of night soil for fertilizer is the development of a considerable degree of indifference to the presence of human wastes in the immediate environment. This attitude is evident in the frequently careless handling of household wastes.

How widespread pollution is is indicated by the fact that, of the more than one thousand households we examined in Shantung cities and villages not one was free of viable *Ascaris* eggs. Although a majority of our examinations were made in poorer homes, the group included some well-to-do farm families and a certain number of middle and upper-middle class city families. The incredible numbers of worms parasitizing the bodies of the people of China exist because both the agricultural use of night soil and the sanitary habits of the people result in the direct pollution of the environment.

Two additional factors must be mentioned to complete the picture of a sanitation condition which has caused fecal-borne diseases to become widespread. First is direct contact transmission resulting from the crowded conditions under which even rural folk live, aided and abetted by ignorance as to how diseases are transmitted and the low level of personal hygiene. Second is pollution of the water supply. Every well that we examined contained bacteria that had come from a human intestine. Furthermore, we found that the number of such bacteria present in water jars was definitely greater than in freshly drawn well water. The common practice of drinking hot water considerably reduces the importance of water in the transmission of disease but enough raw water is consumed to make the water route significant in the spread of disease-producing organisms.

All these factors taken together are the reason why more illness and death occur from fecal-borne diseases than from any other class of causes, and, consequently, why environmental sanitation is the number one public health problem in China.

How can this problem be solved? What must be done to reduce the enormous incidence of death, illness, and lowered vitality stemming from poor sanitation? It is in this field that the greatest advances have been made in the West during the past half century. Why not apply the methods that have worked in Europe and America? Certainly the principles of what must be done are the same. If the grim grip of the fecal-borne diseases in China is to be broken a few simple things must be accomplished:

1. Human excrement must be collected and disposed of in such a way that all pathogenic organisms are destroyed.

2. Pollution of the household environment must be stopped.

3. The water supply must be protected.

4. Personal cleanliness and hygiene must be taught and practiced.

In the West these things have been accomplished by the introduction of water-borne sewage in cities, towns, villages, and even on many farms, and by the widespread use of sanitary latrines in rural areas where flush toilets are impractical; by the development of treated public water supplies; by the education of the people; and by raising economic standards so that individual families can afford the costs of cleanliness and the cost of constructing sanitary facilities.

Application of these processes in China immediately involves serious problems. First and fundamental among these problems is the fact that China's agriculture is absolutely dependent on the use of night soil as a fertilizer. Agricultural yields are as high as they are only because this most abundant source of nitrogen is carefully conserved and used. Our analyses and calculations showed that the plant food constituents—nitrogen, potassium, and phosphorus—present in the excreta of the average farm family in China have a value, at world market prices, equal to almost 10 per cent of the average gross farm business, in spite of the fact that the excreta lose some of these plant foods before they are returned to the soil.

Chinese soils have been worked so long and so thoroughly that they have struck biological balance, and crop yields parallel closely the amount of fertilizer used. If, in the interests of sanitation and public health, it were possible to decree that human wastes be destroyed, the drop in crop yield would certainly be much more than 10 per cent of the value of the gross farm business. The people of China could not stand this loss, nor could any other business long stand a continued loss of 10 per cent of the gross. Obviously, Chinese peasants would ignore such a decree.

Nor could the peasants afford to stop using human fertilizers even if they were aware of the connection between fertilizers and health. There is always the chance that disease will skip the individual, while the economic loss would hit every farmer. Any sanitary method to be workable in China, therefore, must provide for the conservation and return to the soil of as much of the plant foods in human excrement as possible. No system of water-borne sewage that would deprive agriculture of the plant foods contained therein could ever hope to be applied to the majority of China's population. This is true not only because China's agriculture could not stand the economic loss involved, but also because, without expensive sewage treatment and water-purification systems, there is not enough water in China to care for the huge quantities of sewage produced by her dense population. Also, since the purification processes by which organic matter is broken down and made harmless act extremely slowly in water, a system must be used which to meet mere sanitary demands can take advantage of the more rapidly acting purification processes that take place in soil.

To be workable, from the point of view of both economics and sanitation, China's system of environmental sanitation must be what has been called "agricultural sanitation." By agricultural sanitation is meant the sanitation of the environment by means that fit into and assist the regular agricultural processes.

Seven years of work in developing such methods was cut short the day the Japanese attacked Pearl Harbor. The project was financed by grants from the Rockefeller Foundation, and was carried on in the chemistry laboratories of Peiping's Yenching University under the direction of Dr. Stanley D. Wilson and in the Department of Biology at Tsinan's Cheeloo University where I was in charge.

Believing that the solution lay in composting, we carried out hundreds of experiments to determine what happens when household and farm wastes, including night soil, animal manure, and crop residues, are built into various kinds of compost heaps. During all seasons of the year we found that biochemically generated heat caused quick rises in temperature inside the heaps. Aided by occasional mixing to ensure thorough heating of contents and surfaces, all pathogenic bacteria, protozoan cysts, and worm eggs were destroyed within twelve days by the high temperatures generated in the stacks and the human and animal wastes were completely safe to use in any way desired.

In from forty to one hundred twenty days, depending on whether aerobic or anaerobic composting was used, wastes were broken down into a rich organic fertilizer with the general characteristics of well-rotted leaf mold. Field tests showed that our completed compost was an excellent fertilizer with the characteristic relatively slow-acting and long-residual effect of good organic fertilizers, improving the tilth and colloidal structure of the soil, raising its moisture-holding properties, and frequently providing some plant resistance to disease.

Further, our methodical chemical studies showed that when these composts were made of 20 per cent night soil, 50 per cent animal manure, 20 per cent vegetable wastes (such as wheat straw, leaves, or dry grass), and 10 per cent field soil, and when they were allowed to heat in shallow aerobic stacks, were turned once, and at the end of twelve days packed into deep pits for anaerobic composting, about 90 per cent of the critically important nitrogen present in all the raw materials used was conserved in the completed and sanitary compost product. Other experiments duplicating present farm methods for producing soil-compost showed that only 66 to 74 per cent of the nitrogen was retained and another 15 to 17 per cent was lost by drying the finished product before plowing it under, resulting in a total loss by present methods of nearly half the available nitrogen before the fertilizer is used—and this at a cost of great effort, for the farmer has carted soil to the pigpen-latrine and then carted it all back to the field.

The new composting method is definitely superior on every count to that now used by the farmer. First, with the expenditure of much less labor, our method returns to the soil a larger percentage of nitrogen. Second, it kills all pathogenic bacteria, protozoa, and parasitic worms, and becomes a basis for effective sanitation. Third, by greatly increasing the amount of organic matter returned to the soil, it makes possible a vast increase in the amount of chemical fertilizers the farmer can use without doing serious damage to the physical condition of his soil.

Composting, then, *can* meet the requirements of agricultural sanitation, but the introduction of composting is confronted with at least one serious difficulty. It depends on large quantities of vegetable wastes for most of the energy that generates the heat necessary to kill pathogens. To conserve the maximum amount of nitrogen in the compost heaps it is necessary to have a carbon-nitrogen ratio in the raw materials of between thirty-eight and forty parts of carbon to one part of nitrogen. Large quantities of both animal manure and vegetable matter must be used in the compost heaps if the highly volatile nitrogen present in human wastes is to be captured and conserved. To accomplish this, each North China farm family needs a minimum of 3,500 pounds of crop residues, leaves, and grass in their compost heaps, and for the very best results they should use up to 8,800 pounds of vegetable matter. Yet the average North China farm with a crop area of 5.09 acres (farms are larger in the dry north than they are in the wet south, hence the 5.09 average is larger than the 4.18 average acreage for the entire country) produces only a few pounds over 7,000 pounds of crop residue. On the average each family must use over 6,000 pounds of these vegetable wastes for fuel and another several thousand pounds as fodder for their work animals. Thus the farm area does not now produce enough vegetable matter to supply fuel for the kitchen stove and feed the animals. To meet this deficit the rural population gleans every wisp of dry grass from the steep hillsides and from the paths that run through the fields. Even seedlings planted for reforestation find their way into a stove before they have a chance to grow, thus keeping the hillsides denuded and contributing to erosion. It is obvious that composting cannot be applied generally until new sources of fuel are made available.

The solution of the fuel problem would make possible a vast series of benefits in the fields of public health, sanitation, agriculture, forestry, animal husbandry, and in the general wealth of the country. The greatest benefits could stem from the solution of excreta-disposal problems by means of efficient composting—literally millions of lives could be saved every year, tens of millions of illnesses could be prevented, and a great deal of China's backwardness could be reduced. On the basis of the farm data we assembled, we estimated that 900,000 long tons of nitrogen were present in the annual production of fertilizer in the wheat region of China; our method of composting would boost the amount of nitrogen returned to the soil in this area by 40 per cent, bringing the total to about 1,300,000 long tons.

Even this increased amount of nitrogen, however, would fall far short of the optimum quantity recommended by the Ministry of Agriculture, which estimates that a total of 6,300,000 long tons of nitrogen should be supplied annually to the wheat region alone. To provide the 5 million additional tons of nitrogen required to meet the recommendation, chemical fertilizers such as ammonium sulphate would be needed at an annual rate of more than 20 million tons—only 4 million tons less than the entire world production in 1947!

Composting, as a step toward the solution of the sanitation problem, is applicable also to the wet south. Although its introduction would require greater changes in methods of handling and use of fertilizers than in the dry north, the fuel problem of the south is less acute, both because less fuel is needed for heating and because more lush vegetation offers a greater supply. The introduction of composting would require a change from the quick-acting liquid fertilizer now used to a more slow-acting, nonliquid organic fertilizer supplemented by quick-acting chemical fertilizers to maintain and expand production of southern crops.

It is apparent that both fuel and chemical fertilizer production must be vastly increased during the process of introducing agricultural sanitation.

There are at least three ways in which more fuel for the Chinese farm may be provided. First, more fuel can be grown. In all parts of China, but particularly in the wet south, modern methods of forestry can develop and produce more material for fuel than is now available. All too large a percentage of the steep, rocky land unsuited for crops is now producing nothing more than a stand of grass each year.

Just before the war, Dr. Willard Simpson carried out experiments in North China on the production of fuels in the wastelands, reforestation of denuded hills, the prevention of erosion. Considerable success was achieved with the leguminous shrub *Amorpha*. Planted along banks of streams, it helps retain soil during the summer rainy season, propagates easily from seed, cuttings, or divided roots, and produces in its second year a quantity of leaves for fodder and tall woody stalks for fuel. By cutting half the shoots on each clump annually, fuel production was maintained at a high level. *Amorpha* is highly resistant to drought, develops in poor soil, and, because it does not grow too tall and fixes its own nitrogen from the air, it can be grown close to other crops without shading them or robbing them of nitrogen. It can therefore be planted on the boundary ridges of the fields of North China as well as on wastelands. *Amorpha* is but one of the shrubs and trees that can utilize wastelands to many advantages, among them the production of fuel, fodder, and building material.

Second, coal, with which she is well supplied, can replace much of the vegetable material used as fuel on the farms of China. To do so, however, the production of her mines must be expanded enormously. It is to be expected that the first demand for the mineral will be to provide energy for the expansion of industry, but those who develop China's mines must also make coal available to many hundreds of thousands of farm homes and villages, not only by producing it in quantities but also by expanding transport facilities until coal is universally available and cheap enough to use as farm fuel.

Teaching the farmers to use coal in order to obtain better sanitation and fertilizer will in itself be no easy task, for the cycle may seem farfetched—burn coal to save vegetable matter, use vegetable matter in compost heaps to destroy pathogenic organisms and expand organic matter, reap the benefits of better health and more fertilizer. The lesson calls for nation-wide demonstrations as visible proof of the advantages to be gained.

In many areas coal can be made available to the farm from co-operative mines in which the farmers may dig their own coal during the slack winter season. There are many localities throughout North China where such a method of providing fuel is feasible, where coal lies in rather thin outcroppings or in veins near the surface in deposits that would be unprofitable to work with expensive machinery. Groups of farmers under the direction of mining engineers could open and operate such mines all over China, just as Shantung and Shansi farmers are operating them today.

The third, and ultimately the most important, source of fuel for the farms of China will be electricity. It may seem fantastic to suggest that someday the crowded plains and valleys of China will be filled with country homes where food is cooked on electric stoves, but I believe that not only is this a possibility but that it is a necessity if the people of China, all the people, are to enjoy a higher standard of living. There is no cheaper way to distribute in small quantities the vast amount of energy that ultimately must be consumed than by pumping it through electric wires, and China is blessed with two vast sources of electric power: the huge coal beds in the north and northeast, and her mighty water power potential.

During the war the Japanese in northeastern Manchuria generated large amounts of electric power both by burning relatively low-grade coal and by the development of water power. There are many places where coal is sufficiently abundant to encourage the building of huge steam turbine plants. There are, in fact, more places in North China where the lack of water, rather than coal, is a limiting factor for steam-generated power. From such steam-operated plants power can be channeled across the northern plains to light homes, cook food, drive threshing machinery, grind grain, and pump water for millions of peasant farmers.

In the wet south, along the Yangtze and a thousand lesser rivers, someday there must be scores of huge dams and hundreds of small ones to transform the energy of rushing torrents into heat and industrial power.

STARTING WITH SANITATION

One fall day in 1944, when wisps of morning mist were leaving gleaming trails on the rocks and walls of Chungking, I made my way to the steep, water-splashed stone steps that lead down from the city to the boat landing on the Chialing River side. I descended slowly, for the early-morning procession of water carriers crowded one side of the steps, carrying brimming buckets of river water slung from swaying shoulder poles, while a stream of goods carriers poured down the other side. Threading their way back and forth between the ascending and descending cargo carriers were scores of people working their way down to the boat landing, their baggage in their hands or on the backs of accompanying porters. A small steamer was waiting at the landing for a group of us who were off on what proved to be one of the most exciting and interesting two days I have ever experienced.

The steamer cast off its mooring ropes as soon as our party was on board and swung out into the gray Chialing fog and water and headed downstream. Driven by slow-turning engines and swift current, we reached the surge that perpetually marks the confluence of the Chialing and the Yangtze. Once clear of the small-boat traffic we dropped down the wide expanse of the Yangtze, an eight-knot current adding to the thrust of our engines. A line of high-masted junks was visible inshore as we swept in a wide turn around the first curve of the river. On the rocky shores we could see the tow gangs straining in rhythm to their chanteys, struggling with every ounce of weight and muscle to move the deep-laden junks upstream through the rapids formed by the current as it sweeps over the rocks and around the bend of the river. Through my mind there passed a vision of millions of such tow gangs that have fought the Yangtze through the centuries, forcing a passage through its swift waters by sweat and brawn.

Eight hours later our steamer moored to a floating wharf and we disembarked at a small city downstream from Chungking. After a short ride by truck we came to a small river tumbling over a 70-foot waterfall where a neat new hydroelectric plant had recently been built under an overhanging cliff. After inspecting the rewound motor that had been turned into a 3,500-kilowatt generator driven by a water turbine made from odds and ends of scrap material, we climbed the hill from which the overhanging cliff was suspended. As we wound back and forth up the steps we could see the Yangtze off to our right and could look down on the left to the small river feeding the power plant, while atop the hill were two small, comfortable-looking modern houses, perched high above the farms of the surrounding hillsides and valleys. These houses and the power plant below them seemed totally out of place in this wholly agricultural landscape of ancient China.

Entering one of the houses, we were offered seats at a long table on which were bowls of fruit and the customary glasses for tea. In a few moments the American we had come to see entered the room. He was Dr. George L. Savage, chief hydraulic engineer of the Conservation Service of the United States government. When Dr. Savage had introduced his two Chinese assistants and we had leisurely sipped the inevitable tea, the table was cleared and out came the sketches for the dam at the mouth of the gorges, a dam which could tame all the dragons that roil the waters of the Yangtze. We were to hear one of the first descriptions of the now famous Yangtze Dam Project.

Dr. Savage started by telling us of his trip to the mouth of the gorges to see the sites proposed for the dam. At that time Ichang, the city just outside the mouth of the gorges, was still in the hands of the Japanese, and the Chinese had no maps sufficiently accurate to use for sound planning.

However, they did have a captured Japanese ordnance map which seemed to be accurate. About two months before our visit a small party had made the trip downriver, landing well above the Japanese lines, and had slipped down to have a look at the sites, to check the accuracy of the Japanese map, and to observe something of the geology of the mountain formations into which the dam would be set.

Then they returned to the house where we were hearing the story and set to work on preliminary designs for two separate plans. The first provided for a dam to be located farther downstream where the gorge widens, a dam larger than any yet constructed or dreamed of, large enough to contain the power plant in the body of the dam itself. The second plan, the one preferred by Dr. Savage, involved the construction of a somewhat smaller dam farther upstream inside the mouth of the gorge. This second plan seemed more feasible to Dr. Savage because the water could be diverted during the six-year estimated construction period by means of twenty-four tunnels, each one fifty-six feet in diameter, driven through the mountains, twelve on each side of the gorge. This diversion problem is more impressive when one realizes that the building of the Hoover Dam required only four such tunnels. Because records show that there is a peak flood on the Yangtze about every hundred years, the tunnels must be able to carry the normal volume of water with a wide margin of safety.

With the river diverted, the construction of the dam could begin. An immense structure would be required to withstand the 600-foot depth of water, and would use about 14 million cubic yards of concrete, or about 3 million cubic yards more than the Grand Coulee, the largest dam yet built. The entire downriver face of the dam would be a spillway over which excess water of the summer rainy season could flow, controlled by nine doors fifty feet in height,

so designed that they might be opened in a matter of minutes to permit a 50-foot sheet of water to flow over the face
of the dam and provide some protection from possible
bombings.

Above the dam the rapids that Chinese boatmen have
fought for centuries would lie harmless under hundreds of
feet of water at the bottom of a placid lake devoid of strong
currents for hundreds of miles upstream, while below the
dam the great slow-moving Yangtze, which now flows slug-
gishly from Ichang to the sea and occasionally runs amuck
in flood, would become a harmless steady-flowing stream.
So great would be the storage capacity of the dam that the
level of the lake would fluctuate only slightly from season
to season, providing a constant water supply for irrigation,
making possible flood control and reclamation of downstream meadows now regularly inundated, and providing
safe passage for ocean steamers up to 10,000 tons from the
sea to Chungking, almost within sight of the snowy mountains of Tibet. The most creative innovation, according to
Dr. Savage, would be a lock cut from the solid rock of the
mountain that would permit a large steamer to be lifted to
the upper level in one operation.

"The only problem in the entire project about which
there is any question of technical feasibility," he commented,
"is the design of the doors for the bottom of that lock. It
will have to take greater pressures than any movable structure ever before planned by man." Then a twinkle came into
his eye as he added, "I think I have a design that will do it."

Later reports indicate that because of the great consumption of water involved in the operation of such a lock the
plans have been changed to provide the lifting of specially
built river steamers over the dam by means of huge electric cranes.

The most important purpose of the Ichang dam, however,

will be the production of electric power. Dr. Savage showed me how he planned to carve the electric-power plant out of the center of the solid mountain, arched by a roof of more than one thousand yards of solid rock. The huge generator rooms would be at right angles to the twenty-four diversion tunnels, and, when the dam was finished, the upper section of the tunnels would be plugged and the lower section used as runways for water that had already passed through the turbines.

Twenty-four penstocks, cut through the solid rock and lined with cement, would bring water from a point two hundred feet up the mountain side down to ninety-six turbines below, each turbine with a capacity of 110,000 kilowatts. The total capacity of 10,560,000 kilowatts would be more than three times the generating capacity of the Hoover, Grand Coulee, and Shasta dams combined, and about *one-sixth* the total capacity of all generators, both steam and hydro, in the entire United States.

The most astonishing result of the entire project, Dr. Savage stated, would be the low cost per kilowatt. The entire cost of the project, estimated at US$1 billion, would provide electricity at the rate of $95 for each kilowatt of capacity, a figure well below the average for hydroelectric installation in the United States. When the Ichang dam is finished and there is enough industrial and private consumption to justify capacity production of 240 million kilowatt hours daily, the output of energy every day from this single source will equal the muscular energy of China's entire working population.

This single structure could produce enough energy to make a huge contribution to the industrialization of China and to supply hundreds of thousands of farms as well, but the Ichang dam is only one of a system of dams necessary before the Yangtze is completely controlled. Of the other dams planned as part of this system, two or three would equal or surpass the Hoover and Grand Coulee dams in power-generating capacity.

"Until I came to China and studied the Yangtze, I had not really seen hydroelectric generating possibilities at all," said the man who, perhaps, knows the most about the water-power possibilities of the globe. "With the possible exception of the upper reaches of the Amazon there is no water-power site in the whole world that can surpass this Ichang site, and there is no river system that can equal the Yangtze in power production."

"But what about silting?" we asked Dr. Savage. "Won't the river silt up rapidly behind the dam?"

"Well, if nothing at all is done upstream to reduce silting, we estimate that there will be absolutely no trouble for at least three hundred years. If even a few precautions are taken on the watershed, then it will be at least five hundred years before any trouble will start. If all that we know about erosion and river control is applied to the whole valley, as it must be, then there will be no silting problem for at least three thousand years. I, for one, am willing to leave that problem for the men who will have to solve it when the time comes."

As we made our way down from that hilltop house toward the little 3,500-kilowatt power plant tucked under the cliff, a plant which will someday be under water if the Ichang dam is realized, I could not resist the vision of a time when electricity will play a dominant part in solving the problems of energy and fuel for the Chinese farmer. His limited vegetable wastes will go back to his hard-worked soil by way of a compost heap. His villages will become clean and healthy, and his life reasonably free of disease and death.

There are many lesser power possibilities on hundreds of streams in China, but the development of these dams must be correlated with the other basic needs of the people who live in the areas served. Such over-all development projects can not only raise the production level of electricity, but can prevent erosion, provide reforestation, fisheries, game, commerce, irrigation and recreation, produce nitrogen and other essential commodities, and, in the development of the areas themselves, give opportunity and impetus to the improvement of schools and hospitals, and lead toward a more modern society.

Thus, starting with a search for the key to her greatest public health problem—the control of the fecal-borne diseases by sanitation—our project carried us deep into many other problems equally basic to the total rebuilding of China. To stop the transmission of worms and fecal-borne diseases, a new method of household and farm waste disposal which will kill pathogens, prevent insect breeding, and conserve fertilizers is necessary. Composting is such a method. It is applicable to conditions throughout China, but dependent on:

1. The development of new sources of farm fuel that will release large quantities of vegetable matter for both an expanded animal industry and increased composting. New sources of farm fuel can be produced by (*a*) growing more and better fuel on wasteland; (*b*) electrification; (*c*) mining and distributing more coal for use on the farm.

2. The development of a low-cost transportation system capable of distributing coal and fertilizers throughout agricultural China.

3. The development of a program of popular education which will spread the knowledge and encourage the cooperation necessary for adequate and proper composting and better general sanitation.

4. The development of industry which will produce, among other commodities, an increased supply of chemical fertilizers to meet the needs of the soil.

5. An increase in total production and income sufficient

to permit the farmer to use composting, to consume more fuel and fertilizers, and to develop economic means to cleanliness and personal hygiene.

Thus the requirements of sanitation, a logical starting point in the rebuilding of China, are a large order. Given time, it can be filled. In filling it, China is led to a second problem.

Chapter XII

Expanding Agricultural Production

JUST AS IMPROVED SANITATION IN THE CHINESE VIL-lage requires changes in the use of two agricultural fundamentals, fertilizer and fuel, so solutions of the fertilizer and fuel problems require expansion of transportation and industry. Basic to all, however, is the necessity of raising the buying power of the farmer, now so abjectly poor that he cannot even perform the relatively simple services to himself necessary to break the grip of fecal-borne diseases.

There are two common explanations of the poverty of China's farmers. One might be called ideological; the other, technological. The ideological theory is influenced, directly and indirectly, by Marxist doctrine and has been propounded so many times by so many types of people that it is widely believed. According to it, the peasant is poor because he farms land that is owned by big landlords who grind him down with excessive rents. He is the victim of usurious interest rates and unbearable tax burdens imposed on him by a ruling class dominated by the landlords. The farmer is poor because of social and political inequality and injustice, the victim of wrongs that can be righted by social and political changes. The cure recommended is revolution. With the revolution, it is said, the downtrodden will rise up, shake off the shackles, redistribute the land, change the social and political order, and everyone will live happily ever after.

The second explanation might be called technological. According to this theory the cause of poverty is a combination of history, culture, and technological development. The root cause is simply a much too large population dependent on one major source of production—agriculture, and a prescientific hoe-culture agriculture at that. Tenantry, usury, overburdening taxes, and even much of the political injustice the peasant suffers are symptoms of the basic disease —overpopulation plus an obsolete technology. The solution: introduction of modern techniques that will permit rapid expansion of basic production coupled with democratically achieved social and political readjustments brought about over a period of years.

It is of the utmost importance to determine which of these two explanations is correct. To do so it is necessary to evaluate the factors each suggests as causes of the poverty that dominates the life of the vast majority of Chinese. Only on this evaluation can a sound program of expanding farm production be based.

It has been pointed out that there are too many farm families for the amount of arable land available, and that the individual farm is too small for efficient production. But it will be worth while to follow the bases for this conclusion a step further.

Dr. Buck divided the farms he studied into five size groups—small, medium, medium large, large, and very large—and analyzed the efficiency of operation in each group. Sixty-one per cent of the farms fell into the first two groups, and 39 per cent into the remaining three. Centering attention on three groups—small, medium large, and very large—some comparisons are illuminating.

The small farms group included 23 per cent of all those studied and averaged 1.43 acres per farm. The medium large group comprised 28 per cent of the total and averaged

4.92 acres. Very large farms included only 7 per cent and averaged just over thirteen acres. Small farms supported an average of 4.4 persons; medium large supported 6.9; and very large farms were operated by families averaging 10.0 persons.

A study of efficiency on these farms showed that one farm laborer worked 1.5 acres on the small farms; 2.6 acres on the medium large farms; and 4.0 acres on the very large farms. In other words, the very large farms used their labor two and two-thirds times as efficiently as the small farms, and one and a half times as efficiently as the medium large ones.

The study further showed that one work animal cultivated the equivalent of 2.6 acres of land on the small farms; 4.8 acres on the medium large farms; and 6.7 acres on the very large farms. In the use of animal labor, therefore, the very large farm was again two and one-half times as efficient as the small farm and one and one-third times as efficient as the medium large farm.

Although even these "very large farms" do not use labor to full efficiency, the statistics show that, since both human and animal labor can function more effectively on the 13-acre farm, the greatest waste of labor occurs on the smallest farms.

Moreover, large and small farms have the same crop yield per acre. Families working small farms are not able to cultivate their land any more intensively than those on large farms. All Chinese farms are worked to the limits of existing natural and technological factors. However, when total production was measured by the amount of grain equivalent produced by one man during one year it was found that a single worker produced an average of 2,042 pounds of grain a year on the small farm, 3,186 on the medium large farm, and 4,560 pounds on the very large farm.

Moreover, the very large farm was supporting 10.0

persons while the small farm supported only 4.4 persons. This final measure of comparative production is the most significant of all, for it shows the production per capita. For each member of the farm family the small farm produced 495 pounds of grain equivalent, the medium large farm produced 1,054 pounds, and the very large farm produced 1,701 pounds. The very large farm, therefore, produced almost three and one-half times as much wealth per capita as the small farm and one and two-thirds as much as the medium large farm.

The conclusion is clear enough: the fundamental cause of low production and consequent low standards of living in China is that farms are too small. Without any change in technology whatsoever, production and wealth per capita could be increased from 61 to 243 per cent if, by some magic, the average size of all Chinese farms could be raised to thirteen acres. Most of the other causes of the poverty that weighs down China's peasants are symptoms of this overpopulation disease.

The protagonist of the ideological explanation of peasant poverty in China insists that tenantry is a major cause. The facts suggest that tenantry is a symptom of overpopulation rather than a basic cause of poverty. Furthermore, the facts available concerning the prevalence of tenantry seem to minimize the exploiting landlord as a poverty-causing factor in China's farm structure.

Dr. R. T. Ts'ui of the University of Nanking College of Agriculture presented the following table in the July, 1946, issue of the *National Reconstruction Journal*, published by the China Institute in America:

	Percentage of total number of farms		
	1912	1934	1937
Tenants	28	29	30
Part owners	23	25	24
Owners	49	46	46

These figures come from reports published by the National Agricultural Research Bureau of the Central Government, and, while a gradual increase in the proportion of tenants is indicated, they show that less than one-third of China's farms are cultivated by tenants who themselves own no land and that nearly half are cultivated by owners.

The picture of landownership presented by the 16,796 farms that Buck studied showed even less tenantry. Buck's data showed that over one-half of the farmers were owners, less than one-third were part owners, and only 17 per cent were tenants. Furthermore, his data showed that only 28.7 per cent of the total Chinese farm *area* was rented (12.7 per cent in the wheat region and 40.3 per cent in the rice region). In the area with the highest percentage of rented land, the Szechuan rice area, 49.1 per cent was tenant cultivated. Although there are individual areas in China where the percentage of rented land area is high, the proportion of total land rented is no greater than in the United States, where, according to Department of Agriculture figures for 1940, 29.4 per cent of the land area was cultivated by tenants, 28.3 per cent by part owners, and only 42.3 per cent by owners and managers.

In general there are four land rental systems in common use. One-fifth of all tenant farms are leased on a share-rent basis by which both the crop and the risk are divided between the tenant and the owner. One-fourth are leased on a cash-rent basis, by which the tenant pays a fixed rent and takes the risk of profit or loss depending on his crop yield. A little over one-half of all tenant farms are leased on a cash-crop system by which a fixed portion of the crop or its money equivalent is paid as rent. Fourth, accounting for less than one-fiftieth of China's tenant farms, is the cropper system by which the tenant obtains a very small share of the crop because he supplies only the labor.

One method of measuring the rental burden, therefore,

is to determine the percentage of farm production paid out as rent. Buck obtained data on the use of crops that were harvested on 15, 646 farms. Of an annual national rice crop approximating 60 million tons, Buck found that an average of 15 per cent was sold, 56 per cent was eaten by the farm population, 4 per cent was kept for seed, and 21 per cent was paid out as rent. Of an annual national wheat crop approximating 25 million tons, 29 per cent was sold, 54 per cent was eaten, 9 per cent was kept for seed, 1 per cent was used for animal feed, and 4 per cent was paid out as rent. Of sweet potatoes, the third crop in importance, 24 per cent was sold, 63 per cent was eaten, 2 per cent was saved for seed, 7 per cent was used for feed, and less than $\frac{1}{2}$ of 1 per cent was paid out as rent. Of the fourth most important crop, kaoliang, 25 per cent was sold, 53 per cent was eaten, 3 per cent was used for seed, 9 per cent was fed to animals, and 5 per cent was paid out as rent. All other crops show similar disposition, with less than 5 per cent used as rent. It would appear that well under 10 per cent of China's total farm production is used to pay rent, and even much of this rental crop goes to landlords who are themselves farmers and would be classified as "poor" by American standards. Well over half the total production is consumed by the farm population as food, and between 15 and 20 per cent is sold. Some of the money realized from sales must be used to pay the cash rent that one-quarter of the tenants (between 4.5 and 8 per cent of all farmers) pay, but it is probable that far less than 15 per cent of China's total farm production is used for rent.

It seems evident, therefore, that, while there is a group of Chinese farmers on whom the burden of rent is heavy, the less than 15 per cent of production used for rent cannot be the major cause of the abject poverty that dogs 70 to 80 per cent of China's farmers.

On the basis of facts it is possible to predict the effect

that a change in the system of land tenure would have on total and individual production. Buck (page 198) makes the following statement: "A change in the system of tenure cannot be expected to affect the amount of land available for cultivation, as is sometimes stated by those interested in the reform of land tenure; also, according to previous studies, such a change cannot be expected to increase crop production (i.e. yield per acre), for it was found that tenants were better farmers than owners."

If tenantry were eliminated and the farm area distributed about equally among all the cultivators (the Communists are now operating on the basis of this policy), the over-all effect would be to break up those relatively few farms that are large enough to approach a favorable size for economic operation. Again quoting Buck (page 285): "Moreover, the problem of land distribution is not one of equal division of land among all the people, for then no farm would have enough land upon which to earn a living, but rather *one of development of farms of an economic size for each farm family, so that each may have a satisfactory standard of living.*" (Italics are mine. G. F. W.)

One final fact about tenantry needs to be added. When the percentage of farm area which was rented was determined for each farm-size class discussed above, there was little difference between the proportions of land rented in the different groups. Of the small farms, 29.5 per cent were rented; of the medium large farms 29.2 per cent; and of the very large farms 24.3 per cent. There is little relation between the size of farms and the occurrence of tenantry.

In order to buy land, the tenant farmer would have to borrow money, and therein lies a second symptom of poverty. Interest rates in China are normally high, and under the pressure of inflation they have gone so high that they have no sensible meaning. Again it is necessary to refer to Buck's prewar studies for data sufficiently representative to be of use. Buck found that Chinese farmers borrow money for three purposes: to carry on the work of the farm, to supply family necessities until harvest time, and to meet unusual expenses that have not been anticipated and offset by savings. Only about one-quarter of the money borrowed is used for productive purposes, and almost none of it is used for long-term investments such as land buying. Most of it is used for special expenses involving the prestige or the family face. For example, when the grandfather dies he must have an elaborate funeral to demonstrate the filiality of the sons. When a son is married his family borrows money to entertain the guests, pay for the new household equipment, and demonstrate to the bride's family what a good marriage their daughter has made. Buck found that the average expenditure for funerals amounted to prewar CN$102, for weddings CN$127, birthdays CN$63, dowries for betrothed daughters CN$96. At the time of Buck's researches, the average annual income of the farm family was CN$400. Although the amounts may now be multiplied by tens of thousands, the proportions remain the same.

Almost three-fourths of the farm families of China are able to meet these social prestige expenditures out of current income and savings, but those living on small farms with limited production must borrow to maintain social position. Small farm size, therefore, combines with the cultural pressure of family face to create a demand for borrowed money at usurious rates which use up all the savings available and leave little for investment at more reasonable interest rates.

Interest rates for such loans averaged 2.7 per cent per month or 32 per cent per year, according to Buck's figures, and the average amount of debt incurred by borrowers amounted to CN$76 per year which, balanced against the average prewar farm income of CN$400 per year, represents a fairly heavy debt for the 39 per cent of all farmers who were forced to borrow. When interest is added to this CN$76 debt, the amount the farmer paid back at the end of a single year was a few cents less than CN$100, and represented about one-quarter of the gross farm production of the average farm.

There is no farm credit from a national credit market to meet these needs. The banking system of the countryside has not developed sufficiently to accumulate farmers' savings, nor have precarious farming risks, vagaries of weather, bandits, and political disorders been particularly conducive to a peaceful growth of farm loan systems.

Where does the farmer borrow this money? Buck found that the major sources of farm credit, representing 39 per cent of all debts, were relatives and friends. Twenty per cent came from what might be called speculative sources, including wealthy persons, merchants, or shops in nearby cities. Only 2 per cent of the money borrowed came from landlords. It is apparent that the picture of city speculators and large landlords waiting eagerly to foreclose mortgages has been heavily exaggerated. What foreclosures there are, therefore, are due more to international and civil strife added to an already hazardous farm situation than to avarice of moneylenders, even though most moneylenders are probably endowed with a normal amount of avarice.

After rentals and interest rates, a third factor in China's agrarian economy is the heavy land tax. In 1932 Buck found that the average rate per acre on medium-grade land in China was US$1.78, comparing with tax rates of US$0.92 to US$1.15 per acre of comparable farm lands in New England, the middle Atlantic, and the eastern north-central states. Land taxes in China are heavy because farm production represents such an overwhelmingly important part of China's total wealth, while industrialization is still so poorly developed that it can carry only a very small percentage of the tax burden. Furthermore, since it is impossible to conceal land or change the size of fields in order to evade taxation, a tax on land is relatively easy to levy and collect. For the continuing support of armies, farmers have been taxed even more heavily, sometimes being required to pay for years in advance. Such taxes are another symptom of an unhealthy, one-sided economy and of underproduction.

It seems evident that the evils of tenantry, usury, and unreasonable taxes are symptoms rather than major causes of the abject poverty in which 70 to 80 per cent of China's farmers live. The real cause lies in the fact that the individual farmer does not produce enough.

Once the distinction between causes of poverty and symptoms of poverty has been made, the conclusion that the outstanding problem in Chinese agriculture is the low level of production is unavoidable. There are two fundamental steps which can remedy the situation: an increase in average farm size and an increase in production per farm worker. Since the limits of farm size are determined by the total land area available divided by the existing number of farm families, farms can be increased in size only as the total area under cultivation is increased or as the total number of farm families is reduced. Both can be accomplished.

At the present time in agricultural China there are approximately 232 million acres of land under cultivation. In addition, Buck estimates, there are possibly 35 million acres more which might be made suitable for cultivation by irrigation and reclamation, by the consolidation of farm parcels to reduce the acreage covered by boundary ridges, and by the elimination of graves from fields. Also there is another 80 million acres in Manchuria and other outlying areas that might be made suitable for cultivation. The total of these three figures, 347 million acres, represents a maximum estimate of possible arable land in all China. If this land were divided into 13-acre farms, equal in size to the very large farms that Buck found to be the most economic now in operation, farms could be provided for 26,700,000 farm families. There are now at least 56,500,000 farm families in agricultural China proper, exclusive of Manchuria and the other territories in the northwest. At least 30 million families would be displaced by such action and would be forced into new means of livelihood.

If a magic change suddenly produced 13-acre farms operated by the 26,700,000 farm families, each consisting of the present average of ten persons, the total production per person would rise from its present average of 980 pounds of grain equivalent per capita to 1,657 pounds per capita, and the standard of living of these farmers could rise 80 per cent —merely by increasing the farm size. But the same magic would then have to produce other employment to support at least 180 million displaced persons. Since no such versatile magic is available, the increasing of farm sizes (reduction of the farm population) is going to be a major operation in social engineering.

The second fundamental process for increasing the amount of per capita production consists of the use of all the means whereby modern science can raise production per acre—a long and arduous task to carry out in China, but so thoroughly within the realm of possibility that it merits detailed consideration.

Although China's production per acre is surprisingly high, considering the prescientific nature of agricultural methods and the almost complete ignorance of the enormous progress of agricultural technology, opportunities for applying modern principles are almost unlimited. Generally speaking, they fall into three categories: biological farm methods; mechanical farm methods; and, third, co-operative projects and developments which can be carried out most logically by the government.

Biotechnological improvements are of greater importance than mechanotechnological ones because of the limited size of Chinese farms. A tractor cannot be operated profitably on a tennis court, and even if the average farm size were raised to thirteen acres the amount of work required of mechanical devices would be relatively small. The greatest gains may be expected from biological developments.

The first biotechnological development applicable to Chinese agriculture is the improvement of fertilizers. Its requirements are a vast increase in the use of chemical fertilizers and a considerable increase in quantities of organic manures to be applied to the soil. One rough calculation of the amount of nitrogen-bearing chemical fertilizers needed to meet applications recommended for North China soils has been cited. A much more detailed and accurate estimate, based on field experiments to determine the quantities necessary to ensure the farmer a two-to-one probability of profit, indicates the need for at least 20 million tons of chemical fertilizers each year. According to the U.S. Department of Agriculture, the 1946–1947 world production of chemical fertilizers was only 23,939,000 metric tons.

Obviously, to meet her own needs, China must produce chemical fertilizers herself; and she can. Here is a worthy use for the millions of kilowatts of electric power that can be generated by China's rivers. Nitrogen can be pulled from the air in inexhaustible quantities. Extensive beds of phosphates have recently been discovered in Yünnan province, and, with the use of electricity, these phosphate rocks can be transformed into modern superphosphates highly available to plants.

The application of such quantities of chemical fertilizers requires a corresponding increase in the amount of organic fertilizers that must be used as balance. With new sources of fuel provided for the farm, compost heaps can provide that organic matter (and also serve the needs of environmental sanitation). Gains in production through development of fertilizers may be expected to total 20 to 40 per cent.

However, the mere production of millions of tons of fertilizers is not enough by itself. Fertilizers must be distributed quickly and cheaply to the millions of farms where they are to be used. Trains, trucks, and steamers, moving over new roadbeds, improved and extended highways, and up and down controlled rivers must provide the inexpensive transportation that human muscles can never give. To take the primary and most fruitful step toward increase of agricultural yields, China must develop a huge chemical industry and build vast new systems of transportation.

A second biotechnological improvement is the continuation and enormous expansion of programs now under way to produce improved strains of seeds. Already the program of plant breeding initiated by the University of Nanking has spread to many other agencies, notably the National Agricultural Research Bureau, and has produced significant results. In the years just before the war the production of cotton rose sharply following the adaptation and introduction of improved cotton seed. During the war years wheat yields in Szechuan province were increased by improved strains introduced by the University of Nanking.

The slow but highly productive process by which plant breeders can improve Chinese agriculture is also illustrated by results obtained in Shantung at the Cheeloo University plant-breeding station, a substation under the technical direction of the University of Nanking's College of Agriculture. It was supported by the University of Nanking, the Shantung Provincial Famine Relief Committee, and the Shantung Provincial Government. In 1939 the plant-breeding station, after ten years of work, announced a new and improved strain of wheat, superior to any used by the farmers of Shantung.

The story of that ten years of experiment began with the collection of more than twenty thousand strains of wheat from all over the world. The best types from the steppes of

Russia, the plains of Kansas, the fields of Canada, Europe, and Argentina were collected, while the plant breeders brought in the most promising awns from the Shantung countryside as preparatory to a great elimination contest.

Kernels from a single head of each strain were planted in one large field, each in a row a yard long. The following spring each strain was carefully checked to see how it had withstood the winter and examined for desirable characteristics and resistance to rusts, smuts, and other wheat diseases. Hundreds of strains that proved poorly adapted to the climate and showed inability to resist disease were eliminated. Thousands of strains remained in the contest for the second year. Again each was planted in yard rows, this time several rows per strain, in a nonsystematic, random fashion, or, in plant breeder's vernacular, "replicate rows of each strain were randomized," in order to average out the variations in fertility bound to occur in different sections of the field. Again there was an elimination of those strains which did not stand the dryness or the cold of winter, or were diseased. By now it was possible to weigh and compare the yields of the various strains and to single out those producing the most of wheat and straw.

Year after year these experiments were repeated with infinite care to avoid mixing of grains, and, as the years went by, more strains were eliminated and those remaining were subjected to more and more careful scrutiny. The record of yield was more fully analyzed until at last one strain stood out as being the best—a strain that consistently outproduced all others and yielded from 20 to 30 per cent more grain than the average Shantung variety. Ten years of work had at last produced a new, genetically pure strain of wheat that was well adapted to the conditions of the Shantung plain. The strain that had won in competition with famous wheat from all parts of the world was one found in a peasant's field not many miles from the station at Tsinan, Shantung.

EXPANDING AGRICULTURAL PRODUCTION

By the fall of 1939, the new strain had been planted on all available land at the plant-breeding station, and contracts had been signed with neighboring farmers to propagate the prize wheat. According to the terms of the contracts, the station guaranteed a certain minimum income to the farmer, and he in turn agreed to sell his entire harvest to the station for distribution to a larger number of farmers the following year. (Most of the farmers who signed the contracts were members of co-operatives sponsored by the university, and although they had a good deal of faith in us, they wanted to be protected against any possible loss from the use of seed that might prove to be bad.)

The following spring was exceedingly dry. The winter wheat across the provincial plains was not doing well, but the fields planted to the new drought-resistant wheat became famous as harvesttime approached. Across the plains they could be seen as squares of evenly rich, evenly tall blocks of gold standing a good six inches taller than the mixed brown and green wheat in other fields. Some weeks before the harvest, contract holders began to ask if they might retain a portion of the harvest to sell as seed to friends and neighbors. Their skepticism had disappeared, and they were besieged with requests for grain.

At this point the Japanese stepped in and demanded control of the new wheat. Although every effort was made to resist them, they distributed the grain themselves. In a few months came Pearl Harbor. Cheeloo University was occupied and became the 150th Field Hospital of the Japanese Army.

What was done for wheat in Tsinan has been done for millet at Peiping's Yenching University, and the promise of the plant breeder is similarly applicable to every crop that China grows. Someday yields will be 15, 20, or perhaps 30 per cent higher because of improved strains of seed.

A third biotechnological improvement is control of injurious insects and plant diseases. No one knows how great the losses from this source may be, but one report prepared in 1929 by Professor Yen Kei-wei estimated losses to the ordinary rice crop due to insects and disease at CN$227,230,-600, and a total loss of well over CN$1 billion in glutinous rice, wheat, beans, corn, vegetables, fruits, cotton, forests, and stored articles.

Damage to cotton is caused by a number of insects, of which one of the greatest scourges is the cotton aphid. All through the provinces of Shantung and Hopei, where cotton is grown extensively, the aphids attack young cotton plants, affixing themselves to the underside of leaves in a solid coating. There they suck the plant juices, stunting or killing a high percentage of the afflicted crop. Just before the war a group of entomologists of the National Agricultural Research Bureau, working under a young graduate of Cheeloo University, developed an inexpensive and effective method of controlling cotton aphids by using an emulsion of cottonseed oil in water. The emulsion is placed in an old-fashioned washbasin and the laborers go down the rows dipping each plant by hand. Such a tedious method of killing aphids probably would not be practical anywhere else in the world, but because of the very small Chinese farm size and the large number of workers available the system is useful in China, where it requires no equipment and makes use of spare time.

China produces an average of 87 bushels of Irish potatoes per acre, while the United States produces 108 bushels. The major cause of the low yield in China is potato blight. During the war years, the United States Government sent one of our greatest potato experts to China to study this problem, and sent with him seeds of the best breeds of potatoes known to man. He found that blight virus was so prevalent throughout China that experiments could not be carried on except in one small area high up in the hills of western Szechuan province, for it is only by supplying a constant source of disease-free tubers year after year that yields of potatoes can be expected to increase. Immediately a program was set up to produce blight-free potatoes from this blight-free area to supply seed for planting in other districts. At the same time experiments were undertaken to improve the quality of the blight-free potatoes that already existed in this area.

Among the insects and plant diseases that make serious inroads on Chinese crops are the rusts and smuts that regularly attack wheat and millet and mold crickets that frequently go down row after row of millet in North China, eating off each newly sprouted stalk just under the ground.

In the rice-growing region of the south, particularly in the Red Basin of Szechuan, it is not uncommon to see a field of rice almost ready for harvest but with a quarter to a half of the heads empty—pale shadows of normally developed grain—where the rice borer, the larval stage of a beetle, has eaten through the stalk under the water level.

To figures for such destruction must be added the rodent ravages occurring after the crops are harvested. Losses in stored products run high because the enormous production of grain crops, including 60 million tons of rice, 25 million tons of wheat, more than 65 million tons of other grain products, and 16 million tons of sweet potatoes, is now stored almost entirely in mat cornucopias that stand on the mud floors of Chinese peasant homes. Stored in this unprotected way, they are subject to damage by weevils and the inroads of rats and other vermin. In spite of the fact that the Chinese peasant takes all possible care of his stored produce by regular sunning to prevent growth of fungi and development of insects, it seems probable that 5 to 10 per cent of the total production is spoiled between the time of harvest and consumption.

Plant diseases and ravages of insects can be controlled. Such diseases as rust and smut will largely be conquered by the plant breeder, as well as by the treatment of seeds with chemicals that destroy disease spores. Insects can be controlled by the application of both biological and chemical methods found practicable in other parts of the world and adapted to China's particular needs. It is difficult to estimate the increase in yield per acre that can be made possible by such controls, but gains of 15 per cent seem probable.

A fourth biotechnological improvement which must be applied to Chinese agriculture is an adequate forestry program for production of more and better fuel and building materials. There are large tracts of waste- or semiwasteland which, with proper methods of planting and management, can be made to produce quantities of both. Problems to be solved are the selection and adaptation of plants and the training of workers in scientific forest management. Valuable by-products of such a program would include greater retention of vital moisture and the control of erosion. Through proper planting of hillsides, stream sides, and field boundaries, it would be possible to slow down the process by which millions of tons of China's soil are washed to the sea each year.

A fifth biotechnological need is the improvement of animals. The most important food-producing animals are the pig and poultry, among the latter particularly chickens and ducks. These animals are of greatest importance to Chinese food economy because they are scavengers, consuming foods that otherwise might be lost. Both poultry and pigs can be improved by careful breeding of desirable characteristics to increase production of meat and eggs without a corresponding increase in quality or quantity of feed, a difficult task because most of the great advances made in animal industry in other parts of the world have been based on significant improvements in the quality of diet. Some progress in this direction has been made, and the production of farm animals can be further improved by teaching the Chinese farmer how to make wiser use of fodder now available. Another means toward improvement of animals is protection from disease. Both the pig and the chicken in China are highly susceptible to pig and chicken cholera, widespread diseases sometimes responsible for the death of most of the pigs in a village or all the chickens in a family flock. Both can be controlled by relatively inexpensive methods of inoculation. When the Chinese farmer has been instructed in modern methods of animal care and has adopted them, and when he has been provided with improved breeds of farm animals and knows how to protect them from unnecessary death by contagious disease, then the production of the Chinese farm will be further expanded.

Application of all these biotechnological improvements should double the yield per acre and the production of the farm as a whole, and when such doubling is fully achieved, Chinese agriculture will have attained the same degree of intensive scientific development that is now characteristic of agriculture in Europe.

While biotechnological improvements can be expected to provide the major gains for Chinese agriculture, there are important advances to be made through the use of mechanical devices. When farm sizes are increased and the farm population is decreased, a number of mechanical improvements will be required to meet peak work loads at seed- and harvesttime. It does not seem likely that tractors and other large machines can be used extensively except in certain North China areas where dry land farming on flat country exists, and even then the size of tractors would be limited by the small field size common even to 13-acre farms. However, small tractors owned and operated on a co-operative basis would permit plowing of broad tracts where groups of farmers were willing to eliminate their present field boundaries. In South China, where fields are terraced and flooded for rice culture, it seems almost certain that the water buffalo will continue to be the motive power used for plowing, since flooded plots must be kept small to prevent escape of water. However, there is room for the mechanical improvement of the plow and methods of plowing now in use.

Raymond Moyer, now of the United States Office of Foreign Agricultural Relations, showed by a series of tests conducted at Oberlin-in-China school, in Shansi province, that the introduction of more modern plows would increase crop yields and reduce the time required to prepare seedbeds. The introduction of simple, animal-drawn seeding machines for planting winter crops in the south and all crops in the north would certainly be to the advantage of farms as large as thirteen acres.

A second mechanical improvement needed is machinery designed to replace the goose-necked hoes now employed for crop cultivation. The introduction of simple, hand-pushed plows of the type now used by American suburban gardeners could result in enormous savings of time and energy for the Chinese farmer who works dry land. Instead of backing down each row, pulling a hoe stroke by stroke to cut the weeds and loosen the soil, the farmer could walk forward at a steady pace, the small plowshares clearing and cultivating the whole furrow at one passage. Even this type of cultivator could be owned co-operatively and serve more than one small farm during the period of transition and until such time as the single farm became large enough to employ such an instrument full time. In the cultivation of rice, however, it seems unlikely that any tool can prove superior to fingers, feet, and toes for underwater cultivation of closely planted rice plants.

The most critical mechanical problem on the Chinese farm is the harvesting and threshing of huge grain crops. Each spring and fall these two processes require the labor of every man, woman, and child in the farm areas. With increase in farm size and decrease in farm population, hand methods would be inadequate. In the north it should be possible to use small combines in areas where fields can be thrown together without boundaries. In hill country a portable gasoline-powered reaper would be necessary for harvesting in small, inaccessible fields, and an electric- or gasoline-powered thresher that could be carried from village to village would solve the threshing problem. Such a thresher could process the crops produced by an entire village in a day or two and could, therefore, be the property of a group of villages to be used in rotation during the harvest season. In rice country where fields are drained before the harvest, the same methods and machinery would be applicable, but in the hill paddies where water must be retained the year around, present methods of hand harvesting probably could not be replaced by machinery.

After harvesting and threshing, the most important mechanical problem in Chinese agriculture is irrigation, important because southern ricelands must be flooded and because so much of the north must be irrigated if crops are to grow at all. Furthermore, many thousands of acres, particularly in the northwest, could be brought under cultivation if water were available. Owing to prodigious labor by man and animals, China already has a larger proportion of her cultivated land under irrigation than any other country in the world. Community efforts and mechanical aids can divert much of this labor into direct production and increase the efficiency of irrigation.

In an experiment conducted by co-operatives in Hopei province, farmers pooled their efforts and a small amount of capital to dig hundreds of wells, after which water was drawn for irrigation by ordinary hand methods. Yields from fields thus irrigated were almost doubled. At one mission station in Honan province, experiments with a single suction gas engine and centrifugal pump mounted on a small boat irrigated a large tract of land more quickly and less expensively than hand methods.

Once there are electric lines across the countryside, it will be possible to have portable electric motors attached to small centrifugal pumps which can suck the ordinary well dry in half an hour. By moving from well to well, it would be possible to irrigate large tracts of land and increase the yield to the extent demonstrated in Hopei, especially in North China, where moisture is the most important single factor in determining crop yield.

In the rice-growing south there are tens of thousands of situations where portable pumps can be used to facilitate the irrigation of rice fields. The building of the dams that China can and must build for electric power will make possible the extension of gravity-flow irrigation projects in many places. Thus by the introduction of modern irrigation methods the hazards of drought in the north and the cost of irrigation in the south can both be mitigated.

When improved plows and machinery for cultivating, harvesting, and threshing have been introduced, and when mechanical irrigation has reduced the risks, costs, and time of agricultural enterprise and, at the same time, has increased production per acre, China's farmwork can be handled, and handled more efficiently, by a much smaller farm population. While mechanotechnological changes are not so important as biotechnological improvements, they can and must play a significant part in improving the certainty and efficiency of agriculture. The development of these mechanical devices must depend to a certain extent on the development in China of fuels, internal-combustion engines, and farm machinery adapted to the specific needs and conditions of various parts of the country. The trend toward smaller and more compact farm tools for use on garden plots and what we consider very small farms in America is already producing some of the changes in farm machinery that must be carried still further to meet the special needs of China.

Thus far only the biological and mechanical improvements that must be made on the farm itself in order to improve agricultural production have been considered. Some problems, however, will require the application of essentially mechanical processes to units larger than the single farm.

First, there is the problem of flood and erosion control, which must be planned and carried out on a larger basis than the single farm unit. Hazards of agriculture in China are somewhat greater than in other large countries of the world, and one of these hazards is flood. Important among causes of floods are the wide fluctuations in rainfall characteristic of China's climate, an example being the cloudburst over the Han River valley that resulted in the great Yangtze flood of 1935. Also, much of the Chinese wasteland capable of growing forests has been denuded by poor people in search of fuel, a process which has led to rapid and highly destructive hillside drainage, to erosion, and to the flooding of rivers. Two hundred years ago China was one of the most advanced countries of the world in the control and utilization of water for irrigation, but by modern standards her dams and irrigation projects are much too small both for adequate flood control and for extensive modern irrigation methods. Such flood-control installations as the planned Yangtze dam can go a long way toward reducing the hazards of flood that now bring extensive periodic losses to great segments of China's population.

By means of fuel-growing programs and dam construction on streams and rivers, the regular loss of soil now taking place can be brought under control, a control absolutely necessary if the total area of arable land is to be prevented from shrinking year after year as it is washed into the sea.

A second problem, which must be solved by united efforts, is the problem of transportation, so constantly in evidence as basic to the solution of other problems. When famine occurs in China it is almost always due to the lack of transportation. For efficient fertilization, for marketing (because of inadequate transportation facilities there is no national market for farm products), and for lowering costs and raising economic standards, transportation is vital.

Finally, there is the problem of processing farm products, the organization, in the villages of China, of co-operative processing groups able to obtain credit for the purchase of simple equipment, and make it possible for the farmer to send his product to market more nearly ready for the final consumer or in a condition that will make preservation and use of his produce easier. The extra labor thus put into processing in the village can make profitable use of the billions of man-hours of idle time the farm population accumulates during winter months and between the periods of intensive summer crop cultivation. The extent and importance of village industry can be further extended and many new methods introduced to supplement the industries that now produce such things as bean curd, alcohol, and soybean sauce.

In addition to biological and mechanical contributions to the well-being of the Chinese farmer, there are a series of economic and political problems that must be solved, principally by government, if standards of living for those engaged in agriculture are to be raised.

First, because almost all the biological and mechanical improvements suggested require capital, is the problem of farm credit. Until credit is available at interest rates low enough to permit borrowing both fixed and operating farm capital, it is impossible to expect that the farmer will be able to take full advantage of improved methods. At the same time, credit at reasonable rates will give hope to the tenant that he may someday own the farm he operates.

A second problem to be met at a high level is presented by the necessity of establishing and enforcing regulations governing the standardization and marketing of farm products. There is now no nation-wide market—merely a conglomeration of local markets. Transportation and credit are part of this general problem, but the farmer needs additional assistance. In the course of China's modern history, she has lost her leadership in two important international markets because she failed to establish and maintain a system of standardization of products. She lost the tea trade to India because before it was packed for foreign shipment her tea, produced by many small farmers, passed through the hands of a whole series of dealers who could not resist the temptation to adulterate the farmers' products in order to make a temporary personal gain. The tea grown in India and Ceylon was controlled by large companies and delivered to foreign buyers as a standard and pure product. Similarly, China lost her silk market to Japan, where a rigid system of merchandise grading was enforced. Today, because the Chinese agricultural leaders responsible for the development and marketing of tung oil are acutely conscious of the fact that they may lose their dominant position in the market unless they are able to guarantee uniformity and prevent adulteration, strenuous efforts are being made to set up tung-oil extraction plants either under government auspices or with careful government supervision so that adulteration and variations in quality can be avoided.

As China's internal market expands and takes on a national rather than a local character there must be similar grading of products not intended for export if the farmer is to be protected against undue speculation, and if the consuming public is to be ensured high-quality products. One section of such grading codes must include pure food and drug laws.

Since the individual farmer is usually forced to sell his crops as soon as they are harvested, at a time when the market is flooded and prices are at their lowest, the formation of marketing co-operatives would enable him to pool his produce with that of other small farmers, sharing with them in credit arrangements which can be secured on the crop without having to deliver it, and to be protected from having to market all of his crop at the most unfavorable time of the year.

Third, a uniform set of agricultural laws for the equitable protection of farmers from political and economic uncertainties must be enacted. Laws are needed for the further clarification of water rights, equity rights on land and the survey and registration of land, for the correction of taxation abuses and the regulation of rents and credits.

A fourth problem to be met at governmental levels is the problem of landownership. While tenantry, with its concomitant social difficulties, is as much a symptom of overpopulation and a result of poverty as it is a cause of poverty, this problem in many specific situations is important, and the burden it places on millions of farmers, particularly those operating small farms, is heavy. The fundamental solution of this problem can be achieved only when large numbers of farmers now forced to cultivate small farms are shifted off the land and into other productive occupations. Nevertheless, in the period of transition, while the pressure of population on the farm area is being lessened, relief must be provided for tenant farmers who now carry an unreasonable burden of rent. In addition to the provision for cheap farm credit, the laws limiting the amount of rent landlords may charge, both of which have long been on the statute books of the Central Government, must be implemented. It seems clear that one of the reforms that can be credited to the Communists in many of the parts of the country they controlled during the war years was the forced reduction of rents. They seem now, however, to have abandoned this mild reform policy and to have returned to a radical program of land division.

A fifth, and vital, problem is that until peace comes to China as a whole there is not much that can be done to give any farmer the security necessary for rapid agricultural progress, particularly with regard to financial security. All through Chinese history periods of civil strife and political unrest have been characterized by investment in land as preferable to investment in movable goods, which can be damaged or destroyed, a procedure that is indicative of the struggle for survival continually faced by Chinese families and made even more acute during civil war. While the ownership of land can be expropriated by a political regime, roving bandits have not yet learned how to carry it away with them. During such periods of strife there are always thousands of bands of roving brigands who conform to no political ideology but who constitute one of the great risks of the countryside, even to the poorest farmer. To escape this pillaging all people who can possibly do so buy land with their ready cash, thereby forcing up interest rates and tenantry. Peace and the maintenance of law and order throughout the whole country are necessary prerequisites to the successful operation of any system of farm security, but particularly for farm credits and rent control. In the complex, highly competitive, and overcrowded countryside, the prosecution of a relentless class war by the Communists is bound to bring more loss and misery to the people of China than the political reforms they propose can possibly pay for in real improvement.

Ultimately the solution of the problem of tenantry or any of the other problems having to do with poverty and production is dependent upon the development of real democracy among the people. The people themselves must have clear-cut and effective political machinery whereby they may protect themselves against political corruption and unjust extortion now all too frequent. Indeed, liberal, democratic machinery must be set up and made to function if any of the far-reaching changes outlined here are ever to be carried out.

New and extensive educational and administrative programs also are essential to so broad a program, and the Central Government is now in the process of creating the administrative facilities and training programs. At the invitation of Generalissimo Chiang K'ai-shek, a joint commission on agriculture known as the China-United States Agricultural Mission completed in 1946 a five-month intensive study of agricultural needs and problems in fourteen provinces and in Taiwan (Formosa). The commission consisted of ten outstanding American agriculturists headed by Dr. Claude Burton Hutchison, dean of the College of Agriculture and vice-president of the University of California, and thirteen Chinese agricultural experts appointed by the Chinese Government. It included such outstanding authorities on Chinese agriculture as Raymond T. Moyer and John Lossing Buck. The commission concluded its report to the Chinese Government with the following proposals:

"1. That an integrated program of agricultural instruction, research, and extension be developed by the Ministry of Agriculture and Forestry and the Ministry of Education working together which would function through six central research bureaus located at the capital, nine strong regional centers situated in the main agricultural areas of the country, and appropriate agencies of the province and *hsien*.

"2. That action be taken (a) to provide more adequate farm credit and at lower cost; (b) to assist farmers in marketing their products; (c) to improve the conditions of tenancy wherever serious problems now exist; and (d) to provide for a better balanced and more equitable system of land taxation.

"3. That there be established a single government-sponsored bank to serve agricultural credit needs, to be known as the Agricultural Bank, somewhat comparable to the Farm Credit Administration of the United States.

"4. That there be established in the Ministry of Agriculture and Forestry a National Agricultural Regulatory Administration to enforce standardization and market regulations governing agricultural products.

"5. That increased emphasis be placed on the construction of chemical fertilizer plants; on the development of irrigation; on the improvement of plants and animals and their protection from insects and diseases; on reforestation and the scientific management of present forest stands; on the production of fruits, vegetables, and livestock to improve diets and nutrition; and on statistical services to provide current information on crop and livestock production and the market situation.

"6. That definite measures be initiated immediately to encourage the export of important agricultural commodities now being seriously restricted through the present currency exchange rate, the high costs of inland transportation, and inadequate and expensive credit.

"7. And finally that the Government of China give serious consideration to ways of solving the problem created by pressure of population on the relatively limited agricultural resources of the nation which, unless eased, could offset the benefits of increased agricultural production and industrial development if the present trend toward population increase continues."

Chinese agricultural production can be expanded, but this expansion is dependent upon achieving the following:

1. At least half the present farm population must be

shifted to other means of production, thereby making possible an increase in farm size and a resulting improvement in economic efficiency.

2. Biotechnological methods must be modernized and improved so that production per acre can be doubled.

3. Mechanical methods must be developed to accomplish full production with fewer workers.

4. Social and political changes must be carried out to provide the farmer with adequate low-cost farm credit and necessary protection from injustices and unsettled conditions.

5. A vast educational and research program must be carried out to supply the farmer with the knowledge and the specialized materials that he will need in applying new and improved farm methods.

Chapter XIII

Industrial Consequences

As has been indicated, success in providing the Chinese villages with adequate sanitation depends on a related series of improvements in agriculture. The success of these improvements, in turn, depends on basic industrial developments. For the past twenty years a controversy has raged among Chinese trained in modern methods as to the relative importance of agricultural development and industrialization as factors in "national reconstruction." One group, perhaps a majority, has developed an almost mystical faith in industrialization as the answer to most if not all of China's problems. Certainly industry has a vast contribution to make, but developed alone it cannot raise standards of living. Industry and agriculture are mutually dependent. Industrialization must be brought about in a manner which will permit industry to play its basic part in the solution of China's agricultural problems, while agricultural problems must be solved in order to create the higher living standards necessary for the accumulation of industrial capital and the growth of an industrial market.

It is, therefore, necessary to examine the implications for industry of the problems of sanitation and agriculture as well as the direct contributions that industry must make to the rebuilding of China.

The basic needs of the agricultural community which industry must supply are, listed briefly and not necessarily in order of importance: more energy for the farm, inexpensive and efficient transportation facilities, huge quantities of fertilizers, many new insecticides and fungicides, new farm tools and machines, materials necessary for building crop-storage facilities, inexpensive and improved building materials for rehousing the farm population, and many types of new, low-cost, consumers' goods needed to improve the everyday life of the people. Industries built up to do all this must, in addition, provide productive work for that more than half of the present farm population which must be shifted from the land.

Energy for the farm must come from several sources and supply a number of needs. The basic necessity is a fuel for cooking which will permit the farmer to use his present fuel, vegetable wastes, in compost heaps. The ways in which this can be accomplished have already been outlined. In addition to fuel for the cookstove, the Chinese farm, as it increases in size and becomes more mechanized, must have engine fuel. There are scores of applications for the power produced by internal-combustion or electric motors in farm communities—irrigation water pumps, mechanical plows, seeding machines, harvesters, threshers, and the machines of home and village industries, to mention but a few. To meet these needs a dozen types of industrial enterprises must be developed, ranging from mines to engine plants and oil refineries.

Furthermore, the production of the fertilizers, insecticides, and fungicides needed by Chinese agriculture will require the development of a vast chemical industry. And beyond the needs of agriculture lies the whole field of drugs for men and animals.

Over and over again the problem of transportation has appeared in the consideration of one or another phase of the problem of agricultural improvements. The importance of adequate transportation to the development of stable markets for agricultural products is illustrated by the situation that existed in the Chinese wheat market before the war. The big flour mills in Shanghai, and even those at Tientsin in the middle of the wheat region, bought large quantities of Canadian and American wheat. Foreign wheat was imported not because there was no Chinese wheat but because it was more economical to depend on the standardized North American market and reliable ocean transportation than to buy in the local Chinese market. This was true in spite of the fact that the existing railroads were functioning quite efficiently.

Poor local transportation, lack of standardized agricultural grades, and a scarcity of railroad facilities for handling grain on a large scale were factors in making it more profitable for Chinese millers to use foreign grain. If a Shanghai mill needed a few hundred thousand bushels of Chinese wheat, there was no central market where it could be obtained quickly and easily. Millers were forced to send agents into the wheat-growing areas to make thousands of small, individual purchases. Arrangements had to be made to have these thousands of individual lots of grain delivered to the railway. Frequently there was no covered storage space at the small stations where the grain was gathered. It was essential that a guard ride with the grain to protect it from pilferers along the way. When the wheat finally reached the mill a further expense was necessary before it could be milled. It had to be cleaned of the quantities of small stones swept up from the threshing floors and left by hand winnowing. Threshing machinery and an effective system of local and nation-wide storage and transportation facilities are necessary before Chinese wheat can move to market and obtain the same high prices that the modern millers are willing to pay for clean, efficiently shipped, North American wheat.

During the war, air transportation developed so rapidly that today passenger transportation from one part of China to another is relatively efficient and simple, but freight haulage is a different matter. Since the fundamental need is cheap bulk transportation, no matter what airlines may accomplish in handling passenger and high-priced, low-weight express traffic, railroads are the number one problem.

Between 1866 and 1942 China constructed only 12,036 miles of railways. Eight of the original twenty-six provinces are entirely without rail service. Before the war China had 27 miles of rails per million population, Japan 190, Great Britain 437, and the United States 1,940. For every 100,000 square miles China had 274 miles of track, Japan 9,120, Great Britain 21,360, and the United States 7,970. During the war China's 12,036 miles of track were reduced to about six thousand miles of functioning railway, with another 1,500 miles of new construction in the interior not yet ready for use. Since V-J day civil war has destroyed several thousand additional miles.

In *China's Struggle for Railway Development*, former Minister of Communications Chang Kia-ngau suggests that China must, in addition to restoring old lines, build 14,300 miles of new tracks. He proposes a 10-year program, divided into two stages. During the first 5-year period, Dr. Chang proposes construction of about seven thousand miles of railway to connect the political and military centers and to aid in the development of essential mineral resources. During the second 5-year period the emphasis would be on the development of frontier and coastal provinces and the opening of new overland routes to neighboring countries. It is estimated that the construction of these 14,300 miles of new railways would require about US$350 million worth of new material and equipment, much of which must come from abroad. However, in preparing these estimates, Dr. Chang assumed that much of the Manchurian industrial plant would be recovered intact after World War II, and that a large quantity of new material and equipment could be manufactured in China. Unfortunately, the Manchurian industrial plant has been either moved to Russia or destroyed by civil war.

Dr. Chang's hope for 14,300 miles of new rails is actually a modest one. His goal is far short of the 100,000 miles minimum trackage advocated just after World War I by Dr. Sun Yat-sen in his *International Development of China.* In fact any industrial development adequate to the needs of a rising standard of living for the Chinese people will require a railway network much larger than that suggested by either Dr. Chang or Dr. Sun. Dr. Chang's plan, however, represents a sound first step.

In addition to the construction of between 100,000 and 200,000 miles of railways, China must expand vastly her system of highways. At present there are about 75,000 miles of roads and highways of all descriptions. During World War II, 3,742 miles of new highway were built and 15,252 miles of existing highways were improved in free China alone, while the Japanese built an extensive system of new roads in occupied territory. Most of these highways, however, are far from being first-class arteries. Many of those which connect the hsien of North China are no better than second-grade farm-to-market rural roads, and in the mountainous parts of Central and Western China there are many hundreds of hsien cities of 20,000 to 25,000 people with no roads whatsoever. The total highway mileage needed to place even half of China's villages within a mile or two of an improved road is so enormous that a realistic estimate is virtually impossible.

Moreover, there is an enormous need for expanded transportation facilities even where roads and highways now exist. Automotive equipment must be almost totally replaced. Even before the war buses and trucks which traveled the improved roads of North China were unbelievably crowded. Buses commonly carried overflow passengers on every square foot of their roofs, and cargo trucks loaded people on top of freight. After the war, the infrequent buses that ground along the streets of modern Shanghai were so crowded that windows were used as exits and so broken down that, once stopped, passengers often had to push to start them again.

Of the river and coastal shipping that played a large part in the transportation of goods before the war more than 90 per cent was destroyed during the fighting either by Japanese bombs or by American bombing and submarine action against ships captured by the Japanese. China has made a beginning in restoring her shipping tonnage by purchases of American surplus property, and the Ming Sung Industrial Company alone has placed orders with American and Canadian shipbuilders for nearly US$20 million worth of river and coastal steamers. With other companies planning similar restoration, shipping facilities can be expanded to meet the growing needs of a developing industrialization. In addition to the ships themselves, docks, piers, and godowns must be constructed. Because port facilities were major targets during the war (the aim of American bombardiers was phenomenally accurate at Shanghai in particular), because building materials were practically unobtainable, and because economic, political, and social problems interfered, shipping in and out of China was still difficult more than two years after the war. Ships, lined up for miles in the Whangpoo River at Shanghai, waited for weeks to discharge cargo at the few remaining wharves, paying heavily for the privilege. Even after finally being unloaded, goods crowded insufficient godowns to the bursting point, where they remained endlessly waiting for the broken-down transportation facilities to carry them away.

Transportation, then, a requisite for further industrial development, is now completely inadequate. A modest railroad development is at least planned, and the development of water transportation has gone beyond the planning stage to actual orders for equipment. Gradually, transportation facilities will be built up, but until internal peace comes not rapidly enough to meet the urgent need of China's rebuilding.

In addition to those which will provide China's agriculture with fuel, fertilizers, farm machines, and transportation, industries are needed which can produce building materials. As a health problem the need for a new inexpensive flooring material has already been mentioned. There is, actually, a real necessity for the many types of inexpensive building materials required to make possible the complete rehousing of the rural population. Similarly, adequate protection for stored grain crops already has created a demand for a vast number of modern elevators. Ferroconcrete grain-storage structures so designed that much of the construction could be carried out by village people under the guidance of trained foremen using local sand and gravel, requiring only cement and reinforcing metal from outside the community, could be built in enormous numbers. Such granaries would bring an immediate return by saving grain now destroyed by insects and rodents. Among the building materials needed, therefore, are cement and steel.

Thus, although the solution of agricultural problems depends on the development of a wide range of new industries, the process of industrialization, on the other hand, must make an immense direct contribution toward raising standards of living.

China's new industrial development must be so designed as to be capable of producing great quantities of low-cost, good quality, consumers' goods, controlled by the same type of standardization regulations that were advocated for agricultural products. With any expansion in agricultural productivity, and with the shift of population from the land into other types of productive activity, the buying power of the individual will rise. This increased buying power will automatically create a demand for thousands of new products. Shoes serve as an excellent example. In many cases, the eventual cost of wearing cloth shoes is actually more than that of leather shoes, but the individual cannot afford the cash required to buy a pair of leather shoes. Therefore every few months he pays a smaller amount for a pair made of cloth. With adequate transportation to bring hides from the Mongolian plateau and with further extensions of the rapidly developing leather industry, it should be possible for China to provide enough low-cost leather shoes for a large proportion of the population. And so it is with many other products.

Already the beginnings of a number of industries have shown how the production of the industrial worker can contribute to a higher standard of living both for the worker and for other elements in the population. The processes by which this takes place are too well known to Western peoples to need elaborating. In China, as industrial development takes place, those who are themselves engaged in industry will become a significant element in the developing market that permits further expansions of industrial production. The combined demands of both rural and urban populations for goods coupled with a growing productivity on the farm and in the factory must provide the driving force that will make the development of a vast industrial operation possible.

Can all these developments in industry provide a living for the 30 million families, about 180 million people, that must be moved from the farms if the farm size is to go up? Can industry absorb them in addition to the 100 million urban population that already depends on nonagricultural pursuits for livelihood? And what about the additional population that is likely to come into being? Can standards of living be raised for all these people? To what levels must industry be developed to make a significant contribution?

INDUSTRIAL CONSEQUENCES

Let us assume that China builds a capital manufacturing plant which equals that of the United States in 1926–1929 in size and output. This would mean an output of manufactured goods, exclusive of food products, valued at US$40 billion at 1926–1929 price levels. This level of manufacturing, added to the potential agricultural production outlined in the preceding chapter and to the mining, commerce, transportation, public utilities, and personal services that such an expansion of the economy would bring into being, would result in a total national income of about US$85 billion.

A national income of $85 billion would provide a per capita income of $170 for a population of 500 million people. It would provide $130 for each of 650 million, but only $106 each for a population of 800 million. That is, *if* China can develop her agriculture and her industrialization to a level that will produce a national income of $85 billion, and *if* she can keep her total population below 650 million, the average per capita income of her people can reach US$130. The per capita income of the people of the United States averaged $654 after taxes in 1929, and was about $860, 1929 buying power, late in 1947. Since the estimated per capita income of the people of China in the years just before the outbreak of the war was US$20, the development of a capital plant equal to that of the United States in 1929 would raise the present standard of living more than 600 per cent and provide a level of income about equal to that of Italy before the war. Such a standard of living is only 20 per cent of that of the United States in 1929.

The two *ifs* in this assumption are huge. The problem of population control will be considered in the next chapter, the problem of industry here.

Can China hope to develop and maintain an industrial plant as large and as productive as the one which the United States had just before the depression of 1929? Two fundamentals must be considered before answering this question. First, does China have the basic natural resources to build and run such a plant? Second, can she raise the capital it will require?

China's position in relation to coal is patently favorable. According to 1936 estimates, China's coal reserves amount to 236,068,000,000 metric tons. Of the approximately 7 trillion metric tons of coal reserves known to exist, the United States ranks first with $3\frac{1}{2}$ trillion, the Soviet Union second with $1\frac{1}{2}$ trillion tons, Canada third with 1 trillion, and China fourth with $\frac{1}{4}$ of a trillion tons. Moreover, China's coal is widely distributed, with deposits known to exist in every province. The major coal beds, containing four-fifths of China's known coal resources and forming one of the world's largest coal fields, are located in Shansi and Shensi provinces, but the three coastal provinces, Shantung, Hopei, and Liaoning also have extensive reserves running into several billion tons. During the war years additional coal fields were opened in Szechuan, Yünnan, and Kweichow provinces.

Coal production thus far has been largely limited to the most accessible places rather than the most productive because of the lack of adequate transportation. During the war years, the Japanese expanded Manchurian production, particularly at Fushun, where an open-cut mine operates on the thickest bed of bituminous coal in the world. Although this mine has been taken over by the Chinese government, its production is seriously hampered by civil war.

The peacetime production of coal in China reached 30 million tons in the year just before the war, an average per capita consumption of 150 pounds per year. Japan consumes 1,000 pounds per person annually, and the United States 8,000 pounds per person. In 1944 Chinese coal production reached 50 million tons,* of which 44 million were produced

* Wang Kung-ping and Thomas T. Read, *"Controlling Factors in China's Coal Development,"* Pacific Affairs, June, 1946.

by Japanese and puppet governments in occupied areas and only 6 million tons in free China.

Production of coal is low in China, even during periods more nearly resembling peace, and even in accessible places where transportation is available. The average production under such favorable circumstances has been 0.3 of a ton per worker per day, compared with a 0.93 ton average production per worker in European mines and 5.1 tons per worker in American mines. Aside from political upheaval and lack of surface transportation, there are many causes of low production per man. One was pointed out to me by Mr. Cheng, the manager and chief engineer of the T'ien Fu Mining Company of Szechuan. He told me that the use of compressed air hammers and drills designed and produced for American miners resulted in a lower efficiency when used by Chinese miners than could be obtained when using tools specially designed for them. The average Chinese miner, averaging 115 pounds, is too light to handle heavy American tools. This does not necessarily mean that Chinese miners are underfed or ill-treated, for the workers at the T'ien Fu mine (in marked contrast to many Chinese mines) were well housed, well fed and, by Chinese economic standards, well paid. Mr. Cheng believes that tools 20 per cent lighter in weight would increase the efficiency of Chinese miners.

Another major cause for low production is inefficiency of underground transportation. Production in the T'ien Fu mine during the war, Mr. Cheng said, could have been doubled had he been able to install even a simple system of towline transportation for moving his underground coal trucks. The blockade that deprived the T'ien Fu mine of equipment, however, is not the usual drawback, for most Chinese mines are poorly equipped because of both lack of capital and lack of modern technical leadership.

Production in mines operated by old indigenous methods is also held down by the prevailing system of employment and wages. By tradition, an accepted "squeeze" of 10 to 20 per cent of the miner's wages is withheld by the labor contractor, providing this venal gentleman with a large return while the individual laborer receives so little that he lacks incentive to produce efficiently.

Both labor and management are trying to abolish the evils that have grown up in Chinese mine practice. The war and inflation have, in this respect, been beneficial. Skilled mine labor was so valuable that it became necessary for operators to provide adequate housing, reasonably good food, medical care, and substantial wages to keep laborers on the job. If these trends continue, and the individual has an increasing voice in deciding working conditions, mine production will improve materially.

Wang and Read estimate that even with technical improvements it will require a working force half again as large as that of America in order to produce in China 100 million tons of coal each year as compared with an American production of 500 to 600 million tons. To achieve the desired industrial status, China must employ $1\frac{1}{4}$ million miners who can dig 750 million tons of coal per year. When this is accomplished, Chinese miners will be producing at an efficiency about equal to that of European miners, but still only one-fifth that of American mine labor.

China is unfortunate in her position as regards oil. While small oil fields have recently been developed in Kansu province, the total production is still minuscule when measured either by world output or by China's needs. It is still too early to estimate the amount of reserves in the Kansu field, but thus far experts have not permitted themselves to grow overly enthusiastic about it. China does have some oil shale, and fuel for internal-combustion motors can be extracted by hydrogenization and cracking processes, but both the cost and the amount that can be produced are limiting factors. Under war pressure, fuel was produced from shale both by Chinese in free China and by the Japanese in Manchuria, but such production was engendered by necessity rather than economy.

For the purposes of this discussion it may be said that whatever oil China does have will ease the severity of the problem of energy as we outline it, but that it is not now known to be significant enough to justify including it in the main argument. And in spite of the fact that China's potential hydroelectric power is at least five times that of present-day American installations, her coal reserves are the main source of energy that must be depended upon to provide for her industrialization.

Considering the problem in terms of tons of coal, then, the amount of coal China would have to consume each year if she had a total national income of about $85 billion can be estimated. As has been shown, to do this she would have to have a capital plant about the size of that in the United States. Taking the amounts of energy that the American economy is using at present in terms of its coal equivalent* the following deductions can be made:

Industrial plants: The total energy consumed annually in American industrial plants is equal to about 170 million tons of coal. China would have to consume an equal amount. Since technological developments can be expected to continue in the field of energy production and use it is fair to assume that 170 million tons of coal will provide enough energy for an industrial plant as large as that which the United States had in 1926–1929 and have a margin of safety left over.

Railroads: American railroads now consume the equivalent of 156 million tons of coal each year. This amount operates about 240,000 miles of main-line track. If it is assumed that 140,000 miles of main-line track will provide China with an equally adequate railway system in view of the

* Cf. *Fortune* magazine, March, 1947.

fact that her population is concentrated in an area about half the size of continental United States, and if it is assumed that by the time such a system is in operation it will be equipped with coal-burning gas turbine engines with an efficiency of about 20 per cent as compared with not more than 5 per cent for the steam locomotives now in use in this country, it may be estimated that 60 million tons per year will be adequate to operate China's railway system.

Retail deliveries: Fuel for use in homes amounts to about 152 million tons of coal in the United States. If the per capita home consumption of fuel in China does not rise above one-fifth of that of the United States, and if China's population levels off at about 650 million, then China must consume 143 million tons each year. This rate of consumption will be a considerable improvement over present levels of fuel use and would more than provide for the needs of farm cooking. With houses redesigned to trap as much radiant heat as possible, the level of comfort will be considerably higher than it now is. Even so, the Chinese will always have to dress more warmly than Americans and, in the north, will need to keep themselves hardened to cold.

Coke: China will have to plan to operate her total industrial plant on about half the amount of coke now consumed in the United States. This she can do because she will not use so much steel in the production of automobiles, and will substitute the new lighter metals and plastics for steel in many other products. To produce half the amount of coke used in the United States, she will require 47.5 million tons of coal.

Public utilities: The total energy used in providing public utilities will have to equal that used in this country, 148 million tons. This level of consumption, however, would permit the individual only one-fifth as much benefit as the average American now gets. It will be necessary to develop hydroelectric power to the fullest extent possible. The total amount of energy provided from water power can exceed the coal tonnage needed for public utilities. Much of it will go into industrial plants.

Motor fuel: China will be unable to consume motor fuel in the lavish manner of America. In part this will be due to the fact that China has no extensive oil reserves, and in part to the fact that she cannot afford to burn up her coal reserves too rapidly. Since she will be unable to afford the amount of personal transportation and pleasure driving prevalent in America, she will be able to supply her necessary motor fuel by the use of about one-third the coal tonnage equivalent to the motor fuel consumed in America. Full advantage will have to be taken of all advances in motor design. Low horsepower, low fuel consumption motors such as are typical of British cars will have to provide the power for Chinese cars and trucks.

She will undoubtedly import a good deal of petroleum and petroleum products until the chemical treatment of coal has been developed to provide gasoline and other oils in quantity. China will need much less motor fuel for her farms than is used in America since, even with considerable mechanization of agriculture, 13-acre farms will not require as much power as larger farms. Also, in the wet south the water buffalo is not likely to be displaced in rice culture. One hundred sixteen million tons of coal should provide a sufficient annual equivalent of motor fuel.

Other petroleum: The United States is now consuming the equivalent of another 486.4 million tons of coal as non-motor fuel petroleum products. Estimating that China will have to consume half this amount, another 243.2 tons of coal equivalent must be added to her fuel consumption.

Natural gas: The United States is using natural gas to supply the equivalent of 254.5 million tons of coal. Again we have a category that China will have to restrict as far as she can. Allowing a consumption of one-third that of the

United States, another 84.8 million tons of coal will be added annually.

Totaling all the tonnages listed under the eight types of fuel use, China, by careful planning and by eliminating much of the luxury use of energy in heating buildings and homes and in personal automobile transportation, etc., can operate an industrial plant as large as that now being operated by the United States on about 1,000 million tons of coal a year. She will be able to do this in part because she will be forced to continue to use men for many tasks for which we use machines. Such continued manual labor will be forced upon her by a population which, it is estimated, will have grown to at least 650 million by the time she has raised her industrial production to the level America attained in 1926–1929.

From this 1,000 million tons of coal energy must be subtracted that portion which can be supplied by hydroelectric power. Since China is capable of providing hydroelectric energy equivalent to an estimated 250 million tons of coal each year, a remainder of 750 million tons must be mined and consumed to provide a standard of living equal to that of Italy in 1926–1929. From the point of view of need to meet production this is a minimal figure, but from the point of view of China's reserves it is a maximum figure. It must be maximum because consuming at the rate of 750 million tons per year China's known coal reserves would last only about three hundred years, a short span in which to reduce her population and to find new sources of energy.

It is obvious, therefore, that China must plan to develop her coal in the most economical and effective way possible. She must keep well abreast of the newest methods of coal technology. Since it seems likely that a veritable revolution in the mining and utilization of coal is now beginning in America, it is probable that the results of new methods may serve China in helping her use her coal more efficiently than

America has used hers thus far. Certainly by the time China is ready for rapid and large-scale development of her energy resources it may be hoped that these new processes will have been proved and that they will be as effective as they now seem to give promise of being.

There is, therefore, enough energy available to make possible the development of an industrial economy equal to that attained in the United States in 1926–1929.

In addition to basic energy production, China must expand her metal industries. Although she is moderately well endowed with metal resources, China's delay in applying the industrial revolution has its advantages, for the iron of the eighteenth century and the steel of the nineteenth century account for much of the technical progress of the Western world, a progress now shifting in the twentieth century to the use of aluminum, aluminum alloys, and the lighter metals. China, relatively deficient in iron ores, does possess a quantity of the lighter metals now replacing steel.

However, the fundamental metal for the development of Chinese industry remains, for the present, iron and the steel that can be made from it. China has small, widely scattered deposits of iron ores, but only a few large deposits of high quality. Good ore deposits are located in the central Yangtze valley, in Hopei and Anhwei provinces, from which ore has been taken for the past several decades to the blast furnaces of Japan at the rate of nearly a million tons a year. Although these high-grade ore deposits are situated far from beds of good coking coal, it seems probable that there may well be a considerable development of iron and steel production in the central Yangtze area. A second deposit of good ore is found in North China, about 150 miles northwest of Peiping. China's largest iron ore deposits are those of southern Manchuria. The metallic content is low and the resultant metallurgical problem complicated, but under Japanese management, the blast furnaces of Manchuria reached a capacity of almost four million metric tons of pig iron in 1942. On the other hand, the Szechuan iron resources in free China that were tapped during the war contained so much sulphur and phosphorus that even unusual metallurgical methods produced brittle steels.

With a known iron ore reserve of only 1,302,600,000 tons, or enough ore to produce a little over 600 million tons of pig iron, a program of iron and steel development which by 1980 would be producing at an average rate of 30 million tons of pig iron, built up from a rate of only 2 million tons average for the years 1950–1960, would completely exhaust iron ore reserves by the end of this century. Such a rate of development for the iron and steel industry would result in an average annual production of about 50 million tons of steel by 1990 and would provide enough steel for building a capital plant equal to that attained in the United States by 1926–1929. To keep going beyond that point China would have to rely on future technological developments and external sources.

First, she would have to depend on improvements in methods of iron and steel production which would make it possible for her to use deposits of iron that are now considered too low grade to be classed as ores. Second, she would have to plan to import iron ore from the Philippines to stretch her own supplies. Third, she would have to plan to buy scrap steel from more highly industrialized countries. Fourth, she would have to use other metals and plastics wherever possible to substitute for steel. Finally, it may be that now-unknown deposits of ore will be found. By all these means China can produce the iron and steel that can at least build up a basic capital plant which will make possible the level of industrialization being used here as an attainable goal.

China is blessed with only one of the ferroalloys—tungsten—of which she has a large percentage of the world's supply. Ore reserves from which tungsten is refined are estimated at 1,647,500 metal tons. China still holds first place in world production, producing 22 per cent of the world's output, and at times has supplied the major part of the world market.

There is a small production of manganese in Kwangsi province and in Manchuria, and reserves are adequate for domestic needs, but deposits of nickel, chromium, molybdenum, and vanadium appear to be lacking. Mercury is mined from an ample supply in Kweichow and Hunan provinces.

Next to iron, tin is China's most valuable metal. Chinese tin was of such value to the Allied war effort in World War II that many thousand tons of the metal were flown out "over the Hump" into India at a time when transportation facilities were at their lowest ebb. Out of a total national production of 17,278 metric tons in 1940, Yünnan province produced 13,340. The supply of tin reserves in Yünnan alone is estimated at one million metric tons and another half million tons may be deposited in Kwangsi, Kiangsi, and other provinces.

Of the nonferrous metals, China's greatest limitation is her relatively small supply of copper. Although she has been refining and working copper for more than twenty-five hundred years, total reserves are inadequate for the needs of an industrialized nation. During the year 1940, only about 1,500 metric tons of copper were produced, 1,078 metric tons in free China and the remainder in Japanese-occupied territory. Known deposits did not exceed 200,000 tons in all provinces prior to the recent discovery of new deposits in Sikang province estimated to contain 1,824,000 metric tons. While Sikang is relatively isolated, it is not too far from great potential water-power sites.

Aluminum is now being produced in very small quantities, but there are large reserves of bauxite available in the provinces of Liaoning, Shantung, Yünnan, and Kansu, totaling at least one billion tons, and the recent discovery of large and unsurveyed bauxite deposits in Kweichow province, near enough to the site of the proposed Yangtze dam to be served by electric power, holds hope for greater production. The Liaoning deposits are known to have a 50 per cent aluminum content (the Japanese took advantage of this possession during the war to produce quantities of aluminum). If China can produce it cheaply and in sufficiently large quantities, aluminum will help offset the limitations imposed on industry by the lack of copper and the relatively poor supply of iron ore.

Antimony is one of the three minerals (the other two being tin and tungsten) with which China is bountifully endowed. Before the war she was producing regularly over 19,000 tons of antimony a year, representing about 20 per cent of the world's production, exceeded in volume only by Bolivia and Mexico. This production was largely from Hunan province, where the ore reserves amount to almost a million and a half tons.

China possesses adequate quantities of sulphur in nearly every province, and her annual output of more than 5,000 tons can probably be expanded to keep pace with her growing economy. She also produces large quantities of salt from the wells of the southwest, the salt lakes of the northwest, and from sea water, but the production of salt also must be increased to provide China with an adequate and cheap supply for her industrialization, especially her fisheries.

Of the other major basic resources, China is probably weakest in lumber supplies. In many parts of the country, lumber for building materials is scarce and expensive, and much of that used before World War II came from Southeast Asia, the Philippines, and the American Northwest. China does not have forest reserves sufficient to supply the quantities of lumber and pulp required by a modern industrial civilization, but it is possible that developments in the fields of ceramics, glass, and plastics will provide substitutes.

Although the description of China as a geographic area endowed with tremendous mineral resources has been commonly exaggerated, and although technical problems in the development of many of her mineral deposits place definite difficulties in the path of China's industry, her total of natural resources appears sufficient to supply the raw materials for the development of an industrial plant as large as that of the United States in 1929. But can China accumulate the capital plant necessary for such development?

According to estimates made by the National Resources Commission of the Chinese Government, the national income in 1933 amounted to 27 billion prewar Chinese dollars, or approximately 9 billion U.S. dollars. Since it may be assumed, in view of the predominantly hand nature of both the agriculture and the industry of China, that the annual production is somewhere near the total value of the capital plant, the total plant now in existence, including agriculture, industry, transportation, and communications, may be something between 9 and 12 billion U.S. dollars.

Further, it may be assumed that the average annual product over the next fifty years will be about 1 dollar for every 2 invested in capital plant—a defensible assumption based on the fact that in highly industrialized America the annual product is 1 dollar for every 3.9 invested in all types of productive activity.* (The proportion of capital is much less in other industrial countries. In all probability the ratio of product to capital in China is about 1 to 1 now, and, by the time the development of a modern industrial plant is completed, it may well be above the average 1-to-2 figure assumed here. However, in order to simplify the method of

* According to the League of Nations publication *Industrialization and Foreign Trade*.

estimating the capital investment requirement for the development of China's capital plant a 1-to-2 ratio will be used here.)

Second, an average 15 per cent of the annual production may be assumed to be capital goods, and, therefore, the rate of reinvestment in all types of plant including dwellings and farm equipment will average 15 per cent of the annual production. This is the average rate at which the United States enlarged and repaired its capital plant between the years 1920 and 1939. The actual yearly rate fluctuated widely as, undoubtedly, the rate in China will, but again the assumption is workable since it was attained in the United States.

Finally, it may be assumed that the Chinese will use their capital plant in such a way that it will require forty years for it to be worn out, an annual depreciation rate of 2.5 per cent. This assumption seems justified in view of the great care that the Chinese use in the upkeep of most of their equipment and their tendency to use everything long past the time it would be scrapped in other countries.

With these assumptions, and starting with an estimated national income of $9 billion in 1950, by 1960 the national income would rise to $14.3 billion and the capital plant would be worth about $30 billion. By 1970 the total production would reach about $23 billion, and the capital plant would be worth $46 billion. Continuing at this same rate of expansion, the capital plant would reach $75 billion and the total production about $36 billion in 1980. By this time the volume of investment would have grown so that both capital plant and production would start making considerable increases each year. By 1990 the total new investment in capital plant would be approximately $8.7 billion with a value at the end of the year of nearly $122 billion and an annual production of more than $58 billion. By 1995 capital plant would be worth $154 billion and production would be at the rate of $73.5 billion. By the end of the century, plant will have reached a value of $195 billion and production will have attained the level of $93 billion. This would represent the attainment by the Chinese of that standard of living here set as an attainable goal, always provided that the population does not grow too fast, and provided that an average rate of 15 per cent of national income can be reinvested in capital plant.

From the very outset it seems improbable that the Chinese economy will be able to reinvest 15 per cent of its product in new capital plant. This is the one assumption in this theoretical calculation of how China might capitalize herself that seems to me to be impossible to attain, for in 1950 she would have to invest $1.35 billion out of a total national income of only $9 billion. I don't believe there is that much blood in the turnip. But there is a way in which this rate of new investment can be attained: by borrowing abroad and by attracting foreign capital to China. Furthermore, since most of this capital will be invested in fundamental enterprises that will produce a high return considerably in excess of the $1 of annual return for each $2 of new plant which has been assumed, the investment of $1 billion of outside capital a year for ten or fifteen years can do much toward catalyzing the reaction that will start the process by which 15 per cent of the national income in later years can be plowed back into capital plant. In other words, it is possible for China to attain the rate of industrial development suggested here with the help of the more advanced industrial peoples. Both the United States and Canada built up their present plants with the aid of large investments by British and other European capital. If China can do the same thing, such a development will be to the advantage of the entire world.

Foreign capital, however, either as loans to the government or as investments, will avoid China until she has political stability. American Government policy in withholding the $500 million loan long earmarked for China is an indication that we are reluctant to risk such sums in a country torn by civil strife. Yet America cannot afford to stand quietly by and watch China founder economically.

This problem, in turn, raises the question of another dilemma of Chinese policy. Is she to industrialize primarily by means of private enterprise, or is her industrialization to be carried out by government? China herself has been saying that she intends to follow a combination of these two types of development, with heavy basic industry the prerogative of government while private enterprise is encouraged to develop lighter industries. The chief reason given for this division is that, whereas private organizations alone would have difficulty in obtaining the huge sums needed for the development of heavy industry, a government would be better able to float long-term loans. Furthermore, those dealing with these problems have determined that China shall not again be caught as unprepared to defend herself as she was in 1937. Under the impetus of the plan to develop heavy industry through government, the National Resources Commission immediately after World War II assumed control of a wide range of industries, both light and heavy, that were formerly operated by the Japanese and their puppets in occupied China. In fact there was much complaint that an overeager bureaucracy took over much more than was planned. The term "bureaucratic capitalism" was coined by the press to describe the wholesale appropriation of industry by the government.

In February, 1947, when an attempt was made to control soaring inflation, this policy of too much government operation of industry was reversed, and it was announced that all government holdings except in heavy industry would be sold to private companies. It now appears that private enterprise may be given much wider scope for development.

Quite aside from any considerations of class or special interest, the problem of how best to develop China's industry quickly and efficiently is a knotty and difficult one. It is true that no private enterprise can hope to match a stabilized government in assuming responsibility for long-term loans. At the same time it is also true that government operations in the name of social necessity, but subject to political intrigue, are frequently inefficient. The relative inefficiency of many government operations in countries with a long and thoroughly democratic tradition such as that of the United States, in spite of a competent civil service and years of experience in preventing waste and graft, is all too well known. Both inefficiency and graft may be expected in even greater proportion in China, where government by law is still far from realization, and where the familyistic ethics of Confucianism still sanctions to a marked degree the age-old practice of the official class in taking advantage of its traditional position to improve family welfare. When this tendency is coupled with the extreme scarcity of trained or qualified administrators and technicians, it becomes almost a mathematical certainty that government-operated industry will be inefficient. So those who honestly and earnestly plan for the welfare of the Chinese people find themselves caught between the inefficiency of government-operated industry, on the one hand, and the limitations of insecure private enterprise, on the other. It is my opinion that every industrial operation in China must be carried out under the most rigorous scrutiny to determine the efficiency of operation, for only as government-operated enterprises meet private competition without any favoritism and only as private enterprise has the support of a stable government in attracting foreign capital and making full use of modern efficient management can China succeed in her gigantic task of industrialization to meet the needs of her people. The capital for the industrialization of China can be found when there is peace within China and a policy permitting equal opportunity for both government loans and private investment. Much of this capital will have to come from the United States.

I have been outlining resources and suggesting rates at which industrial developments must be made if the standard of living of the people is to be raised. How does this picture compare with the actual situation in China today after ten years of international war and two years of postwar civil struggle? Mr. C. Yun, the director of the United States Office of the National Resources Commission of China, writing in the July, 1947, issue of the *National Reconstruction Journal*, reported that China was then producing coal at the rate of approximately 10 million tons a year and that she hoped to raise production to 30 million tons within three years. This would mean a restoration of prewar rates of production. He further reported that China has about 1 million kilowatts of installed and recoverable electric power capacity, and that she should install a further 1.5 million kilowatts within the next five years. China is now producing only 100,000 tons of steel products and 85,000 tons of fertilizer each year, but production of these items should be raised to at least 500,000 tons of steel and 700,000 tons of fertilizer as soon as possible. Indeed China has a long way to go before she will have enough industrialization to begin to make possible a decent life for her people.

Yet there are many able Chinese who are thinking about and working with these problems. One important group is in the National Resources Commission under the able leadership of Dr. Wong Wen-hao. That they are thinking realistically and effectively is indicated by the principles listed by

INDUSTRIAL CONSEQUENCES

Mr. Yun in the article mentioned above. He lists the principles that underlie future Chinese industrial developments as follow:

1. To supplement, implement, and increase the mobility of agricultural production which is the bulk of China's national wealth.

2. To balance international payments.

3. To give the common man a better living.

4. To develop natural resources and give employment equitably to people in all parts of the country.

5. To create an ever-increasing national income and at the same time to discourage overconcentration of wealth among a few.

6. To set up industries of suitable magnitude commensurate with requirements and working efficiency.

7. To strike a right balance between centralization and decentralization of management.

8. To secure efficient co-ordination between public and private enterprises.

9. To encourage foreign capital investment and participation.

10. To ensure social security and an equitable wage system.

11. To improve the working conditions of wage earners.

12. To promote co-operation between labor and management.

13. To promote industrial democracy.

14. To provide fuel and power for private initiative and spontaneous investment.

That they are also thinking soundly about what China needs now is indicated by the following list from Mr. Yun's article:

1. Fertilizer Plants
2. Animal Product Processing Plants
3. Tung Oil Refineries

4. Tungsten Ore Concentration Plants
5. Tin and Antimony Refineries
6. Electrical Manufacturing Plants
7. Mechanical Equipment Factories
8. Shipyards and Steel Fabrication Shops
9. Iron and Steel Mills
10. Cement Mills and Other Building Material Factories
11. Railroad Equipment Factories
12. Caustic Soda and Soda Ash Plants
13. Dyestuff and Plastics Factories
14. Petroleum Refineries
15. Rice and Flour Mills
16. Canneries and Food-Processing Plants
17. Pulp, Paper, and Rayon Factories

China has the natural resources that, with careful planning, can provide for the development of a capital plant and a productive capacity equal to that attained in the United States by 1929. To develop this plant and productivity she must have the help of more advanced peoples in terms of technological know-how and in capital investment. With such a plant she can provide productive work for the more than thirty million families which must be shifted from the land to permit the increase of farm size to an efficiency level that will permit agriculture to provide a better standard of living for farmers. She already has many of the men needed to start these processes and they are thinking in the right direction. One great question remains. Can all this be done in such a way and over such a period of time that the population will not outgrow all the gains that agricultural improvement and industrialization can make possible? Can China control the growth of her population?

Chapter XIV

Population Control

ALL THE PROPOSED STEPS TOWARD INDUSTRIALIZATION and increased agricultural productivity, all the processes necessary to enable China to play her logical role in a world community, all plans for her progress are and will be futile unless her population growth can be controlled. Unless her production of consumers can be held to a rate of increase slower than that of her production of goods, a rising standard of living will be impossible and her attempts at rebuilding a failure.

With China already overpopulated and faced with the necessity of industrializing, a basis both for estimating the effect of the future on her ratio of people to production and for approaching the problem of population control can be constructed only by studying the facts of population growth in countries already industrialized.

In all preindustrial, rural economies largely dependent on agriculture, the death rate as well as the birth rate is high. The introduction of modern techniques into such an economy has two immediate results: an expansion of food supply and consumers' goods which permits people to live who formerly would have died of hunger or exposure, and a rising national income which makes usable the modern medical knowledge necessary to reduce the death rate from disease. The lowered death rate is achieved largely by the reduction of infant mortality, thereby causing, a few years later, an expansion in the young adult group that further increases the population by creating a rise in total births. At the same time the customs and habits appropriate to a rural agricultural economy continue to sustain a high birth rate. In the early stages of industrialization, improved economic and medical conditions may even cause the fertility rate to rise. The result is a widening gap between births and deaths and a rapid increase in population. This rapid increase has been the first effect on population size in every country in which industrialization has taken place.

The story of Europe in the past hundred fifty years illustrates the process. Entirely aside from the many millions who emigrated, that portion of Europe's population which remained in Europe has tripled since 1800, and has doubled since 1850. The greatest growth came during the latter part of the nineteenth century and the early part of the twentieth, reaching a rate of increase of as much as 12 per thousand of population per year, or 12 per cent per decade. While the crude death rates of most European countries dropped below 20 per thousand by the late decades of the nineteenth century, birth rates did not fall below 30 until several decades later. The rate of increase thus produced was so great that had it been operating over the two thousand years since Roman times, Europe would have a population of 10 trillion persons—five thousand times that of the present population of the world. The industrial revolution and the medical revolution, which developed with it, created a rate of population increase that could not be sustained.

It was not sustained because the second effect of industrialization and rising standards of education and living began to take place. Although the drop in death rate came first, Europe's birth rate, when it did follow suit, declined more rapidly. The declining birth rate was caused by a number of factors. Among them were the delay in marriage resulting from a lengthened period of education made necessary by the demands of a more complex and skilled technology. Further, in an industrial society women became more independent economically and often chose to delay marriage or remain unmarried in the interest of a career. Moreover, as modern medical services and rising standards of economic well-being increase the certainty of survival for children, families tend to limit the number of children by the practice of birth control. In congested urban communities children become a burden rather than the economic asset they are on the farm. In Europe, all these factors made themselves felt and the birth rate fell. Now Europe has what the demographers call a "mature" population conforming to the characteristics of "incipient decline." If the birth-rate tendencies in Europe (exclusive of the U.S.R.R.) which existed between the two wars continue, by the end of the century the population will have definitely declined. Such a decline would have occurred even without the destructiveness of war. With war deaths and the effects of war on births, production, and food supply the process probably will be hastened.

The same two effects of industrialization on population have been at work in Japan. Accurate information concerning the Japanese population extends back only to 1920, when the first modern census was taken. At that time Japan had a population of 56 million. By 1940 it had grown to 73.1 million, an increase of 31 per cent. All the increase was concentrated in industrialized urban areas. In 1872, about 77 per cent of the Japanese population was engaged in agriculture, a percentage close to the present figure for China. By 1930 only 48 per cent of the Japanese were still on the farm and by 1940 the proportion had dropped to 40 per cent. Yet this apparent shift from rural to urban majorities did not result in a reduction of the total number of persons on farms. The total rural population in 1940 was about the same as it had been in 1920. The increase in urban population was the result of an over-all population increase. By the time World

War II began, Japan's birth rate had begun to decline. Industrialization, although it came later to Japan than to Europe, took sixty years to begin to lower the birth rate.

When the British finally finished taking over India in 1881, the population numbered 259 million. Since 1881 India has been free of major wars. The introduction of public health services and the development of transportation have reduced the number of deaths due to great epidemics and starvation. But the birth rate has remained high. The result is a population increased by half from 1881 to 1941, when it reached 389 million. Since 1921, with the birth rate 12.1 points higher than the death rate, the population has been increasing at the rate of 12.1 per cent each decade. If this rate of increase should continue until the end of this century, the population of India would reach 786 million. As yet, industrialization and modernization have not progressed far enough to affect the birth rate.

Populations in other Southeastern Asiatic countries where modern sanitation and public health have been introduced are increasing at rates even higher than that obtaining in India. For example, the average rate of increase in the Philippines was 20.8 per cent per decade from 1902 until 1941. In the Netherlands East Indies the rate of increase since 1920 has averaged 17.8 per cent per decade.

Against this simplified picture of the major factors that have determined population changes elsewhere, the problems of China may be considered.

It is perfectly possible for China, if industrialization and public health measures are generally applied, to attain a rate of population increase similar to that of India, a rate even higher than that of Europe during the latter half of the nineteenth and the first decades of the twentieth century.

How rapidly can the checks on population growth developed by industrialization and rising standards of living be expected to take effect in China? In England, where the industrial revolution started, more than a hundred years passed before the birth rate began to drop. In Japan sixty years were required. At best, without conscious effort to speed the process, it normally takes many decades before the natural checks on births are imposed by industrialization.

It seems certain that if the modernization of China follows the pattern set by other parts of the world, the first effect will be a vast expansion of the population. While such data as we have concerning the Chinese population in the relatively peaceful years just before 1937 indicate population growth, it is also possible that the war and the present upset conditions in China may have slowed down or even completely halted this increase. Nevertheless, population growth would be the normal trend because modern knowledge and application of medicine and public health measures begin to take effect before the alteration of mores eventually checks the birth rate. When civil fighting ceases and communications are restored, population growth will certainly begin again. It is perfectly clear that with a birth rate of 40 or more, any drop in the death rate will result in a rapid net increase of population.

China can raise her standards of living only as she applies modern knowledge to the productive processes on the farm and in the factory to the advantage of a population that stays within quite definite limits. If, in modernizing, she also increases her population at a rate similar to that of Japan, ending up with as many people on the land as there are now, then there is little hope of raising the standard of living. Farm sizes would then remain the same, in spite of the fact that a number equal to half the present population is shifted to other employment. If production per man in the rural districts does not increase sharply there will be no domestic market large enough to support an extensive industrial development. If China is to improve her standard of living she cannot afford to double her population in the process of shifting from an agricultural to an industrial economy, but if death rates are lowered as much as they have been in India, China could have a population of 800 million by the end of this century. The natural resources of China cannot possibly produce a decent standard of living for that many people. These resources will have to be worked to the limit in order to provide a standard of living that is equal to only one-sixth of the American standard in 1929 if a population increase of no more than 33 per cent takes place. The crux of the problem is the necessity of bringing about a drop in the birth rate at least as great as the drop in the death rate.

At the very outset it must be admitted that no country has yet prevented population expansion during the period of industrialization. However, no nation has ever begun to industrialize with as much knowledge available concerning industrialization and population control as is available to China. This knowledge and its application constitute the one slim hope for China's solution of the population problem. Since it is of importance to the human race and to the future of world history that she succeed, it may be worth while to compile a series of theoretical birth and death rates that must be attained if the population is to increase no more than 33 per cent in the next half century.

Taking an estimated present population of 500 million, and assuming that the birth rate will be about 40 and the death rate about 32 per thousand when the civil war finally subsides and peace is restored, the rate of population increase for the decade 1950–1960 would then average 8 per cent. Since this seems likely, the gain in population by 1960 would be 40 million. If the birth and death rates for the decade 1960–1970 could be lowered to 38 and 30, respectively, the rate of increase would still be 8 per cent, or a gain of an additional 43 million by 1970, bringing the total population to 583 million.

POPULATION CONTROL

In the third decade, the birth rate would have to be lowered another four points to 34, while the death rate probably should not be lowered more than one point to 29. By 1980, at 5 per cent increase, the population would have grown to 612 million. A similar lowering during 1980–1990 to 30 and 26 would add only 24,500,000, and the next decade might lower the rates to 26 and 23. With such controlled reduction in birth and death rates, the population by the end of the century might be held to 650 million, with the rates well on the way to balance and eventual decline.

A national income of $85 billion will provide an average individual income of only $106 for a population of 800 million. The same national income will provide $130 for 650 million. If China can hold birth and death rates to the figures given, she can provide her population with an income 23 per cent higher than she can if she follows the pattern of India.

Three processes must be developed concurrently if the controlled decline of birth and death rates are to reach the levels noted: existing checks on population growth must be left much as they are until positive means of reducing births are developed and practiced; a medical-health program designed to bring about a rapid reduction in births to keep pace with declining deaths must be activated; the process of industrialization must be speeded so that natural restrictive factors, such as those which finally leveled off Europe's population curve, will help limit the growth of population.

The development and application of these three processes probably constitute the most difficult and far-reaching tasks that must be accomplished in the rebuilding of China. They are difficult because they involve the mores of Chinese society, far-reaching because they affect every individual, family, and institution in the entire country.

Customs, economics, and religion are concerned, and the attitude toward the family itself. The pressures now acting to maintain the family as the basis of Chinese society are powerful, for they are the pressures of survival. It has been through the continuity of families that both the individual and the nation have been maintained for centuries. The family is the economic unit on which everything else depends. There is no economic security for the aged except the possession of land and of sons to work that land. As long as this basis for economic security remains, the Chinese peasant is under pressure to have sons.

At the same time centuries of religious belief about the nature of the family stand behind the demand that it be maintained. The whole significance of the reverence for ancestors, which has been called "ancestor worship," is that the living believe themselves to be in an unbroken unity with their dead progenitors. Furthermore, they believe that the spirits of the dead continue to live as long as the living members of the family continue to remember them. When all the descendants of the departed die and there is none left to remember, then the spirits of the departed die also. Thus the Chinese speak of the "death" of a ghost. To keep the spirits of one's ancestors alive one must have sons to carry on the family name and keep the memory of the ancestors alive. Thus the economic pressure to have sons acquired, centuries ago, a powerful religious sanction that eventually became crystallized into Confucian filiality. This combination of tradition and economics obviously forms an obstacle of serious proportions to the limiting of families, yet there is evidence that this formidable obstacle can be overcome.

Before the outbreak of the last war in China, the medical department of the Mass Education Movement at Tinghsien in Hopei province carried out a birth-control project among farm families in which the parents were in their early thirties and had several living children including at least one boy.

The approach was first made to the fathers, all of whom

were graduates of a Mass Education school and members of one of the local alumni groups. The medical officer, in a series of meetings with these young men, explained to them the whole problem of birth control and pointed out that each additional pregnancy meant an economic loss. If the new child lived, the family had one more mouth it could not afford to feed after all the pain and trouble of a confinement, and whether living or stillborn, there was the loss involved in having the mother handicapped in her work for several months and the risk of her death. The great majority of the young men were quick to see the advantages of preventing future pregnancies.

Chinese are thoroughly practical, ready to take advantage of any improvement once its value to them is proved. Following such meetings the young husbands agreed that public health nurses should teach their wives how to use a simple contraceptive. But even with this co-operation the program ran into problems, for under conditions common to Chinese rural homes it is not easy to employ contraceptives, either because they are too expensive, too complicated, or too dependent on the use of techniques such as douches that the home is not equipped to provide. Nevertheless, the investigators found that there was some degree of success in prevention of pregnancies. The experiment was interrupted by war before extensive conclusions could be reached.

The next ten to twenty years must show progress in the development and general application of effective contraceptive methods that will meet the needs and problems of the rural population if the birth rate is to be lowered to 34 by 1980. There is no question in my mind but that millions of families, both rural and urban, can be taught how to use some practical means of birth control and that such a program, if vigorously promoted, can be successful in limiting population to a level consistent with economic potentialities.

A drastic reduction of the hazards that now confront the

Chinese family and the Chinese individual would create more of a willingness to accept and use birth control. The restoration of peace and order, first on such a list, is essentially a problem of stable government, for with stable government greater economic security is possible. Since current conditions provide no protection for the savings of those who are able to accumulate them, sons are now the only practical security. Even in the cities, where a good deal of money is held by certain groups, there is not enough economic stability to risk investments in productive enterprise.

As peace and order come gradually to China, there must be developed a nation-wide system of banks that will gather in the savings of those who have surplus money, and underwrite loans at reasonable rates. Banks are essential to the welfare of every aspect of Chinese life, not the least of which is the security of families, especially rural families. When individuals and families can rely on returns from savings, then the hazards of old age will be drastically reduced, and the present reliance on sons can be lessened to permit limitation of family size.

A second means by which a greater degree of economic security can be achieved is through the development of insurance. Life insurance was well established in the cities of China before the war and provided not only individual security but the capital for productive enterprise. Inflation has now wiped out all existing long-term insurance, but with peace, order, and monetary stability both personal and group insurance will again develop.

Ultimately, however, the only means of enhancing the economic security of the family and the individual is the drastic raising of standards of living. So again one returns to the point where the vicious circle must be broken. The standard of living can be raised only as production is expanded and as population growth is checked to permit production to catch up. The limitation of the family becomes one of the most important factors in providing security for the family; and here is the most acute dilemma of all, in terms of both practical policy and moral values: existing checks on population growth must not be removed until the controls exerted by direct family limitation and industrialization are well established, perhaps for a period as long as thirty years. The death rate, therefore, must not be reduced too quickly. Medical-health policies must be shaped with great care with better health stemming from more knowledge and co-operation on the part of the people themselves and not from the superimposition of preventive measures. It is obvious that the first objective of the medical-health program must *not* be the simple, natural one of saving lives: instead, it must be the development of means whereby the Chinese people will reduce their birth rate as rapidly as modern science can reduce the death rate.

The proposition is made with an acute awareness of its radical nature. For one trained in public health it will seem rank heresy to propose that during the next twenty to thirty years not even severe epidemics in China should be attacked with every means available to modern medicine. I suggest that public health measures which can save millions of lives should not be practiced in China on a nation-wide scale until the stage is set for a concurrent reduction of the birth rate. Existing misery and poverty can be permanently eliminated only when there are fewer, healthier people, with longer life expectancy and greater economic security. The future welfare of the Chinese people is more dependent on the prevention of births than on the prevention of deaths.

Until the long-term factors that reduce births take effect, health improvement efforts should be concentrated on those population groups in which the chances of reducing simultaneously the birth and death rates are best. In some cases, the groups singled out for special health efforts would constitute a geographical unit, such as the Tinghsien area where the Mass Education Movement was in operation before the war, while others might be limited to special groups within a community.

Such a medical-health program can be slanted toward physical, economic, and spiritual improvement, but it must be based on the fact that limited amounts of food and resources can nourish and supply only limited numbers of healthy human beings.

In working out the realities of such a plan it is constructive to select a given area and develop the program along foreseeable lines. A typical Shantung county, or hsien, with a population of about 200,000 constitutes a case in point. To serve a community of this size, the public medical-health program must combine in one system the treatment of the ill as carried out by the private practitioner in the United States as well as the functions of a public health and sanitation department. To meet economic realities, this county medical-health program must be tax supported, and at the same time collect fees from those who can afford to pay for hospitalization and treatment. This pattern of combined services already has been tried with apparent success in several experimental areas during the past few years.

The first task of such a public service is to win the confidence of people whose medical beliefs are now thoroughly rooted in tradition. Although a century has passed since modern medicine was first introduced to China, and although much headway has been made in creating a desire for modern health practices and services, a scientific health program cannot be completely successful unless the people understand and carry out the advice and instructions of doctors and medical officers. In many instances, the people must choose between new truths and old fallacies.

Since modern medicine has established its greatest prestige through miracles of surgery, it would seem that the most rapid means of establishing confidence would be to center the medical-health program around a hospital where first-class surgery can be practiced. In addition to surgery there should be a strong department of internal medicine stressing the use of the vast array of new specific drugs and pharmaceuticals now available for treatment of diseases. The policy pursued in carrying out these practices should be one of public education—teaching every patient the origin, significance, and prevention of his disease. There should, therefore, be trained workers whose duties would be limited to instruction of patients, and each hospital should have carefully prepared motion pictures to impart a clear understanding of commonly treated conditions. If a patient leaves the hospital without attaining some understanding of the facts underlying sanitation and medicine and without a new faith in modern medicine, the hospital will have failed in its duty just as much as if it had permitted the patient to die.

But, doctors may protest, the average hospital is already overloaded with work. Such a program of teaching patients about anatomy and physiology, about bacteria and disease transmission, about processes by which different agents cause pathological change in the human body, must be done at the expense of treating fewer patients. That is exactly the point.

The ultimate purpose of the medical-health service in China is not solely to treat illness and save lives, nor even to prevent disease, but to contribute to the long-range well-being of the entire population by bringing about a drop in the birth rate to equal the drop in the death rate, to assure the nation of fewer but healthier citizens living in greater economic security. It is only through this process that the standard of living can be raised to a point at which full health protection for everyone can be made available and paid for.

Judged by this standard, the first purpose to be served by treatment of surgical and medical cases is to build the prestige of modern medicine in order that its workers may be able to lead the community toward a rational application of medical knowledge to the needs of society. Second, it provides an opportunity to teach all types and classes of people some part of the vast range of facts they must acquire before control of population growth will be possible. Third, it saves lives and restores individuals as useful members of society. Fourth, by humanitarian activities it helps build a new and deeper conception of the value of life. There can be no doubt that this fourth purpose is a fundamentally important function of a public health program, both for its immediate activity and for its long-range purpose.

On the surface it may seem a contradiction in terms to advocate a policy that would do nothing to lessen the force of disease and death in vast portions of the population and at the same time to insist that as a moral obligation deep consideration must be given to the humane demands of the ill and needy. Yet a closer look will show that there is no real conflict between these two seemingly contradictory ideas. If the population is ever to be limited, one of the fundamental things that must be built into the thinking and feeling of people throughout China is a new concept of the value of individual life. Only as parents become concerned with the protection of the children they have against the economic losses represented by additional children will they take the trouble to limit the number of children they bring into the world. When life is cheap children are cheaply born.

After surgery and medicine accompanied by effective education, the second most important activity of the medical-health program should be a carefully developed obstetrical-pediatric service, also accompanied by appropriate and practical education. The end product of this second activity should be the widespread knowledge of contraceptive techniques and a willingness to use them. In this field direct efforts to limit the population can be made, but these direct efforts are not the first responsibility of the combined obstetrical-pediatric service. To attain the goal of smaller but healthier families, there is no more logical place to begin than with reproduction and child welfare. As the infant mortality rate declines, the pressure to ensure family survival by means of excessive childbearing will be eased.

Two methods are possible for the development of obstetrics and midwifery in a county medical-health unit. One is the mass approach, most likely to be followed at present, providing a qualified midwife for all normal pregnancies and providing a doctor for all abnormal cases requiring obstetrical care. Because all available personnel, under this plan, is put into the effort of saving the lives of babies at birth, little or no resources are left for pediatric follow-up. Under this approach many lives are saved, but for what? A foundation cannot thus be laid for a reduction in the birth rate or for the economic or physical improvement of the nation.

The second approach combines obstetrical with pediatric services and concentrates on the development of the normal child and its rearing. This would, of course, limit the number of children that could be given the protection of modern services at birth, a limitation that would probably extend for the next thirty years. But it would mean that much more effort would go into the whole health history of each child thus protected, and it would be through this pediatric part of the program that the hope of controlling the population and providing a stronger, healthier China could be realized.

The pediatric follow-up program would consist of the following activities: (1) A planned program of inoculations and vaccinations to protect the child from contagious diseases, most of which are now preventable. (2) A program to instruct the mother in child care, including an emphasis on practical nutrition that will create more concern for economic and adequate dietetics and, consequently, a desire for fewer, healthier children. Such a child welfare program would create groups of healthier families as examples and sources of knowledge for other families. The growth of such groups would permit the organization of mother-and-child groups to spread modern knowledge and to develop new motives and new practices. (3) A program of regular physical checkups with appropriate action to care for defects.

Ensuring the survival of two or three children for families so fortunate as to share in the pediatric program will open the way for further instruction in the use of contraception. The wife who already has an established confidence in the medical personnel is more inclined to accept further advice, particularly when she is assured of sturdy and healthy children. Instead of ten to twelve pregnancies resulting in four, five, or six children of questionable health, the family may have three or four pregnancies that produce two to four healthy children with a full life expectancy.

The third activity of the county medical-health unit should be a program of health education through schools, adult education classes, follow-ups on former patients, and through families and groups served by the obstetrical-pediatric service, with the same objective of lowering both death and birth rates and creating a smaller but healthier population.

This program must make the most vigorous use of every means of instruction. Already many ingenious methods have been used to dramatize facts about health and disease for the Chinese people. Great health fairs have included exhibits graphically portraying facts about the body, disease, treatment and prevention; in rural Shantung we employed health plays, posters, and demonstrations as tools to destroy a little of the old incrustation of ignorance and misinformation common to the people of China. But in the coming thirty years these simple and tested means must be vastly expanded, and to them must be added the projected picture, the movie, the illustrated magazine, the radio, and other new media that are even more effective.

Environmental sanitation, as already outlined, is one of the most important aspects of the health program and may be listed as a fourth activity of the medical-health program. Assuming that the basic facts concerning transmission of pathogenic organisms from person to person are taught successfully by the medical-health program, the ensuing activities in developing sanitation should be made in the homes of former hospital patients and in homes where the obstetrical-pediatric program is already at work. Since the number of families involved at the beginning of this work would be too few for a community-wide program, the first step would be concentration on the sanitary problems of the individual household.

Pollution of the household environment by small children should be stopped and the family toilet facilities should be modified and improved to permit collection and disposal of excreta in such a way as to prevent the spread of pathogenic organisms. The family water supply must be kept pure. Much of this work to make the household environment safer can be accomplished by a minimum expenditure of money. What is needed most is knowledge and the desire to change a few harmful life habits.

With this rudimentary work in a group of selected households, the necessary understanding and confidence and desire could gain a foothold for community-wide introduction of composting as a sanitary measure. At this point the medical-health program becomes coupled to the agricultural program. The aim of the latter must be to teach the same families the advantages of creating new fuel sources which would permit the composting of their crop residues. In addition to the sanitation factors, therefore, the agricultural advantages of composting must be taught and demonstrated. With knowledge and demonstrated proof of the practicality of a healthy environment, on the one hand, and the means to improve agriculture, on the other, the foundation is laid for the introduction of community-wide composting.

A fifth major activity of the medical-health unit operating in a typical hsien is the prevention and control of contagious diseases such as smallpox, diphtheria, scarlet fever, measles; the communicable diseases such as tuberculosis and venereal diseases; and the insect-carried diseases. The cost of saving lives by attacking these diseases is the lowest, perhaps, of any preventive work, yet I have ranked it last in terms of urgency. There was a time when I would have ranked it second, if not first, in order of importance, but that was before I had studied carefully the effect of population expansion on the welfare of the Chinese nation and people as a whole. Now it is apparent to me that all efforts to control these diseases should be relegated to a minor role in the medical-health program for at least the next fifteen to twenty years. When industrial developments are well along, when the obstetrical-pediatric program has begun to lower the birth rate, then is the time for vigorous attack on the communicable diseases. By the end of this century this group of killers should be put under control, but if checks on population expansion are to remain, these diseases must not be controlled too soon. In all truth there will be more work in other branches of the medical-health program—work that will lay a sound foundation for a smaller and healthier population—than there will be personnel or money to implement. Only minimal efforts should be undertaken in that portion of the program concerned with contagious, communicable, and insect-carried diseases.

The economics of medical-health protection for the people will, for a time, limit its size seriously. Assuming that levels of salaries and commodity prices can eventually approximate those of 1937, and then 7 U.S. cents per capita (the amount set in prewar experiments) could be levied for the support of a county medical-health program, then a hsien of 200,000 population would contribute U.S.$14,000 per year, enough to support a skeleton program and to finance an equipped hospital worth $50,000.

If 80 per cent of the $14,000 annual budget were used for salaries, under the conditions mentioned, a staff of sixty-nine people could be maintained, consisting of nine doctors, no dentists, fifteen graduate nurses, half of them trained in midwifery, four pharmacists and technicians, a business staff of four, twenty-five orderlies, servants, and cooks, and twelve students and apprentices in nursing and other auxiliary work. Such a staff could make a beginning at developing the program outlined. Doctors and nurses might be divided as follows: (1) general administration: three doctors (director, hospital superintendent, and director of field program) and three nurses with parallel duties, all of whom would share actual medical work as well as carry out administrative duties; (2) hospital services: two doctors, four nurses, in addition to the superintendent; (3) field services: four doctors and eight nurses.

The obstetrical-pediatric service would have three doctors and six midwifery-trained nurses assigned from the beginning. These nine people, even with transportation limitations, could deliver between 1,000 and 1,200 babies each year, immunizing and giving health services to each in the years following. With a birth rate of 40 per thousand, there would be approximately 8,000 births in the hsien each year, about 7,000 of them receiving no modern care. It is quite obvious that the number of families contacted for the thousand annual births would increase within a few years to a point where the needs of mothers and children under the care of the service would tax the time and energy of all available staff members and still not include more than a quarter of the annual births.

Budgetary expansion to provide more staff members could be accomplished by the charging of graded fees or by increasing appropriation from taxes or both. The charging of graded fees would mean that money now spent for herb drugs and outmoded "medical" services would be channeled into modern productive uses. Through appropriation from taxes, a larger proportion of the taxes paid would be spent in the direct service of the people who pay them.

By the end of the first five years, instead of the original 7 cents per person per year, or 0.33 per cent of the total income, it should be possible to increase appropriations to equal 1.5 per cent of the income, thus providing an annual budget of $60,000 and permitting expansion of the hospital to one hundred beds and the staff to forty doctors and dentists, sixty nurses, eight technicians and pharmacists, thirty apprentices and students, fifty orderlies and servants, and a business staff of ten. Financed and staffed in this way, the health unit could then begin to reach most of the new births and still follow the development of children already under its care. At this point the general introduction of birth-control methods could begin.

By the end of the first decade, it should be possible to expand the budget for the hsien unit to $100,000 and still not exceed 2 per cent of the people's income, a rate of expenditure less than half of that invested in medical care by Americans. By the beginning of the second decade, the income of the people in the hsien should begin to rise as a result of the agricultural and industrial programs. The effect of the combined programs should permit a medical-health budget of $2 million by the end of the century to care for the then 260,000 citizens of the hsien, a standard of medical care and public health protection equal to about one-fourth of that enjoyed by the American people at the present time. This level of relative service could be attained only because the yearly income of trained personnel in China would be considerably lower than that of their American counterparts.

There are 2,019 hsien in China, plus a number of special municipalities and other similar administrative units, justifying a plan constructed in terms of 2,100 units of local government for which such programs must eventually be provided. It is apparent that even the maximum figure of 12,000 doctors that may now be available in China is not enough to provide the minimum nine doctors for each of these 2,100 units. After providing staffs for medical schools, hospitals, and municipal units already existing, there is little or no personnel available for any new projects. To support the programs outlined as they might be operating throughout every hsien at the end of the century, at least 120,000 doctors and 800,000 nurses will be needed, in addition to administrative, teaching, and personnel for private medical activities. It is therefore necessary to plan for the training of at least 150,000 doctors and nearly one million nurses by the end of the century. The expansion of educational facilities to such a level is no small problem.

A bold and realistic medical-health policy and the development of a nation-wide medical-health program are two of the three processes most likely to prevent an increase in population which would spell doom to any improvements in living standards. The realization of these two aims is by no means easy. It will require much courage and foresight to pursue a policy which will permit existing population checks to continue where an intensive medical-health program cannot yet be developed, and it will not be easy to create and operate a medical philosophy that emphasizes the prevention of births more than the saving of lives. Yet only heroic measures such as these can ultimately change China from a country with high birth rate, high death rate, and low life expectancy into one in which both deaths and births are at a low level and a vigorous people live long and useful lives.

The third process that must contribute to the limitation of population is speed in the growth of industrialization.

Every effort must be made to shorten the process of industrialization as a check on population growth. If, instead of England's one hundred years, or Japan's sixty years, this process could be accomplished in a 20-year period, then the factors inherent in raising standards of living and creating a society based on a more complicated and advanced technology would be deterrents to population increase.

During that 20-year period, half the farm population would have to be moved from the farms into industrial work; farm production must be doubled; the total production of industry must be multiplied at least thirty times; dams, reclamation projects, and irrigation must contribute to the increase. Every one of China's natural resources must be developed to the limit. Furthermore, at the end of that 20-year period, the population must have completed the remaking of its health status as outlined, and the nation must have a better educated, highly skilled population. If all this were done, the vicious circle of population growth would be broken, standards would rise appreciably, and China would have set an example for the two-thirds of the human race now living at the survival line. Such a solution must eventually come about if our type of high-energy society is to survive for many generations.

Yet even to state the problem in these bald terms is to demonstrate that it is sheer wishful thinking to suppose that such modernization can be effected in the *next* twenty years. There is no hope that these many complex problems can be attacked and solved that rapidly.

Must it be concluded, then, that the situation is hopeless? Must the discouraging difficulties be accepted as proof that man has been able to gain the promise of winning freedom from the tyranny of nature for his whole worldwide family only to be doomed to failure? I don't believe that they must. It is possible to build toward the accomplishment of most of these goals principally during the last twenty years of this century in such a way as to hold hope for raising the standard of living. It is because the process will require a total of at least fifty years that I have so strongly emphasized the fact that existing checks on population must not be upset too soon.

The immediate objectives of the policies to be carried out in the field of industrialization must be to lay the necessary groundwork for rapid development toward the last of this century. Attention must be paid to transportation systems. Mr. Chang Kia-ngau's program for railway building must be completed and exceeded. Most of the 100,000 miles of railway that Dr. Sun Yat-sen wrote about should be completed, with the one basic modification that the needs of industrial transportation, particularly between coal mines and iron and other metal deposits, should receive special attention. Sources of power must be developed. In the great coal fields of Shansi and Shensi modern mining should have high priority, while the opening of many coal mines in other parts of China and the development of plants for the turning of coal into gas and gasoline should be hastened. The construction of a number of the larger water-power projects, such as the Ichang dam, is a necessary part of the program. All the energy which that mighty dam could produce would not be generated from the beginning. Its great potential would be fully put to work only as the process of modernization progressed. The Kansu oil fields must be made to provide as much oil as possible. There is always the possibility that extensive exploratory drilling in that area will open up now unknown reserves of oil that could very considerably ease the problem of motor fuel for the trucks and buses that will travel the many thousands of miles of new roads and highways that will be constructed. In Szechuan, new chemical industries should be started on a pilot basis. Iron and steel production in Manchuria and in North and Central China must be developed rapidly. Attention must be given to the modernization of the tin mines and of tin smelting in Yünnan and the production of aluminum in Kweichow. The mining of tungsten must be expanded.

Thousands of plants for the processing of these raw materials and the manufacturing of consumers' goods must be built. The already well-developed textile industry must be rapidly expanded to provide woven goods for other Asiatic peoples and to help provide some of the foreign exchange required to finance industrialization.

Every enterprise must be planned to serve as the seed from which many other plants can grow. There will be tension between the demands of immediately profitable operation and those of long-range developments, especially in deciding when and where any given plant is to be located. Too much money must not be put into plants that depend on long-range developments before they can begin to produce a profit for the community, and yet the long-range best use of resources must not be sacrificed entirely to the need for an immediate return on investment. The actual order of development will be largely determined by the ability of a particular situation to meet both these demands. The vital question of how much "planning" and how much free enterprise are to guide the execution of this program of industrialization will have to be solved.

The solution of the technical and financial problems involved in the rapid development of a modern system of industrial production will not, in itself, ensure that this development will make possible a rise in the standard of living. Although the creation of an active industrial plant that produces efficiently is considerably more than half the problem, the social consequences of the process is an exceedingly important, though the lesser, portion of the problem. For example, one of the major purposes of industrialization must be to move many families off the land in order that the over-all effect of these new production facilities will contribute the most toward raising standards of living. It is only by shifting families off the land that the farm size can be increased sufficiently to provide a farm business of an efficient economic volume.

To meet the social demands that must be a part of the contribution that industrialization makes to the expanding life of the nation, a pattern of industrial employment suited to China's social and cultural genius must be developed. The dominating characteristic of that genius is the importance placed on the family, and the set of loyalties that are essentially keyed to the family pattern. There are a number of leaders in the field of industrial development who are seeking ways in which this pattern of family loyalty can be expanded to include the new industrial community that must grow up around modern enterprises. First, they would like to bring whole families into their organizations, preferring them to single workers without families. Second, they seek to make the worker and his entire family a part of a total social organism based on the company, which includes the medical, educational, recreational, and other social facilities of a well-rounded life for the managerial and working staffs and their entire families. With the company thus assuming for the whole group responsibilities parallel to those formerly assumed by the large family or clan, they are seeking to build up the same sense of loyalty and equalitarian mutual responsibility within the whole company, management and labor together, that exists in the best of the old clan units. This type of organization is neither socialism nor individualistic capitalism, but it has some of the characteristics of each. It seems to me that this and many other types of group organization must be experimented with before the new units of social organization that will grow around new enterprises are finally developed.

This new set of social patterns which industry will bring into the corporate life of the Chinese people will have a profound effect on the patterns that evolve in the villages where agriculture will remain the chief occupation. Many new and scores of old industries, much expanded by the application of modern techniques, will continue to be based in the villages and small towns where they can draw on the labor of farm folk. In so far as this is true, the effect of industrialization on the birth rate will be reduced and a greater burden will fall on the direct checks which family limitation must exert. Nevertheless, such decentralization of many types of productive activity will undoubtedly prove desirable.

If all these feats of sociological engineering are carried out by the end of this century, the year 2000 should find the population of China radically redistributed, probably geographically, but certainly as to means of livelihood. About 40 per cent, or 260 million people, of the total 650 million population will still be on the land, but they would be operating farms that average thirteen acres each. About 30 per cent, or 197 million people, will be supported by those who work in industrial and handicraft production. Nearly 15 per cent, or 100 million people, will be dependent on commerce and transportation. About 13 per cent, or 85 million people, will be engaged in the professions, management, domestic service, and other personal service occupations. Finally, some 2 per cent, or 13 million people, will be dependent on mining.*

But before these millions of workers and farmers can make full use of scientific methods to produce and to increase production, a complicated series of educational problems will have to be solved.

---

* This proportional distribution of population by occupations is similar to that of contemporary France.

Chapter XV

Education—the Prime Mover

THE WHOLE, MASSIVE TASK OF REBUILDING CHINA IS an imposing complex of interrelated problems, no one of which can be solved independently. The solution of the whole requires the solution of each; and the solution of each requires the solution of all.

The seemingly simple and obviously humane desire to draw up a program of sanitation which will permit children to play on the threshing floors, in the hutungs, and in the crowded courts of North China villages without also playing host to a growth-stunting mass of parasitic worms has led to a discussion of ways and means to solve a geometric progression of problems. To sanitate the village and eliminate the worms it is necessary to solve the problems of the fuel, fertilizer, and economic welfare of village people. These, in turn, cannot be solved unless agriculture is modernized and production per acre doubled, both impossible without an industrial program which will permit half the farm population to move from the farms, provide adequate transportation, inexpensive power, millions of tons of chemical fertilizers, whole echelons of farm tools, and an economic basis for an efficient standard of living.

An efficient, productive standard of living, however, cannot be provided unless the over-all program is accompanied by success in preventing population expansion from outstripping production expansion. Therefore a medical-health program must be coupled with a forced-draft speed of industrialization to provide both direct and indirect population expansion checks and thereby make possible rising standards of both health and economic life.

Each of these operations is a problem of such magnitude that any one of them would tax the ingenuity and courage of the leadership available to any nation on earth. Yet the nature of the situation is such that they must all be tackled at once. They are so interrelated that no one of them can be solved without the assistance of the correlated solutions that are being worked out to all the others. Furthermore, the problems involved in the rebuilding of China must be solved if human society is to take the next, imperative step forward.

The central necessity, which the problems of China so fully illustrate, of raising the standard of living of that two-thirds of the human race which still must endlessly struggle merely to stay alive, poses an over-all problem the solution of which is as important to the future welfare of the world as is the international control of atomic energy or the development of a system of effective international relations. Actually the far-reaching changes required to solve the whole complex of problems faced by China and the other overpopulated, undermodernized countries are more extensive in time and space and more difficult to carry out than is the solution to the problem of atomic control or of international government.

The only prime mover that can make possible the success of this gigantic feat of sociological engineering is education. The problems of education in China can be considered under four main headings: (1) literacy—the basic tool of knowledge; (2) secondary education—the beginnings of skill and specialization; (3) technical education; and (4) higher education.

The first duty of education anywhere is to make available to the entire population the basic tools of reading and writing as a means of communication and further knowledge. Even though China probably has 100 million people who might be classified as literate because they can at least read and write a simple letter, she must expand her primary education system to at least three times its present size if all children are to have four years of schooling. In addition, she must provide adult education for many millions.

Popular education must go beyond the mere teaching of reading and writing, for the objectives of modern education include the development of discerning and responsible citizens, the provision of a background for a more abundant life and the training necessary to earn a better living. Once literacy is acquired, the community must impart useful knowledge of many types through many media. In modern terms, literacy implies, over and above simple reading and writing, an ability to read and understand pictures both still and moving, the capacity to listen intelligently to the radio, and to make use of magazines and newspapers.

Audio-visual aids of learning are rapidly spreading in China in spite of inflation and upheaval. The Ministry of Education is now in the process of purchasing a third of a million dollars' worth of American equipment and film as the first step in the development of an extensive program of audio-visual aids, and plans exist for supplying many hundreds of still- and motion-picture projectors and radio receivers to mass education centers all over the country. Already these centers are bringing a wide variety of information to many adults and special groups.

The vast range of subjects that must be taught to adults as well as to younger people is illustrated by the quantity of health education material required to support the medical-health program outlined in the preceding chapter. It must include the simple, basic ideas about chemistry, physics, and biology out of which grow knowledge of the human body and its functions. It should include a good deal of anatomy, a great deal more of physiology. Millions of people must be provided with the opportunity to learn about respiration and how the body burns its food to provide energy. They will need to understand the circulation of the blood, how food and oxygen are transported to every tissue and cell, how waste products are carried to the lungs and kidneys and excreted, how the muscles are attached to and move the bones of the skeleton, making possible all those actions by which man has mastered his environment, the co-ordination of that gigantic telephone switchboard, the brain, with its millions on millions of connections, and the subtle control that the body attains through those chemical regulators, the hormones. Adults must be taught about the processes of reproduction; they need to know about the chromosomes and genes that determine heredity, and they should come to understand the significance of fertilization and something of the marvelous interplay of chemical controls that make possible the implantation, growth, and birth of a baby. An almost limitless amount of entrancingly interesting knowledge about the human body and how it works will have to be made the property of millions of men, women, and children.

In addition, the whole field of nutrition must be taught. It is not enough to know that the body requires calories for energy, proteins for growth, fats to supply necessary parts of the intricate machine, and vitamins and minerals to meet still other special needs. People must be taught what foods provide those things, in what balance they should be consumed to give adequate nutrition, and how to grow, harvest, and prepare them so as to retain the maximum amount of body-building elements. As a valuable by-product of this kind of knowledge will come changes in land use and choice of crops.

Another area of health education embraces the nature and causes of common diseases, including the deficiency diseases and how they affect the body. The concept of disease caused by living organisms, whether they be in the virus, bacterial, protozoan, or parasitic animal class, must be hammered into the consciousness of the population until it begins to change behavior patterns. Over and over again the way in which these organisms are passed from one person to another will have to be explained and demonstrated to the people. Together with this type of information, training will be needed in the home care of the sick and in simple methods by which the sick can be isolated to protect other members of the family.

One of the objectives, therefore, of health education must be to tear down the misconceptions of disease that now determine the conduct of family and community, and to destroy the gullible faith now placed in herbs and other types of unscientific treatments. The Chinese people now spend enough money on old-fashioned medicine and for medical services of questionable value to pay most of the costs of an extensive and effective modern health program. Only long and patient learning can turn them away from these misconceptions and eventually shift the flow of this money into more productive channels.

Personal hygiene should take an important place in the health education program. Both the need for and the best methods of maintaining personal cleanliness need to be taught. Cleanliness is expensive—witness the huge amounts the American soap producers spend on advertising—and it costs the American people vast sums of money and much hard work to keep themselves and their clothes clean. In the long run the level of personal hygiene can rise only as the standard of living makes possible increased expenditure for soap, water, heat, and other cleansing agents. However, with appropriate knowledge and willingness to work, it is possible to practice a degree of cleanliness and personal hygiene with the expenditure of very little money, and it is this knowledge and impetus to expend energy and time on cleanliness that education can impart.

Environmental sanitation comprises still another huge area to be included in the health education program. A knowledge and understanding of the ways in which disease-producing organisms are transmitted from person to person can change behavior patterns, control community activities, and stimulate engineering efforts that will break the pathogenic cycle and bring better health in a cleaner, happier environment.

Great effort must be put into teaching how to care for children and how to protect and how to limit the family to numbers that can be supported. The logic of the ratio of population numbers to standards of living will have to be presented to assist in checking the growth of population.

Health, however, is only one field of adult and popular education. For rural groups there is the whole stratum of information about soil, plants, and animals that underlies modern scientific agriculture, a subject as extensive and important as that of health and perhaps even more important to the welfare of the people because it is directly related to the improvement of their livelihood. Then there is much new information about machines and mechanics that both rural and city people must acquire to improve the efficiency of many productive activities in home industries as well as small-scale factories.

Beyond the common modern knowledge in fields of health, agriculture, and industry there are almost unlimited horizons of information about the universe, the world, history, society, culture, and politics, all of which should be included in the program of adult and popular education as the only means of expanding the knowledge and experience of both the great group of adults who have already passed the age when they can attend primary school and for those millions of children who can hope to have no more than four to six years of primary schooling.

There can be no modern productive society, there can certainly be no real democracy as we understand the word, without a literate majority in China. It must be a literacy that reaches far beyond the mere ability to read and write, and employs the written, printed, and recorded word and picture to make accurate information a part of the working and aesthetic life of the people. Primary education for all children is an integral and basic part of this drive for literacy.

China's primary school system is as large as that of the United States, in terms of numbers of schools and total attendance. China has about 350,000 primary schools with a total enrollment of between 20 and 25 million pupils. In 1940 the United States had 207,000 such schools, with 21,-106,000 pupils. Although this is a respectable showing for an overcrowded, poverty-ridden country, only about one-third of China's children of primary school age are in school, compared with 94 per cent in America. The total value of buildings and equipment of Chinese primary schools is only a small fraction of the more than six billion dollars invested in American primary schools. Furthermore, most of China's pupils attend schools that provide only four years of instruction.

To meet the need for primary education, China will have to expand her schools to three times their present capacity and will have to invest capital equivalent to twelve or fifteen billion American dollars in order to equip them adequately.

A primary education system not only has the task of supplying the basic tools of knowledge to all citizens while they are children, but also it should seek to discover those more able children who should be given the opportunity for advanced training in secondary schools. The importance of this function of primary education in a society that hopes to make the most of the native human qualities born in each generation cannot be too strongly emphasized. A system of education that seeks to discover and give opportunity to the more gifted throughout the whole population is essential because it takes advantage of the laws of heredity. While it is true that a larger percentage of children from exceptionally able parents make distinguished records than do children of ordinary parents, it is also true in every generation that ten times as many exceptional children come from ordinary backgrounds merely because there are so many more of the latter than of the former. Society must be geared to provide able children of ordinary parents with the full opportunity to develop which their parents are both economically and culturally unable to give.

Thus, in order to furnish the tools of knowledge with which both adults and the oncoming generation will be able to produce the crucial transformations needed, China will have to expand vastly her popular and adult education programs and must triple her efforts in primary education. In doing so, she will always have a struggle to keep her system of primary education so democratic and sensitive that able students will receive recognition and help regardless of social or economic background.

The secondary school—called middle school in China—is the channel through which the more able children can acquire the skills and begin the specializations that lead to positions of primary and secondary leadership in the life processes of the community. In the United States the rapid expansion of secondary education has been the outstanding feature of educational development during the past fifty years. In 1890, less than 360,000 American young people were enrolled in secondary schools; by 1940 enrollments had increased twentyfold to more than 7 million students constituting 72 per cent of the American population of high school age. The effect of this expansion on education and on the productive skills of the American people cannot be calculated. China must experience a similar development of her middle schools in the course of the next fifty years. She has already made a commendable start.

In 1936–1937, China had 3,264 middle schools with a total enrollment of 627,246. In 1942–1943, in spite of the war, she had 3,455 registered middle schools in free China alone with an enrollment of 1,101,087. When the war ended most of the schools that were operating in occupied territory were taken over, bringing the total to more than 4,000 secondary schools with enrollments of well over a million and a half. In relation to population, secondary education in China is roughly equal to that of the United States fifty years ago, and it may be that another twentyfold increase can be accomplished by the end of this century. To achieve this expansion, China will require 124,000 middle schools with a total enrollment of 28,800,000 students. Even if secondary education does not reach these figures, however, the achievements of the immediate past indicate that secondary education can provide skills to many millions of individuals.

The millions of Chinese with junior and senior middle school training are destined to play a large part in the modernization of China. They will man the millions of jobs at the foreman and junior staff level and, for many years to come, will provide the bulk of the teachers for the vast number of new primary and adult educational units yet to be organized. They will supply the co-operating personnel in nursing, midwifery, pharmacy, and laboratory technology, who, along with more highly trained nurses and doctors, will form the working teams that make the medical-health program a reality. Millions of them will provide leadership in developing the organizations of modern agriculture, while millions more will be needed to help build up industrial operations ranging from mining to the manufacture of con-

sumers' goods. Clerks and white-collar workers, so important to the organization and management of modern governmental, industrial, commercial, and social enterprises
of all kinds, will be recruited from among these secondary
school graduates.

To accomplish these goals, the secondary education system must become not only larger but also a great deal more
flexible. Constant experiments must be made to determine
the methods and curricula best adapted to the specialized
needs of a changing society and economy. Although the
nation-wide educational standardization now imposed by
the Ministry of Education has produced a certain amount
of rigidity and stagnation, there is evidence that there are
among the educators of China men who possess the imagination and ability to lead in the creation and adaptation of
educational methods to meet changing requirements.

Technical education may be either a development of
specialization derived from that of the middle school or an
organization quite separate from the formal school system.
The variety of types of technical training that will be required by China is as wide as the needs of a modern society
for technicians. Many technicians will be trained in technical middle schools. Thousands more will have to be trained
in special technical schools providing from two to four years
of college grade instruction. Many types of technical short
courses already have been offered in special institutions.
Cheeloo University operated a popular two-year college
grade course in radio technology in the years just before the
Asiatic war and now offers similar two- and three-year
courses in hospital laboratory technology and in pharmacy.
The man who directed the radio course and many of his
students played significant parts in the organization and operation of the air-raid warning net that served the people
of the interior so well during the war years. The University
of Nanking operated a two-year course in automobile repair

and turned out hundreds of the mechanics who kept the trucks of blockaded free China moving in spite of war shortages and difficulties. Today the same university is offering a two-year course for technicians in the field of audio-visual aids and another in rural leadership. Other institutions have similar offerings in other fields, and in addition to an expansion in this pattern of technical short courses, China would do well to investigate the applicability of the junior college to the rapid production of great numbers of technicians in many specialties.

There are many types of technicians who can best be trained on the job in industry. One example of this I found when I visited the Tien Fu Mining Company near Chungking, where Mr. Cheng, the manager, an American-trained mining engineer, offered a course in foreman training and engineering that was open to experienced miners and mine foremen from his and other nearby mines who had ability but no formal training as engineers. He and the other engineers at the mine were conducting classes and practical demonstrations underground. A number of the young men studying while working showed promise of becoming efficient engineers capable of operating mines themselves.

As the tempo of industrialization increases, China may find it advisable to set up practical training programs using methods developed in America for on-the-job training of operators and foremen. The methods are well established, and their adaptation and use can help China solve the problem of training the technicians she needs.

The purpose of higher education is to train and educate top leaders capable of undertaking the actions necessary to solve the multiform problems already outlined and many others too numerous to discuss in detail. By training is meant the imparting of technical knowledge and skill, and by education is meant the developing of the moral character, philosophical understanding, and discernment necessary to the conception and implementation of sound policies. Education must be of such a quality that policy decisions conform to universal, moral truths so that their execution will serve the public welfare without causing the sort of disaster that Hitler brought upon Germany and the military-ruling class brought to Japan.

Within this comprehensive task of preparing leaders, higher education must educate both specialists and generalists, develop managers, and break the curse of the scholar.

Among the many types of specialists higher education must produce are those needed for the development of modern agriculture. The joint China-United States Agricultural Mission, discussing some of the problems of agricultural education in the report of its 1946 investigations, observed that twenty-five agricultural colleges organized in seventeen of China's thirty-six provinces during the past thirty years have already graduated six thousand men with a greater or lesser degree of specialization in some phase of agriculture. This number is altogether inadequate to the needs for such specialists. According to the mission's report, this paucity is one of the two weaknesses of higher education in agriculture, requiring the present limited personnel to cover more fields and more activities than efficiency permits and stretching the limited public funds available over more services than they can adequately support. There are, in fact, more agricultural colleges, schools, and experimental stations than there are specialists to operate them effectively.

The second weakness of higher education in agriculture noted by the mission was the lack of graduate training, forcing students to go abroad for advanced study and training in teaching and research. The student is removed from his own environment and its limitations, all too frequently returning from his overseas study to flounder for years as he tries to adjust what he has learned to the more limited facilities and the different problems of his native land.

To remedy these defects the Agricultural Mission recommended that the operation of experiment stations, now maintained either by the Ministry of Agriculture and Forestry or by agricultural colleges under the Ministry of Education, be unified and placed under the direction of one man who is concurrently the dean of the college and the director of the station. Present financial support and relationship to the ministries can continue as they are now, but curricula, research, and extension work are too complemental to exist as nonrelated entities. Such consolidation would produce fewer but larger centers with better libraries, equipment, and other facilities for scholarly and productive work; staff members would have the stimulation of daily contact with workers in related fields, and group co-operation on broad agricultural problems would be encouraged and facilitated. Both manpower and facilities could be more effectively used and unquestionably the educational and research results would be greater, in both quality and quantity, than are now obtained from a larger number of small, inadequately staffed, and poorly equipped centers.

The mission recommended that the National Government of China organize and support nine main agricultural centers to be located in the nine agricultural regions into which the country is naturally divided, with a first-class college and experimental station in each regional center, each center to serve a number of provinces and be correlated with the provincial schools in its region. The mission also recommended that at least three of these colleges be developed as rapidly as possible to a point at which they can give advanced degrees in agriculture and enable young men to do their advanced study in China, going abroad for special observation and investigation only after they have had a number of years of experience. In this way the future leaders in Chinese agriculture would be thoroughly grounded in the life, problems, and limitations of their own country, and, when abroad, they would not need to divide their attention because of requirements for advanced degrees, but could give full time to their particular specialty and its adaptation for application in China.

It is probable that most of the Agricultural Mission's recommendations will be implemented as rapidly as disrupted conditions will permit. With many elements of the proposed program already in existence, the new pattern can provide China with the plant breeders, the horticulturists, the agronomists, the agricultural economists, the agricultural engineers, the economic entomologists, the chemists, the geneticists, the specialists in agricultural education and extension, and the dozens of other specialists who in the course of the next half century can develop and adapt the knowledge necessary to double yields per acre on existing farm land, reclaim hundreds of thousands of additional acres now too dry or too marshy, too saline or too eroded to grow crops. In addition to those involved in production, the new program must prepare other specialists who will organize and standardize grading and marketing to ensure domestic use of Chinese products instead of imported products and to improve and maintain the position of Chinese agricultural products in world markets and so provide much of the foreign exchange required for further development.

Together with the expansion of facilities to train agricultural specialists, China will have to give much attention to the training of all types of engineers. Today China has only about ten thousand men with engineering training of any degree. Although she has a number of engineering schools, she has had to depend, in this field as in agriculture, too much on foreign training with the same tendency on the part of those trained abroad to lose contact with the Chinese environment and its problems.

The inclination of Chinese engineering schools to train

engineers who are too academic and too far removed from the practical needs of industry, a failing that is augmented by the foreign training of most Chinese professors in engineering, prompted suggestions from a group of North China industrialists to Yenching University when it reopened after the Japanese occupation. "We need a different type of engineering education here in North China," the industrialists said. "We are tired of having to hire men who have degrees in engineering but whose training is so theoretical that they lose face in the eyes of workmen because they know so little of the practical problems and are so poor in using their hands. Many of these men eventually work out, but it costs us too much to allow them several years to learn things they should know when they come to us. We want to co-operate with your university in establishing a type of school where the students spend half their time on the job during their period of schooling. We will open our plants to the program so that your students can learn how to do at the same time they are learning the theory of what should be done. Furthermore, we want you to get a group of experienced American engineers on your staff to form the backbone of the faculty. We are aware of how difficult it is for the Chinese engineer to break down old habits of the scholarly class in regard to work with the hands. Western teachers have many advantages in this respect because they have always done things with their own hands and because they have had so much wider experience with the actual problems of industry than most Chinese engineering teachers."

Chinese industry already feels the need for more and better engineers, and is keenly aware of the need to break the "curse of the scholar" in future training programs. Outside assistance is welcomed.

As in agriculture and engineering, the education of medical personnel will burden the facilities of higher education. In the preceding chapter it was shown that to provide a level of medical care equal to about one-quarter of that enjoyed by the United States in 1940, it would be necessary to develop a corps of 150,000 active medical doctors and a million active nurses. The expansion of medical education required to provide this number of medical personnel illustrates the magnitude of the training problem for higher education.

Altogether there are about 12,000 Chinese who might qualify as medical doctors with some degree of modern training. Nearly fifty medical colleges carry on some kind of instruction; only about twenty are now in condition to make a real contribution to the training of doctors, and not a single one of these twenty has every post on its teaching staff filled. There are about 5,250 students now in medical colleges (including those taking what is considered in America to be premedical work), graduating 400 new doctors each year, and there are about 1,100 medical teachers on the job. The present rate of graduations is barely enough to replace losses by death and retirement and to maintain the total number of active doctors at its present inadequate level.

If 150,000 doctors are to be at work by the end of the century, higher education in China will have to increase rapidly in quantity and quality. The twenty best medical colleges must augment their staffs and enlarge their student bodies so that by 1955 they would be admitting entering classes averaging 130 students and graduating a combined total of 900 new doctors each year (assuming four-year medical courses without premedical work, as practiced in most American medical schools).

Then, beginning in 1956, a new medical college would have to be opened or a second-rate one improved every other year until the total number of first-rate colleges reached twenty-five in 1964. In 1965 it would be necessary to open another new college, and, beginning in 1966, two new colleges would have to open each year until, by 1972, a total of forty medical colleges were in operation. Beginning in 1973 four new colleges would need to be opened each year, thereby providing a total of sixty medical colleges by 1977. From 1965 on, all medical colleges would have to average two hundred new matriculations each year.

To carry out this program the number of medical teachers would have to increase from the present 1,100 to 12,000 by about 1975. This means adding 2,500 new teachers in addition to replacements in the first ten years, 3,600 in the second, and 4,800 in the five years after that.

If such an expansion is accomplished and the combined death and retirement rate for doctors averages 25 per thousand through 1966, 20 per thousand through 1976, 16.6 through 1986, and 14.2 to the end of the century, then the number of active doctors can be expected to increase as follows: 1955—13,200; 1960—16,700; 1970—30,800; 1980—61,200; 1990—109,800; and 2000—150,000.

These estimates indicate that the facilities for medical education, which are among the most complicated and expensive required for any field of study, will have to be expanded at an impressive rate in order to produce sufficient personnel for the medical-health program outlined, unless the process is speeded up by the lowering of standards.

With only five thousand active nurses, the job of building up the corps of trained nurses to a strength of one million in the next fifty years would seem to be six times as great as that of increasing the number of doctors to 150,000 by the year 2000. Fortunately, the training of nurses is neither so long nor so expensive a process as the training of doctors.

Although higher education, if it is to provide the personnel for rebuilding China, will have to produce many hundred thousands of specialists, it will have to train even more generalists prepared for work in the rebuilding. By generalists are meant the managers and community leaders who will organize and operate specific enterprises using the knowledge and directives supplied by the specialists. If higher education is to fulfill its broad share in the solution of China's complex problems, the training of generalists *per se* is essential, even though many of them will have had specialist's training.

By way of illustration, it is constructive to outline the need for one type of generalist who might conceivably be called a sociological engineer, together with the method of training for such work in a rural community.

From the discussions thus far it is clear that the 80 per cent of the population living in the villages and on the farms must be the foundation for the rebuilding process. It is also clear that specialists already have gathered a great mass of information that could be used to improve the welfare of this huge number of rural people if personnel existed who could teach them and guide them in the application of these better methods. What is almost the most pressing need, therefore, is a new type of community leader to live in the village and to be the link between the specialists and the people. Ideally, there should be many such workers in every group of villages, each one to some degree a specialist—a farm demonstration agent and a home demonstration agent, workers in home nursing and sanitation, and leaders trained in the methods of adult education and the organization of credit and consumer co-operatives, to mention but a few. But the rural community is still too poor to afford a highly trained person for each of these jobs, and for a long time to come the specialists in these various fields will have to look to a whole province or at best a number of hsien for their support. The real arena of change and improvement is the individual family and village, the territory of the sociological engineer.

The primary qualifications of sociological engineers are

an ability to work with people and a capacity for leadership. They should be trained in a special college of rural reconstruction with social sciences and the humanities as the basic core of their education. They should be thoroughly grounded in Chinese history, literature, and thought in order to understand the force of the traditional culture as it determines the behavior patterns of the common people. Together with a grasp of the basic culture and how it functions in daily life, they should have a thorough understanding of the fundamentals and methodology of both sociology and economics in order to detect the social and economic forces at work in the community they are to guide.

On this foundation of existing culture and of social science must be erected a superstructure of general knowledge in a whole series of fields. Sociological engineers will need, for example, enough basic training in agriculture and agricultural economics to be effective teachers of the improved methods recommended by the specialists. They will have to understand the problems of the home and family in order to help organize and operate mothercraft classes and teach better methods of nutrition. They should know a good deal about public health, with special attention to health education and sanitation, in order to serve as a link between medical-health personnel and the villager. Home industries and the best types of supplementary productive activity for their districts would also have to be included in their course of training. They would need to understand the methods and functions of credit and consumer co-operatives so that they could help to organize and conduct them within the community. Finally, the one field in which they should have specialized training is popular education, for they must be the masters of all the media by which ideas are developed and propagated.

Sociological engineers would have to make their living by serving in many different capacities. Some would be teachers in primary or secondary schools. Some would be the secretaries of individual co-operatives or groups of co-operatives. Others would be on the payrolls of hsien governments or be supported by churches or the Y.M.C.A. Whatever the job they were paid to do, they would have to give their energies over and above that job to the task of being the mediator, the mentor, the friend, and the servant of the people.

Over and above training in the techniques and skills of a great variety of fields, such sociological generalists would have to be truly educated, for they must understand and be dedicated to those philosophical, moral, and religious purposes which can supply incentive for the immense amount of unselfish labor required. Above all, they must understand the complex interplay of existing forces that must be turned to good account in the process of rebuilding.

The rural reconstruction college organized by the Mass Education Movement already has begun to evolve such a training program. Even now, Cheeloo University is formulating plans for a college of rural reconstruction, but it will require a number of years of creative experimentation to produce a curriculum adequate for the training of community leader generalists.

The rural community is not the only segment of Chinese society that will require thousands of generalists. Industry, mining, transportation, and commerce also will need them in huge numbers. Effective management for all types of enterprise is one of China's acute shortages today and will not grow less acute as the gigantic modernization process gets under way. The training of managers is one of the responsibilities of higher education. In company with managers anywhere, these new managers in China will have the usual duties of combining diverse elements of technical processes, labor, and management into efficient and productive social organisms and of gearing their own units into existing national and world economic structures. In addition to these customary duties, they will have to contend with problems born of China's cultural traditions and China's lack of modern skill and training.

China's traditional culture with its familyistic ethics and its carefully defined set of human relations creates many problems for the administrator which are different, if not in kind at least in degree, from those which are met in the United States—a fact brought sharply home by personal experience in directing an organization staffed almost entirely of Chinese.

One set of problems derives from the high degree of personal sensitivity which the Chinese culture develops in its people. They are the problems of "face." Face, a factor in the relations of people anywhere, is, at base, simply the dignity of the individual and the esteem in which he is held by himself and his fellows. The skillful manager anywhere must know how to protect the self-esteem of each of his associates and how to maintain the balance of respect that must exist between them. However, in America more emphasis has been placed on developing a robust self-criticism and on attempting to be objective about problems, with the result that face is not the acute problem of personal relations that it frequently is in China.

It is, for example, difficult to make promotions based on merit in a Chinese organization. Except in rare cases where the performance of an employee or an associate has been so outstanding that everyone in the organization recognizes the merit of the case, every member of an organization is inclined to take a promotion given one person as a loss of face to those who are not promoted. When an administrator must make rather subtle decisions in evaluating the effectiveness of the performances of the members of his staff, for example in cases where the matter of quality as well as quantity of work is involved, the average Chinese finds it hard to credit the administrator with complete objectivity. Such a reaction is a by-product of the family system of ethical values. Because the Chinese believe it is the duty of a member of the clan to give undue and undeserved advantages to his clan members, he who is not closely related by blood or friendship to his boss is inclined to conclude that the latter's judgment has been and will be influenced by some relationship factor rather than by the merits of the case.

Another by-product of family- and friendship-centered ethics and loyalties is the tendency toward the formation of cliques based on some commonly held subloyalty within a larger organization. Although the pattern of clique formation occurs in all countries, it is especially acute in China, where organizations are based more on personal relations than on abstract loyalty to a profession or a social ideal. Indeed, the Chinese have functioned so long on this personal and essentially familyistic basis that they are skeptical of the effectiveness of any motivation that cannot be seen to rest on family or friendship ties. The strength of this code is one reason why it has been so extremely difficult for China to become unified politically. Even today, the soldiers of one army or unit will not obey the officers from any other; in fact, they will not obey any officer they do not recognize personally as belonging to their outfit. The effective manager must, therefore, carefully build his organization so that these loyalties center in himself. If he has cliques in his organization he must keep them in balance and be careful to see that all the subleaders around which the cliques are built are connected effectively to himself by personal ties beyond those of formal responsibility and general friendliness usually considered adequate to maintain smooth working relationships in an efficient American organization.

Because of these traditions of loyalty and a number of other problems peculiar to management in China, the task of educating the managers and policy makers is both an urgent and a difficult one. China desperately needs a number of institutions like the Wharton Graduate School of Business Administration to lead the way in developing effective education and training in this field. But beyond the need for such graduate schools lies the necessity for all colleges and universities to place far more emphasis than they now do on the development of a general understanding of social and economic forces and the integration of technical processes into social situations. By so doing they will provide all educated men and women with the intellectual background necessary for an understanding of the problems of administration. From the colleges and universities must come the individuals who can develop into the generalists who manage the rebuilding of both the rural and the urban life of China.

The contribution already made by Christian higher education to the total higher educational process in China would be hard to exaggerate. The missionary movement of the Protestant churches brought modern education to China just as it brought modern medicine. Not only were the first schools —opened in the 1830's—and the first college level work— begun in the 1860's—set up by the church, but also the first academy for the teaching of mathematics and modern science financed and managed by the government of China was organized by a Presbyterian missionary. In addition, the first Chinese students sent abroad to study went as a result of missionary efforts and in many cases were supported by church groups. It was the missionary group that, early in this century, battled to change the restrictive interpretations of the American immigration laws so that Chinese students could be admitted freely to this country for study.

Through the pioneer work of the Christian schools and colleges in China, modern science and Western technology as well as Western philosophy, literature, history, art, and music were all introduced into the curricula that now are accepted as standard for all levels of education. As one observer has said, "The Christian mission to China has offered Western civilization to the Chinese on a silver platter."

With this brilliant record of pioneering behind it, the question arises as to whether there is further need for privately sponsored higher education under Christian auspices. For at least three reasons the answer appears to be that there is.

First, China needs a set of ethical and moral values on which it will be possible to build a modern nation and from which can be derived much of the unselfish motivation for rebuilding her life. At a number of points in this book China's traditional culture, largely based on Confucianism with the family as the central ethical value, has been shown to lack some of the qualities on which a modern nation is based. Some system that can lift loyalty at least a single notch above the family must be introduced and gain wide acceptance before the fatal divisive tendency so apparent in Chinese life can be overcome. Today there are three systems which claim to provide the widely based motivation that China requires and which contend for the allegiance of the Chinese people. These are nationalism, which would place the state and the race in the position of highest value and depend on patriotism as the motivating force; communism, which would place the working class in the position of highest value and draw its driving force from the passions of class struggle; and Christianity, which seeks to put the whole human family in the position of highest value and to draw its motivation from the passionate desire to do God's will in serving the highest interests of all classes and all groups because they are bound to a common brotherhood as sons of one Father.

The choice of nationalism may well lead to a statism of the extreme right with dictatorial power wielded by a group that would turn to the past for its inspiration and might well take China down the fateful road from which Japan has just been violently thrown. The choice of communism would almost certainly lead to a dictatorship of the left and another type of statism with regimentation and collectivization. The choice of Christianity can lead to the slow but steady development of democracy on the Western pattern. Christian higher education must continue in China, strengthened and improved so that it can play its part in making available to the Chinese people those universal values which provide a motive force for the building of a modern nation.

Second, Christian higher education in China must continue because it represents a substantial group of institutions that are in a position to continue the kind of pioneering work they have done in the past. In many ways they are admirably organized to undertake experimental programs that it might be unwise to apply universally until they have been proved in practice. Because they are private and because they are not numerous the Ministry of Education can permit them more latitude for experiment than it can permit the larger and more numerous national institutions. In addition, because the Christian colleges have had strong connections in both Europe and North America they become logical points for the importation of new ideas and practices in education.

Third, Christian higher education has an important place to fill in China's educational system because its institutions are well suited to take a part as a catalyst in the synthesis of a new, world culture. One of the imperative, long-term tasks of our day is the development of a culture sufficiently universal to contain and support the most universal and reliable values in all the great cultures of today and to refine them to comprise a new world culture on which a future, world-wide organization of people capable of maintaining peace can be built. Ultimately this new culture will be hammered out in the brains and the lives of men and women who are deeply concerned with and affected by the several vital cultures that exist in various parts of the world. The Christian colleges in China are one of the places where these strong cultures, particularly those of the East and the West, meet and crossreact. Only through long years of such action and reaction will the new world culture eventually take form.

The Christian colleges, moreover, perform a unique task in China because they contribute the drive of a religion that releases a willingness to sacrifice for the greater good and can, thereby, help supply the motivation that the rebuilding of China requires. Thus they are in a position to continue experimental work in the process of education and can make a real contribution to the synthesis of a new culture.

In general, then, higher education must be vastly improved in quality and expanded in scope to meet the challenge of training the specialists, educating the generalists and managers, and helping generate the moral motivation to meet the tasks of modernization. The problem of quality can be solved only by the men and women who man China's educational system. Since there is no question about their native ability to produce that quality (in many cases they are now doing so), there is every reason to believe that the problem of quality can be solved. The question of quantity, however, is not so certain, and the efforts that must be made to expand in quantity may well hinder the development of adequate quality. A second and closer investigation of the problem of how much higher education must expand to fulfill its mission is illuminating.

Now that the postwar process of taking over institutions that remained in occupied territory, of returning those which fled to the interior, and of re-establishing those which were forced to close down has been almost completed, China, at last count, is reported to have 182 universities and colleges with a total of 110,000 students. This is an average of about 600 students per institution.

The rate at which medical education should be expanded to provide enough medical specialists has already been outlined. At the present time about 5 per cent of all those enrolled in colleges and universities are in medical schools. If we take this ratio as being normal, then by about 1980, when all sixty of the medical colleges that are planned for are operating with a total enrollment of 60,000 students, there should be about 1.2 million students in higher education as a whole. If the present number of students is doubled each ten years from now to the end of the century, a rate of expansion that would tax heavily the capacities of all trained educators and every economic resource that China can muster, then by 1980 instead of 1.2 million students in institutions of higher learning there would be only 880,000. By the end of the century, however, there would be about 3.5 million in such institutions.

To attain this rate of expansion, it would not be necessary to establish any new institutions during the next twenty years provided the plants, equipment, and personnel of existing colleges could be expanded to accommodate an average of 2,400 students each, or four times the present average enrollment. In the decade following this 20-year period, assuming that the average enrollment remained at 2,400, 184 new colleges would have to be organized. In the decade 1980–1990, 366 new institutions would have to be opened, while 732 would have to be opened between 1990 and 2000. By the end of the century there would then be about 1,500 institutions of higher learning with average enrollments of 2,400 students, or a total enrollment of over 3.5 million. In 1940, the United States had 1,800 institutions with a total enrollment of less than 1.5 million, but the population of

China is four times as large and her present need many times greater.

Such a rate of producing trained people for China is none too high. If attained, the number trained would be less than half, relative to population totals, the number of Americans who are given college training. However, from the point of view of the cost and likelihood of this expansion, China will be forced to modernize with fewer trained people. Here the question is raised as to how small a force of highly educated leaders can accomplish the rebuilding of China. Only history can give the answer, but Chinese educational leaders have accomplished so much during the war years, in spite of insuperable obstacles, that one hesitates to prophesy.

Men and women in the field of higher education are now operating under almost unbelievable hardships. A great majority of them have acted as heroically as any people on earth, whether leading students into exile to escape the enemy or operating under enemy control to provide some kind of education for Chinese youth, a heroism the more great because it has been unspectacular to the point of drabness. The very substance of life for most of them has been an increasing poverty, partially described by English Professor Chang Ching-tan in the July, 1947, *National Reconstruction Journal:*

" . . . contemplate the sufferings and sorrows of Chinese professors. Burdened with problems of firewood, rice, oil and salt, they have little time to study. Even if they had time, books and equipment are nowhere to be found . . .

"What is more, professors and educators are suffering even more badly in spirit. In China today the word 'liberal' is a synonym for 'leftist,' and 'democracy' for 'communism,' so no wonder that most of the professors have their lips tightly sealed. . . . At present the highest income for a teacher is CNC$900,000 per month, whereas the lowest is only CNC $200,000. One can realize the seriousness of the situation more clearly when one remembers that, at the time of this writing CNC$900,000 is as much as US$75 only, and that commodity prices continue to rise."

The lot of college students is almost equally difficult, as Dr. Chang points out in the same article under the terse heading "Like Master, Like Pupil":

"In a recent press interview, Secretary General [of Nan-kai University] Hwang Yu-sheng humorously asked, 'Is this a university or a poorhouse?' One should like to know how the one is related to the other. The fact is that the chief business of school authorities nowadays is to find means to fill the stomachs of the students. As is well known, they are far from successful in this respect. Apart from the want of adequate food, the Chinese college students are short of textbooks, not to mention reference books, and thus they must draw entirely on the lectures of professors, which, after all, do not mean much in the way of college education. Therefore it is not just hearsay that the general level of higher education in China has been considerably lowered in recent years."

These are the people who are the seed from which the whole vast structure of education—higher, secondary, primary, and popular—must grow. From one point of view these war and postwar years have tested the educators of China as few groups have ever been tested, and they have come through with unmatched courage. From another viewpoint they have for so long been pressed down by the consequences of an international and a civil war that have eaten at the vitals of Chinese economy and social organization that it seems impossible for them to rise to the position of prime movers in the creation of a new and modern China with an ascending standard of living. The gap between goals and means of achievement is a measure of the seriousness of China's present situation.

Chapter XVI

The Challenge of China

THIS BOOK BEGAN WITH THE THESIS THAT CHINA IS an important key to world peace because the two basic struggles of our time come to focus here as nowhere else. These struggles were defined as the cultural struggle to extend the industrial revolution to include all peoples and the political struggle to determine what system will govern the modernized world.

Fundamental to this thesis was the assertion that the American way of life can survive only if China succeeds in rebuilding herself in such a way as to raise the standard of life of all her people. America's high energy-consuming, high standard-of-living society can endure only if that major portion of mankind now existing on the bare survival line achieves standards of living much nearer hers. Nor can America's way of life survive if most of the world involved in these struggles becomes totalitarian, for she will destroy the economic and organizational base of her existence if she is forced to fight a series of wars in an effort to destroy totalitarianism. Ultimately, all Americans have a life-and-death stake in the rebuilding of China.

The first half of this book described China as she is, and attempted to portray the topography of the battlefield on which these struggles are taking place. After presenting a set of criteria for remaking the life of China, the latter half of the book has moved on to outline in some detail the actual problems involved in rebuilding and to suggest a series of constructive programs that could advance the standard of life of the Chinese people. Attention has been focused on basic human problems and on the technical means available for solving them. It has been shown that in order to raise the Chinese standard of living to a level about one-fifth of that existing in America in 1929, it would be necessary to carry out a series of almost superhuman developments that would reach and alter the corporate and personal life of every person in China. Yet, at the technical level, imposing as the problems are, there is a fighting chance of solving them.

How does the rough but realistic 50-year program for creating a modernized nation suggested here compare with events occurring in China today? By contrasting this program with the actuality, is it possible to obtain clues that can guide Americans in the formulation of a policy toward China that will meet the demands of their own fundamental interests in the successful rebuilding of China?

A realistic account of events in China today does not make exhilarating reading. Stated simply and bluntly, the dominating fact is that a thoroughly ruthless struggle for power is being fought by two groups, neither of which is capable of a quick or decisive victory. This struggle is more complicated and more difficult to check because it is played upon by forces outside China, and because it ranges across all fronts, military, political, economic, and social. While part of a world-wide clash between extremes of right and left, the lines of demarcation between the Chinese opponents are not easily drawn. Each group, Kuomintang and Communist, is a mixture of many elements.

The Kuomintang (Nationalist party) includes a wide range of opinion, all deeply affected by the fact that they are Chinese. The extreme right within the Kuomintang is primarily neo-Confucianist in thinking and opposed to communism as much because it is an alien philosophy as because the Communists propose to overturn the political scale of power. The ultraconservative attitude of this group is due partly to an aggressive support of ancient Chinese virtues, stimulated by a sense of inferiority to the material wealth and power that have been created by the West, and partly to a deep loyalty to the traditional philosophy and social organization that once served China so well.

Among other elements in the Kuomintang are several local warlords who joined the party and government because they could not stand alone as independents against the wave of patriotism that swept the country in the face of mounting Japanese aggression. Some of these men were making a good start in the improvement of their domains when war came; some are recalcitrant mandarins of an old-fashioned vintage reminiscent of the defunct but imperial Manchu court, while still others are little better than bandits turned respectable.

Among the center groups are bankers, business people, and trained technologists, of which the so-called "Political Science" group is one of the most important. Many of the men in this category were educated in America or England and are well versed in the American and British theory of democratic institutions. Many are good administrators who uphold efficiency and honesty in governmental and private operations, who wish to establish an equilibrium between government-owned and -operated heavy industry and privately owned light industry. Within this center element are also a number of able and conscientious scientists and educators like Dr. Wong Wen-hao,* head of the National Resources Commission, and Dr. Hu Shih, father of the Literary Revolution, former ambassador to the United States, now president of Peking University.

In the left wing of the Kuomintang are men who support a more complete socialism, state ownership and operation of industry, and who also have supported a policy of closer relations with the Soviets.

* Now Premier.

Similarly, the Communists include a range of viewpoints. Some of the best-informed Chinese observers in North China analyze the Communists as composed of three major groups. First, there is the powerful and thoroughly Marxist party leadership. Among the leaders some may espouse a political theory arrested at the pre-Stalinist stage of Russian development when communism was still more humanitarian and less an instrument for retaining power, but many, particularly those who, like Li Li-san, have recently returned from Russia, are likely to support the more power-mad elements of contemporary Moscow. While this leadership is aware that all policies must be adapted to the Chinese scene, it follows the Moscow line closely, particularly in international affairs.

A second group within the Chinese Communist party includes a number of agrarian reformers who are primarily Chinese and secondarily Marxists. In their desire for fundamental readjustments in the social and economic relationships of the countryside, they are to some degree using communism as a tool, even as the Marxist leadership of the party uses them as tools for seizing power in the Chinese state. It is the influence of this second group that has caused writers reporting on Red China to question whether Chinese communism is party-line communism or not, for this group is less doctrinaire and probably more compatible with the center and left elements of the Kuomintang than the thoroughly Marxist top leadership of the Communist party.

A third group in the Communist camp is made up of liberal individuals deeply concerned for the welfare of the people who have been forced out of Kuomintang China by growing persecution of anyone branded as Communist (i.e., anti-Kuomintang), and who have attached themselves to the Communist movement for lack of a better vehicle for their convictions.

In addition to these three groups, there are remnants of

the old warlord set that have joined the Communists as much for expediency as for conviction. Some military units of this type have already shifted to the Nationalist side, just as some have deserted the Kuomintang to join the Communists. It should be pointed out that neither the groups within the Communist party nor the cliques that make up the Kuomintang are independently organized. During the past decade, however, several liberal parties, independent of both the Kuomintang and the Communist party, have developed. The active membership of the Democratic League, the National Socialists (no connection with non-Chinese groups of the same name), the Young China party, and others of this liberal movement, is composed largely of Chinese authors, playwrights, artists, professors, and others of China's literati.

Early in 1947, the single-party Kuomintang Government opened its doors, at least nominally, to participation by other parties meeting certain demands, but the liberal element has, for the most part, held out for further reform and more equal privileges before taking part in the National Government as it exists today. The largest opposition party refusing to join was the Democratic League, which the Kuomintang banned altogether in October of the same year.

While the members of these liberal parties constitute a well-informed section of the Chinese population, they demonstrate little group co-operation, comparatively weak political guidance, and no militant leadership with which to implement their liberal views. Furthermore, the only two political parties in China with persuading armies and police are the Kuomintang and the Communists, while the liberals frequently find themselves harassed by one or both contestants.

Although they are, in total numbers, a pitifully small fraction of the Chinese people, most of whom are too much absorbed in the struggle to keep alive to know or care much about political theories, the Nationalists, Communists, and liberals are the political powers in Chinese life. What of the actual performance of the two leading parties? What are their long-term policies? What are they doing, and how does it affect the prospects of rebuilding China?

Communism in China, since being forced from the cities after its split from the Kuomintang in 1927, has been essentially a political movement designed to gain power through stressing and manipulating the poverty and conflicts that exist in the rural community. Communist leadership takes pride in having adapted Marxism to the agrarian situation in China, and is largely responsible for the creation of the oversimplified concept that China is a two-class society in which the "landlords" oppose the "peasants." The chief instrument by which the Communists strive to gain power is the class conflict engendered by means of such a "two-class" concept. They have become extremely facile in manipulating tensions until the poorer segment of the community is goaded into a type of action which permits the small Communist group to gain power.

During the war the Communists carried out a program that had the effect of stimulating the people in the regions they controlled toward change and, in many instances, toward definite improvements. They have survived because they have carried out policies that they could persuade at least a segment of the population are good. This, backed by the ruthless use of police and military force, has been the source of their political effectiveness.

After co-operation between the Communists and the Kuomintang collapsed and the Kuomintang set up its blockade, the Communists were forced to depend, even more completely, on support by the rural people. Under pressures of blockade, Japanese attack, and the demands of guerrilla warfare they perfected semidemocratic techniques of control, among which was a system of simple democratic government by People's Political Councils at levels from the village up to the highest unit in the Border Area government. The councils were elected by the people, only one Communist being permitted for every three individuals elected. Care was taken that all classes were represented, including landlords, farm laborers, tenants, and peasant owners. In practice, because it was the only organized group with a consistent program, the Communist third in the councils was in a position to shape the course of events. However, the people did have a sense of representation.

A second element in the Communist program was one which sought to correct the worst abuses of heavy rents by a moderate program of rent control—lowering rents and guaranteeing their payment, a definite departure from former land division by force, but made expedient by the different circumstances encountered in the north as compared with the south, where the Chinese Communists originated (in the north there are fewer landlords and many more owner farmers, and the landlords hold smaller tracts of land). This policy stimulated those who had money to invest it in other productive enterprises and to be less eager to put it in land. Although the land program considerably improved the lot of tenant farmers, the old drastic laws were applied to those who gained the displeasure of the Communists or the people, and the fact that such punishment could be easily contrived was undoubtedly a factor in getting the well-to-do to cooperate with the lowered rent program.

A third element was a system of graded taxes, with the poorest tenant and owner farmers entirely exempt from taxes if their total income did not exceed a certain designated mark. Taxes were then graded to become heavier as the size of income went up, placing the greatest burden in supporting the government and the war on the more well-to-do.

A fourth factor in the Communist wartime program was a production drive. One of the chief means was the organization of labor exchanges through which groups pooled and exchanged their labor in the interests of greater efficiency in production. In addition to the fact that about one-quarter of all the people in many districts joined such labor exchanges, the popularly elected local governments were used to put pressure on all individuals and groups including students, government workers, and soldiers to produce some of their own necessities.

Still another factor in the Communist program was an effective system of mass propaganda which dramatically explained what was needed and how it would help in the fight against the Japanese. The patriotic motive was an important ingredient in the success attained.

Using these methods the Communists were able to survive and to expand the area of their influence during the war years. Their efforts were reported in glowing terms by Western visitors to the Yenan area, and they were credited with having raised the agricultural production of that region by about 50 per cent. Although the Communists deserve credit, they ascribe the increase in production more to political efforts than the facts warrant. Much of this gain, probably most of it, was the result of returning to cultivation land that had previously fallen into disuse. There are extremely few areas in China where expansion of land under cultivation is possible, but one of these happened to be the Yenan region where fairly good land was not in cultivation because of historical and climatic factors. It is situated near the western fringe of the area where the yearly rainfall is just sufficient to permit agriculture and where the danger of drought is real and constant. In the middle of the nineteenth century the male population of the area was reduced by conscription for the imperial armies fighting the Taipings. Since the conscription took place during a period when a series of excessively dry years brought drought and famine, the population dropped below the total necessary to maintain the cultivation of all the land and to operate the local irrigation system.

When the Communists moved in, the population increased sufficiently to permit the irrigation and replanting of some of the land, and the war with Japan provided additional labor by forcing many refugees into the region. Finally, the Communists recruited armies in the more populous regions to the east and set them to work reclaiming and cultivating land while on garrison duty in the Yenan area.

In other words, the Communists were able to raise production in the Yenan area because of existing physical circumstances. Although they must be credited with the ability to recognize the opportunity to increase the output of their area and for obtaining the co-operation to do it, their success in Yenan does not mean that the same methods could produce similar increases in other areas where the population is more dense and all or almost all the land is already under cultivation. Whatever their success in increasing production and improving the livelihood of the people in Yenan, the Communists do not now have the agricultural technicians needed to solve the biotechnological and mechanical problems involved in the rebuilding of Chinese agriculture. Neither do they have the experience in, nor an adequate conception of, the complexities of the gigantic program of industrialization China must undertake.

During the relatively stable years of war with Japan, the Communists instituted and carried out a fairly effective program that gave the people a voice, however controlled, in the affairs of their local government and a mild land reform that was effective to a real degree in improving the economic position of the poorer segment of the population in particular. On the basis of these benefits and by making full use of anti-Japanese feelings, the Communists greatly strengthened their position in North China.

Since the end of the Japanese war and the beginning of intensification of the civil war, there is abundant evidence that the Communist program in relation to the people has undergone important changes. The evidence comes from sources that range from the Communist radio to eyewitness accounts of what is actually taking place in the areas dominated by the Communists. In total it indicates a return to a much more ruthless program of land division and a tightening up of party control, accompanied by an intensification of the use of force against the "enemy" segment of the Chinese population. In other words, the Communists have reverted to the full-blown methods of the class war directed toward the one objective of overthrowing the existing government in China and taking power by force. It is necessary to examine this new policy both for its immediate effects and for its possible long-term trends.

Land policy is the key to the application of Marxism to the Chinese rural community. It is also the major tool, together with direct military action, used by the Communists to gain and hold power in the countryside. And as a weapon of propaganda it has become one of the major means by which the American mind has been confused while attempting to decide what should be done in China. This land policy, both in its theoretical presentation and in its practical application, is based on several rather simple propositions, not all of which are necessarily sound when thoroughly examined.

The argument, as presented in idealistic terms, is as follows:

1. The undeniable poverty that weighs down the vast majority of the Chinese people is due principally to the extortions of high rent extracted by landlords from the helpless and downtrodden tenants and poor farmers over whom they have gained both economic and political power.

2. Owner farmers are *ipso facto* both economically and socially better off than tenants.

3. The fundamental reform required in rural areas is a

redivision of the land since, by this process, (a) the preponderant power of the landlords will be broken by taking away the source of their wealth and (b) tenant and small owner farmers will be greatly helped by giving them the undisputed ownership of enough land to produce a decent standard of living.

4. A peasantry freed from the shackles of tenantry and the political control of a landlord-dominated government will quickly move forward to the solution of all its problems.

In previous chapters* facts have been presented which cast serious doubt on several of these propositions. First, it is not at all proved that tenantry and landlordism are the principal causes of poverty among Chinese farmers. Such a conclusion completely neglects both overpopulation and prescientific farm technology as factors in the low production per man characteristic of Chinese agriculture. Furthermore, it ignores the facts that not more than one-third of China's farmers are tenants and more than half now own all the land they cultivate. Second, it has not been clearly demonstrated that landownership in and of itself brings a better standard of living, even though the social desirability of farmers' owning their land is accepted. Buck, after careful study and analysis, made the flat statement that he had found many situations in which tenant farmers were better off than the owner farmers of the same area.

There can be little doubt that confiscation and division of the land would destroy the wealth of the relatively prosperous farmers, both landlords who rent out land and farmers who cultivate farms above average in size. It is apparent also that, while an equal division of the land would improve slightly the lot of those who now operate the smallest farms, it will not make possible a decent average standard of living. A program of land division, when judged by the long-

* See especially Chap. XII.

range demands of raising standards of living, is diametrically opposed to the process required. Only when Chinese farmers are able to cultivate larger, not smaller farms, regardless of ownership, can rural standards of living rise. The effect of land division is to destroy those farms which are large enough to be economic and so bring all farm folk nearer to the same dead level of abject poverty.

What actually is needed is a shift of those farmers forced to cultivate very small farms to other productive activities in order to permit the addition of the land they till to medium-sized plots and the consequent creation of more farms that fall into the larger size groups. In the long view, land division, as advocated by the Communists, will effectively prevent a general rise in the standard of living both by the process of condemning all farmers to the operation of farms that are too small to provide a better living and by destroying such accumulations of wealth as may help provide the capital required to develop other means of productive activity.

Since tenantry is not the shackle that binds the Chinese peasant to a life of poverty, it follows that striking that shackle off would not free him for automatic or rapid progress. Furthermore, redistribution of the land would not play a large part in freeing him from the more fettering shackles that bind him because it cannot help reduce the population dependent on agriculture or speed the process of industrialization by which the basic means of production can be vastly expanded. And it would be of little help in breaking the shackles of ignorance and misinformation that are almost equally important factors in the poverty of the farmers.

In spite of the fact that the hard facts, examined from a long-range point of view, lead clearly to serious doubts as to the ultimate workability of the idealistically stated Communist land program, that land program is the key-

THE CHALLENGE OF CHINA

stone to the growing political power of the Communists in
North China. That Communist power continues to grow on
unsound roots is an apparent paradox with several
explanations.

One of the most important sources of Communist strength
is the loyalty of those who have received land under the
land division program. It has been reported by correspondents who have visited the Communist-controlled area that
additional land has been given to ten million families with
a total population of approximately fifty million. The Communist leaders attribute much of their strength to the
loyalty of these millions who have benefited. Their claim
is reasonable. In actual practice, those who have received
land are the poorest and frequently the most disgruntled
elements in the population. Furthermore, both the acceptance of land and loyalty to the Communists are quick ways
to power and influence in the community and a sure way
to put oneself outside the pale of the old order both in the
community and as represented by the Central Government.
Anyone taking the step is committed to fight to keep the
Communists in power or risk punishment by any local or
Central Government group that may gain power. Once across
the divide there is no way back.

Backing up this large group who have gone over to the
Communists for the immediate gain of land and power are
a skillful propaganda program directed along class war lines
and the threat of ruthless force. Since families are held ac-
countable for the conduct of young men conscripted into the
Communist armies, disobedience entails the definite possibility of torture for one's family. By such ancient and universal methods the grip of the Communists on the countryside is tightened.

The land program can be fully understood, however,
only in the light of basic Communist revolutionary doc-

trine. The following extracts taken from *The Theses and Statutes of the Communist International*,* dealing with the agrarian question, throw light on the matter, particularly when they are compared with the main points of the Chinese Communist land program.

After defining the rural "proletariat" and "semi-proletariat" the *Theses and Statutes* read as follows:

"5. The landed peasants or farmers are capitalists in agriculture, managing their lands usually with several hired laborers. They are connected with the "peasantry" only by their rather low standard of culture, their way of living, their personal manual work of their land. This is the most numerous element of the bourgeois class, and the decided enemy of the revolutionary proletariat. The chief attention of the Communist Party in the rural districts must be given to the struggle against this element, to the liberation of the laboring and exploited majority of the rural population from the moral and political influence of these exploiters. . . .

"6. The revolutionary proletariat must proceed to an immediate and unconditional confiscation of the estates of the landowners and big landlords, that is of all those who systematically employ wage labor, directly or through their tenants, exploiting all the small (and not infrequently also the middle) peasantry in their neighborhood, and do not do any actual manual work. . . .

"No propaganda can be permitted in the ranks of the Communist parties in favor of any indemnity to be paid to the owners of large estates for their expropriation. . . .

"In countries where large landholdings are insignificant in number, while a great number of small tenants are in search of land, there the distribution of the large holdings

* As adopted at the Second World Congress, July 17 to August 7, 1920, at Moscow and printed in New York: Central Executive Committee of the Communist Party of America, 1921.

can prove a sure means of winning the peasantry for the revolution, while the preservation of the large estates can be of no value for the provisioning of the towns. *The first and most important task of the proletarian state is to secure a lasting victory.* [Italics mine. G. F. W.] The proletariat must put up with a temporary decline of production so long as it makes for the success of the revolution. . . . "

It is illuminating to compare this with the "Basic Program on the Chinese Agrarian Law," promulgated by the Central Committee of the Chinese Communist party on October 10, 1947, and published by the New China News Agency, official news agency for the party. The important articles as they appeared in an article by Wang Sze-zee in the *China Weekly Review*, November 15, 1947, follow:

"Article 1: The agrarian system of feudal and semifeudal exploitation is abolished and the agrarian system of 'land to the tiller' is to be realized.

"Article 2: Land ownership rights of all landlords are abolished.

"Article 3: Land ownership rights of all ancestral shrines, temples, monasteries, schools, institutions, and organizations are abolished.

"Article 4: All debts incurred prior to the reform of the agrarian system are cancelled.

"Article 6: Except as provided in Article 9, Section b, all land in villages owned by landlords, and all public land shall be taken over by the village peasants' unions, and together with all other village land, in accordance with the total population of the village irrespective of sex or age, shall be unified and equally distributed; with regard to quantity, surplus land shall be taken to relieve dearths, and with regard to quality, fertile land shall be taken to supplement infertile, so that all village inhabitants shall equally share the land, and it shall be the individual property of each person.

"Article 10; Section d: Landlords and their families shall be given land and properties equivalent to that of the peasants.

"Article 10; Section e: All families of Kuomintang military officers and soldiers, government officials and personnel, party members and other enemy personnel, whose homes are in rural areas, shall be given land and properties equivalent to that of the peasants.

"Article 11: The Government shall issue to the people deeds of ownership of the land, and moreover, recognize their rights to free management, trading, and under specially determined conditions, to renting their land. All land deeds and all notes on debts contracted prior to the reform of the agrarian system shall be turned in and shall be declared null and void.

"Article 12: The property and legal operation of industrial and commercial elements shall be protected from encroachment."

The real purpose of the land program in China is to gain control of the state by building a following from among the poor, by destroying the more well-to-do who might oppose the Communist leadership, and by giving Communists and pro-Communists power through the process of dividing the land, which is the real wealth.

It is clear that the standard of living of the masses can rise only as agricultural production is doubled and industrial production vastly increased, and both processes depend on a shift of millions of people off the soil and on a supply of capital for the development of an enormous industrial plant. There are, in the light of these considerations, real dangers in the basic Communist program of land division. First, there is the danger of dooming those who have to stay on the farm to a piece of ground that is too small to provide either a full use of time or a decent standard of living, even should scientific methods succeed in doubling the yield per acre. Second, there is the danger of destroying the accumulations of capital that now exist and so making the financing of the necessary industrial developments almost if not entirely impossible.

It must be remembered, in this connection, that the Russian Soviets took over relatively large accumulations of wealth in the form of gold, jewelry, and real and industrial property from the wealthy of the czarist era for the basic capitalization of their new state industries. Nevertheless, the Soviets were forced to collectivize the land at the cost of millions of lives in order that the state, as sole landlord, might be in a position to exact a good *sixty per cent* of the entire produce of all farmers for the building of an industrial capital plant. If a similar program comes for China with her dense population and smaller accumulations of wealth, the murders will have to run to many times the few millions of Russia. Even under the worst conditions of tenantry in China today, far less than 60 per cent of the total production of all farmers goes for rent, even though some individual tenants may have to pay that much. The Communists make claims of benefiting the whole population, but in reality they have yet to prove that their program can do so. The acid test for them must come when they face the problem of how they will build the capital plant required for China's industrialization.

If they come to power and the present trend in world politics and world economic development continues, it seems certain, in spite of statements to the contrary made during the war by their leaders, that the Communists will not appeal for or welcome American aid in the building up of capital plant. Also it seems likely that America would be reluctant to provide large quantities of capital, from either private or governmental sources, to a Communist-dominated China and that Western Europe will have little capital to export for many years to come. It follows that a Communist

China would be forced to turn to the Soviet Union as the only outside source of capital. The Soviet Union, with huge war losses to make good and the necessity of building up consumer goods production toward a rising domestic standard of living, is not likely to have the excess production required to capitalize China for many years.

It seems reasonable, therefore, to conclude that unless a drastic realignment of world forces takes place, the Communists will encounter extreme difficulty in obtaining the huge quantities of outside capital required for rebuilding China.

The land issue has been skillfully used to confuse American thinking about China. The need for redistributing the land has been the subject of so much uncritical writing that many well-informed and thoughtful people have come to believe that the change most basic and important to China is redistribution of the land. From this fallacious assumption it is easy to progress through the following steps:

1. Land reform is the best way to help the Chinese people.

2. America should support a government in China that helps its people.

3. Since the Communists are dividing the land they are doing the most for the Chinese people.

From this line of thinking comes confusion as to what American policy should be in the present complex situation. Out of it comes much resistance to doing anything at all. There are indeed many problems and questions concerning the best policy, but the oversimplified argument about land reform should not be permitted to play as large a part in our thinking, both conscious and unconscious, as it now does.

The actual, immediate effect of the land division policy as a part of Communist political strategy, coupled with the class struggle that is the propelling force of the civil war, is immense suffering to huge segments of the Chinese population. Some of the ways in which this suffering comes about are illustrated by the story of a peasant woman who lives in the central coastal province of Kiangsu, where the cities of Shanghai and Nanking are located. She had come from the northern part of the province and had worked for many years as nursemaid in a middle-class Chinese family in Shanghai. She lived as frugally as Chinese can live and sent her savings home to her mother, the only remaining member of her family, who lived on a 10 *mou* farm (one and two-thirds acres) in the home village. With these savings squeezed from her meager earnings the two women slowly bought additional fields till they had twenty-four mou, or just four acres. When war came to Shanghai the nursemaid was forced to return to her village and during the latter part of the war the two women managed their farm with the aid of hired labor.

When the Communists came into the district the women were classed as "landlords" because they hired labor even though they had only four acres. Fourteen mou of their land was promptly taken from them and divided among other families, leaving them their original ten. Not many months later the Nationalists captured the area. Those who had received the fourteen mou ceased cultivating their plots because they feared punishment for accepting them from the Communists. Because the two rightful owners feared torture from night-prowling Communists, they did not dare cultivate it either. Even if they had dared they could not have found enough labor to do so because most of the able-bodied men fled the district to escape conscription by one or the other of the armies. As a result, fourteen mou of good land are idle in a district where there is not enough food. These fallow fourteen mou are a single case among the many by which the class struggle applied to the Chinese countryside has thrown thousands and thousands of acres of land out of production.

The home village of a friend who lives in northeastern

Shantung province was taken over by the Communists in 1947. As they moved in, more than 10 per cent of the population of the whole district moved out, most of them able-bodied men. In the thirty-five families living in the village only ten males remain. Not one of them is in the active years of fifteen to sixty.

Add to this rural disruption and suffering the continued destruction of the industrial plant resulting from the civil war and a picture of the cost of the present struggle to the Chinese people begins to take shape. By early 1948 it was reported from China that more people were displaced from their homes, fleeing from the bitter effects of the civil war, than were driven to the roads by the Japanese invasion at its worst.*

Under the pressure of spreading class conflict, the visions of peace, unity, and rapid progress that gladdened the hearts of the Chungking crowds that celebrated V-J day, had, by early 1948, been forced into a receding and uncertain future.

The Chinese Communists are Communists. Their basic long-term policies are directed toward the achievement of a proletarian revolution for the purpose of gaining control of the state. In this program they have the backing of the Communist parties and fellow-traveler groups of the world and the active moral and material support of the Soviet Union. Ultimately, judgment as to whether communism could rebuild China and raise the standard of life of the people must be based on an estimate of the relative effectiveness of communism as a system for solving basic human problems. There can be no doubt that it represents a force that will deeply influence the course of events in China for many decades to come. But the facts of China and of her needs are inescapable, and, in spite of communism's reported successes

* These reports have been confirmed by firsthand information received from Chinese friends whose homes are in the disturbed areas.

in parts of China for limited periods of time, they form an untenable basis for believing that her problems can be solved by a doctrine which claims class conflict as a dogma and has shown an invariable predilection for totalitarian methods.

Opposing the Communists are the Kuomintang and the Central Government. Under the impact of the problems created by almost ten years of international war, by a continually intensifying civil war, by Communist propaganda attack, and by many failures and limited successes, the prestige of the Kuomintang has declined. An evaluation of its policies is valid only if they, also, are examined in terms of their effects on the rebuilding of China.

During the war Kuomintang China fell back more and more on the old bureaucratic type of administration based on the educated-official class and the retention of the privileged position of the gentry. The tendency toward corruption, inherent in a society in which the concept of moral obligation to the community has not yet spread widely enough to displace the older system of family loyalty, increased as war-generated attrition put growing pressure on the economy. Partly because of philosophical inclination and partly because of the necessity to work with what it found in the backward interior, the Kuomintang has sought to solve its problems along the old lines. The result has been a retrogression from its stated ideals and an ensuing loss of popular support.

Illustrative of the way in which this catering to the gentry has operated to decrease popular support are the methods used to conscript the millions of soldiers required by the National armies during the war. Soldiers and soldiering have always been looked down upon by the Chinese, an attitude that has been intensified in recent decades by the suffering undergone at the hands of warlords and by the knowledge that a large percentage of the sons taken are lost forever through death or because they become professional soldiers or bandits. Instead of a selective service system by which individuals could be conscripted, the number of soldiers to be provided at each draft was based on the number of families in the community, and local officials had to deliver their quotas to the recruiting center. This system, plus the general disrespect for soldiering, led to a demoralizing reaction throughout huge areas of Nationalist China. The prestige of a family in the community could be measured by its ability to avoid sending its sons to war. The man with no money to buy his way out and no powerful friends to protect him was forced to go, while the rich and influential could avoid conscription altogether. This process has intensified the attitude long held by the people of China that one avoids contact with the government whenever possible.

Similarly, as the government, driven by the necessities of war, assumed responsibility for more and more commerce and industry, both direct opportunities for manipulation for private or group profit and situations in which accusations of such manipulation might be made have vastly increased. Although a great majority of the officials of the Central Government are honest men who carry on their work against constantly mounting financial difficulties, the small, corrupt minority are spotlighted and, by implication, destroy the reputation of the honest. Thus the Kuomintang is held responsible both for the real cases of corruption and for the greater number of cases in which an insoluble situation goes from bad to worse and is interpreted as resulting from corruption.

Nevertheless, the number of cases in which incompetence, dishonesty, or corruption has resulted in serious governmental failures, as the territory occupied by the Japanese was reoccupied, are altogether too numerous. One of the worst of these failures was that compounded in Formosa, where a combination of arrogant overlordship, hasty and inefficient grasping for government control of all business and industry, and serious grafting for personal gain resulted in a revolt that was put down by armed force. To a lesser degree and on a smaller scale, this situation has been repeated in a number of parts of China.

But the negative chapter, true and important as it is, is not the whole story. The Kuomintang has the support of many elements in the population and, in spite of inflation, is accomplishing much in the fields of education, agriculture, and public health to help the common people. It is the Kuomintang-controlled areas into which pour the vast hordes of people fleeing civil war, adding further burdens on the government. Because in many specific areas the problem of landownership is acute, the Central Government, while not sponsoring widespread and confiscatory redistribution of the land, is working on programs whereby tenants will be able to purchase the land they farm. In the recent past, a number of tenant purchase plans have been set up. Many of them have failed because they did not provide the purchasing tenant with adequate guidance, because they were located on poor land, or because the prices asked were too high.

In 1942 a successful tenant purchase plan, known as the Peipeh Tenant Purchase Project, was set up near Chungking. This experimental project was started in a community of 126 farm families in the nineteen pao of Chao-Yang-Ching, with the Peipeh district government buying the land from the landlords and the Farmer's Bank of China providing the financing. The Ministry of Agriculture and Forestry provided the necessary technical advice and assistance, and a Co-operative Farming Organizer's Office was opened in the community to give technical aid.

The 126 families, with a total population of 426, included 19 absentee landlord families, 16 local landlords, 2 landlords who rented part of their land and worked the rest,

29 owner-operators, 3 part owners, and 47 tenants.* Rice, wheat, corn, and sweet potatoes, the major crops, were grown in a hill-type rice culture system.† The rental charged before the tenant purchase program went into effect was 60 per cent of the principal summer crop, usually rice, with the tenant retaining all the winter crop, or an average rental equivalent to about 30 per cent of the year's production. Under the repurchase plan, the tenant continues to pay the bank the same rental until the debt is paid off and the farm becomes his.

The project has every indication of being successful, a success significant not so much for the large earnings made by various undertakings, nor even for the gradual transfer of land to the tenant purchaser, as for the great change in attitude demonstrated by members toward the general welfare of their community. A new primary school was built with labor contributed by the members, with construction materials purchased from the earnings of a co-operative piggery, and with stone recovered from an old house on property belonging to a landlord. Roads have been improved, public buildings have been repaired and maintained, tung trees have been planted on a public-owned hillside and along roads, exhibits and fairs have been held, home-guard training has been set up, and an arrangement made for settling disputes.

It is this type of economic readjustment of landownership that promises to solve the land distribution problem in areas where tenantry under absentee landlords has created a situation that requires solution. As a nonpolitical means of land adjustment, it can be carried out without leaving the community split by class bitterness. Furthermore, it

* Raymond Moyer, *National Reconstruction Journal,* Vol. VIII, No. 1, July, 1947.

† See Chap. III.

can fit into the basic process that must shift millions of families off the land altogether.

Early in 1947 many of the lessons learned in the Peipeh project were incorporated with other proved techniques of rural reconstruction developed by the Mass Education Movement and set into practice in the ten hsien which make up the third prefecture of Szechuan province. With the full backing of the Central Government and the appointment of its research director as prefectural magistrate, the Mass Education Movement, a private organization, took over full responsibility for the prefecture. Already significant progress has been made in combating illiteracy, reforming taxes, building up economic rehabilitation, improving health, and in general carrying out a well-rounded program that holds great hope for the future.

In spite of all the propaganda to the contrary, the Central Government and Kuomintang China have achieved a great deal more than have the Communists in undertaking the complicated practical programs that can eventually rebuild the country. Nationalist China is far better equipped with technicians and technical experience. Although they represent a very small fraction of the total required, the Nationalists have available more trained people in agriculture and engineering, more educational institutions capable of providing qualified leaders, and more established industrial plants than the Communists. Already first steps have been taken toward the solution of technical problems in the fields of agriculture, engineering, public health, and other activities. However, in spite of possessing more of the requirements for an understanding of the technical and human problems of rebuilding, the Nationalists still fall far short of grasping the scope, mass, and detail of the aggregate task.

Although there are individual medical men and some

groups who have given objective thought to the population problem as a factor in the raising of living standards, there is an almost complete lack of understanding of this problem among most of the nonmedical leadership in the Kuomintang and, in some quarters, a strong tendency to support the fallacy that population increases are desirable. This error is compounded by the fanatic doctrines of some European leaders in their misguided efforts to make small, indigent states militarily independent at any cost. The theory is also supported by some of Dr. Sun's writings in which he made a projection of American population increase through immigration and natural growth from colonial times to the beginning of this century and came to the fallacious conclusion that there would be hundreds of millions of Americans by the end of the century that would constitute a "white peril" which should be met by an expanding Chinese population. Because Dr. Sun was the founder of the Kuomintang and because his writings are considered oracular by many, large segments of the party leadership are totally unprepared to consider the population problem realistically.

The Communists seem little better in comprehending the population problem, largely because they have not seriously analyzed the difficulties involved in achieving a higher standard of living. Both groups are prone to rely on propaganda rather than facts.

Blinded by their Confucian predilections, the Nationalists fail to grasp the really fundamental changes in thinking and in human values required for rebuilding the nation. The habit of looking upon human life as a cheap commodity has become so ingrained through the centuries in all classes of Chinese society that it is difficult for individuals and groups to act as though all men are worth consideration.

Both Nationalists and Communists rely too heavily on the effectiveness of totalitarian planning. The Kuomintang, only slightly less than the Communists, believes in state ownership and control of the means of production. There are too many inherent dangers in such totalitarianism to believe that strict government control can ever be successful in rebuilding China, even though there must be a great deal of central planning and experimentation. This conviction is based on the doubt that the detailed planning of any small group which happened to gain political power by force, or even by election, could be omniscient enough to succeed. The mistakes in judgment of such a necessarily small ruling group are likely to be so numerous and so great as to stall the processes of rebuilding, to say nothing of the corrupting and perverting influence that total power exercises on individuals and groups. Furthermore, when means of production are managed by politically selected individuals, both inefficiency and gross technical errors are too liable to be glossed over and protected under the pretense that social benefits excuse operating at an economic loss. No society has yet demonstrated that totalitarian planning can really raise standards of living. While Russia has given some promise of developing her vast resources under such procedures, she has not yet shown much headway in achieving the higher standards of living that are found in free capitalist economies.

Moreover, totalitarian planning, in addition to its inherent weaknesses, is particularly unsuited to the genius of the Chinese people. They are individualists with the family substituted for the individual. They carry familyism to an extreme that creates one of their worst weaknesses, a limited ability to co-operate with anyone outside the family. On the other hand, they are capable planners when family interests are concerned and so skillful in circumventing government decrees that any highly centralized plan developed to the last detail with the rigidity characteristic of totalitarianism would beat itself to death against a mass of familyistic individualism. China can be rebuilt only when thousands of individuals and families, as well as the government, are inspired to release inherent creative capacity and initiative to plan and carry out those plans. In so far as they are totalitarian in philosophy, both the Communists and the Kuomintang lack the understanding necessary for rebuilding.

In its swing toward nationalism and its assertion of the sovereignty restored by the abrogation of the unequal treaties, and in its strong trend toward government control of industry, the Central Government has, since the end of the war, created conditions that make it difficult for foreign capital to function successfully in China. These government policies, coupled with the problems of inflation, have brought effective business in China to an almost complete standstill and, consequently, have drawn the criticism of American investors and potential investors. The governmental situation has been complicated further by favoritism and corruption on the part of government officials in direct charge of various types of business relationships. The result has been a growing feeling, on the part of many American businesses, that they are not wanted by the Chinese and a doubt that they will be able to share in the future development of the country.

However, in spite of the immediate difficulties that dog and delay effective financial and business relations between Americans and China, the long-term prospects of working out a basis for effective operation seem to be good, provided the country does not become Communist or break up into a number of more or less independent regions. This optimism is based partly on the fact that the Kuomintang has within it the well-established idea, rooted in the writings of Dr. Sun, that outside aid is desirable and can be sought without loss of sovereignty. A more solid basis is the fact that the long-term needs and self-interest of both peoples make such economic co-operation a necessity. In all probability there will be a period of trying struggle, with both sides forced to make a number of concessions before this new basis of operation finally takes form. Given time, patience, and a solution to the civil war, such a basis can be achieved.

If the Chinese Communists are really Communists, then are the Nationalists really Fascists, as they are so frequently represented.

There is a well-organized and active secret police force in Nationalist China. It was organized by the Russian advisers who guided the development of the revolutionary drive that Generalissimo Chiang led northward from Canton in the late 1920's. It parallels that other offspring of the same parent organization, the secret police of the Communists. Separated by the party split in 1927, the two organizations are very similar and are used in much the same way by both sides. The world hears little about the Communist secret police in China for the same reasons that it hears little about it in Yugoslavia or Russia. More is heard about the Kuomintang secret police because, in spite of all that is said and written to the contrary, the Central Government of China still permits more foreign correspondents to see and write more about it than do the Communists.

The existence of a secret police controlled and used largely by the Kuomintang party rather than the government of China means that civil liberties, as we know them, are far from secure in any part of China. It means that the Chinese Central Government is not a democracy. Furthermore, the Central Government does not claim and never has claimed to be a democracy.

The difficulties of democracy in China stem from many sources among which are the poverty and limitations described in earlier chapters. Perhaps the greatest handicap to democracy in China, however, is the fact that a cultural heritage thousands of years old stands in opposition to a concept introduced but a few decades ago. The cultural weight of the conservative, bureaucratic, emperor-centered form of government that was China's through the ages still carries forward with tremendous momentum. That China does not have a democracy in the Western sense of the word is due as much to this inertia as to the infiltration of modern fascist ideas.

Although the Kuomintang-dominated Central Government is not democratic, it also is not Fascist. Both the party and the government are clearly on record as determined to move toward democracy. Since the end of the war, by drafting and promulgating the constitution and holding the first national elections, they have taken important steps toward setting up that democracy, even in the midst of a continuing war situation. Although there are individuals and groups in the Kuomintang who oppose the development of effective democracy, it must be emphasized that there are great segments of the party and the government who do want to place real power in the hands of the people. On this long-range trend toward democracy America's policy must rest its hope of rebuilding China.

It has been my observation that power within the Kuomintang party swings to right or left according to the faith the Chinese feel they can place in American co-operation and support. After Pearl Harbor, and after the loss of the Burma Road isolated China from America, power within the Kuomintang swung steadily toward the extreme right. This swing was not reversed till hump tonnage of supplies being flown in built up and until General A. C. Wedemeyer gave full support to Generalissimo Chiang. Then power moved more into the hands of the center groups. After V-J day, when the United States launched its campaign to force a coalition government on China and stopped aid till such a coalition was formed, power again swung toward the right. Over and over again the actual effect of our attempts to force reforms and improvements in the Chinese government as a price for increased help has been to strengthen those elements which represent the very things America wishes to weaken.

A Chinese friend, arriving in America late in 1947 after months of close contact with the people of Shantung province where the struggle between the Central Government and the Communists has been acute since shortly after the surrender of the Japanese, summarized the attitude of the great majority of the people in this way: "The people still believe in the ideals of justice and democracy that the Kuomintang professes, but they are deeply disappointed that the Central Government does not do more in carrying them out. The people do not believe in the ideals and policies that the Communists proclaim; they are desperately afraid that the Communists will win and impose them anyway."

For the most part the struggle in China is interpreted in simple political terms. We are repeatedly told that if an honest government dedicated to the welfare of the people would only destroy the special interests of the landlords and redistribute the land China could be well on the way toward solving all her problems. Or, stated in the doctrinaire terms of the Marxists, we are told that China's poverty is the result of the exploitation of the working class by the land-owning class; that China is a feudal country where the people are enslaved by the educated-landlord-official class which wishes to see no changes lest its power be lost; that all that is required to set China on the road to abundance is to generate class hatred so that the masses will rise up and destroy the ruling class; that the then newly liberated masses will, if they remain loyal to the dogma of Marxism and continue to suppress any opposition to it, almost automatically work out all the other problems of rebuilding China.

I wish that such a simple diagnosis of the problem were true. I wish that the Chinese people could solve their problems that easily, for, even in China, it would be far simpler to raise enough steam to kill off a class or two than it will be to do what actually must be done. Unfortunately, the problem is not that simple.

China is like a human being sick with cancer. A malignant growth compounded of overpopulation, ignorance, and material poverty and aggravated by years of international and civil war has been gnawing at her vitals for so long that her government, like blood corrupted by deep-seated maladjustments, has become anemic and ineffective. Although governmental reform, like a blood transfusion, will give the patient temporary strength to withstand surgery, the malignant growth itself must be removed before the slow rebuilding toward health can take place. The tragedy of China today is that so many would-be doctors, mistaking the symptoms for the disease, believe that new blood is all that is needed, that better government is a panacea.

The truth is that there is no simple, no easy, no quick solution. China must have her transfusion and then her operation. To recover she will be forced to draw upon the last ounce of vitality in every tissue and cell in the national body. If the effort involved damages her whole organism, as civil war now is doing, then that vitality may be drained beyond hope.

What is happening in China today goes deeper than political and social revolution, deep and shattering as those revolutions are. Essentially China has become a gigantic testing ground where it will be determined whether or not the human race can move into an era of high energy consumption in which all people everywhere can share. Ultimately the very capacity of the human race to continue to exist is at stake. Can man learn to control himself and his environment? Is it possible that man's moral stature measures up to his knowledge of the workings of nature? Can man rise above his own selfishness and shortsightedness? Can he rise above his barriers of clan, and race, and class? Can he learn quickly to transcend the old confines of national boundaries? Does he possess mental eyesight capable of seeing as far as his own ultimate, total self-interest?

And beyond all is the grim test of whether, even after some sort of solution to the political problems has been worked out, the human race can make the sociotechnical adjustment required to put its environment to work in its own ultimate interest. Even with the best and most ideal government and social organization possible, will it then be possible to conquer the stubborn stuff of which the earth is made; to free and distribute and use the vast energies of men and nature in such a way that life can be served? In the titanic problems they face in Asia, not only the Chinese, but all men are on trial, and ultimately the survival of Western civilization hangs on the outcome.

This is the challenge of China. This is the challenge of China to America, for when the United States as a nation, both in its official capacity as a government and in its private aspect as an aggregate of separate group and individual activities, knows how to conduct itself in relation to China so as to foster this gigantic rebuilding successfully, it will have found a policy that can support American fundamental interests throughout the world.

America's interest is basically in the preservation of the American way of life on as permanent a basis as possible. In concrete terms this means the preservation of personal freedom and the rights of the individual, for we still "hold these truths to be self-evident, that all men are created equal, that they are endowed by their Creator with certain inalienable rights, that among these are Life, Liberty, and the pursuit of Happiness." It means the continuation of the democratic institutions of representative government under which every adult has the right to have his opinion expressed through his vote and affect the decisions and laws that establish the conditions of his life. It means the preservation of a free competitive market operating under rules made and modified by the democratic process. It means the continuation of capitalism under democratic control so that it does not develop into socially irresponsible monopoly. It means the continued development of an industrial economy capable of producing the goods and services required by a high standard of living. It means the strengthening of those moral and ethical concepts which form the foundation of social responsibility for all men, all classes, and all groups, a by-product of which is the protection of minorities from the tyranny of the majority.

This American way of life can exist in the world only when most of the world's people are moving in the same general direction. The rebuilding of China can take her in that direction. What, then, are the concrete objectives of American policy that can help ensure the future by helping to make the rebuilding of China possible?

If China is to be rebuilt, American policy must first be directed toward the prevention of another world war. Only if the tensions between America and Russia are reduced and world economy spared the threat and trauma of another war can China hope for the peace she must have for her rebuilding. This condition is particularly vital in China, where the clash between the American type of social and political organization with that of the Soviets is the dominating dynamic of civil war.

Next, American policy must be directed at achieving a real test between America's type of democratically controlled capitalism and communism as competing systems for raising standards of living. Ultimately only the outcome of such a crucial experiment can determine which system is the better. This test must be made, not only between the American economy and that of the Soviet Union but also in Europe and Asia. America's competitive imperative is to keep her economy strong and to keep it operating in behalf of all elements in the population. To achieve these ends, America's economy must remain sufficiently flexible to meet changing world conditions. An unalterable standard by which America must judge the terms on which changing conditions are to be met is the basic moral demand that lies at the root of her concepts of democracy: that all men are in and of themselves worthy of just and equal rights, including the rights to share in determining the course of their own lives.

A third goal of American policy must be the development of the means and techniques for co-operating with the Chinese people in accomplishing the vast range of tasks that must be undertaken, without the acts or motives of imperialism and without the suggestion of a "colonial" relationship. Part of the problem here is the necessity of resisting the pressure of what some may think are the military demands of America's position in the Far East. America must not let fear of Russia frighten her into hasty grabbing for influence on a purely military basis. Ultimately, a rebuilt China can be a strong, reliable military ally, but only in proportion as real strengths within China grow and expand.

In rebuilding toward those strengths, China will need much help from America. One example is a key project such as the Ichang dam on the Yangtze River. The dam can be completed only if technical aid and capital in the form of machinery and materials are supplied by the United States. Perhaps a workable pattern for co-operation in such a project would be a jointly run public corporation on the pattern of the TVA, in which American management would work to carry out basic policies established by the Chinese and, in doing so, train Chinese administrators who would eventually assume complete control. To succeed, America will have to respect the pride and sovereignty of China and develop a pattern of political co-operation with her without domination by the stronger of the two partners. Only by constantly emphasizing the American sense of democracy and knack for respecting and working well with all kinds of people and by suppressing the adolescent impatience with what Americans consider backwardness can the delicate balance that such co-operation requires be achieved.

A fourth objective of America's policy must be the development of ways in which her immense wealth can be put to work within the framework of capitalism for the rapid expansion of the benefits of the industrial revolution to the Chinese people, without economic loss, on the one hand, or unjust exploitation of people and situations, on the other. In other words, America must help China achieve economic efficiency without influencing her actions, either economically or politically, to an imperialistic degree. Here indeed is a challenge to enlightened capitalism. On one hand, it represents risks of a severity that free capital rarely has been willing to face. On the other, however, it offers financial gains beyond modest profits and an opportunity to achieve the greater gains of a more secure world—gains that continue into a lengthening future in which democracy, freedom, and a high standard of living can survive. There must be no misunderstanding: America's economic co-operation with the Chinese, and with peoples everywhere, must be on a sound business basis; it must be able to pay reasonable returns on investments. Such co-operation will require imagination, courage, and a willingness to look to the future while assuming heavy, immediate burdens. If American capitalism refuses to assume these burdens it must accept a large share of the responsibility for the development in the world of those conditions which will eventually make it impossible for capitalism and the American way of life to survive.

A further objective of American policy must be to foster a truly democratic revolution as the social and political dynamic for the rebuilding of China's life. We must never forget that our own nation was founded on, and its wealth and power have grown out of, a major political revolution. That the right to rule rests neither in feudal lord, king, or hierarchy, nor in race, class of birth, or social status, whether it be of owners or workers, but is reserved for all the people to exercise through their duly elected representatives, is a concept put into practice by what remains one of the most fundamental of revolutions. It gives to each human being the greatest degree of dignity, holding that man is no more the chattel of the state or of any class or economic system than he is rightfully the slave of any other individual. It is a political dynamic that can reshape the lives of the underdeveloped peoples of the world.

It must be recognized, however, that it is not easy for the wealthiest, the most powerful nation on earth to find the means whereby such a revolution can be stimulated in the far corners of the earth. One of those means must be a constant effort to make America's democracy fully operative in its own land. In concrete and specific terms, America must continue to move with increasing speed toward the solution of our own problems. We must make it possible for nearly one-tenth of our people to escape the status of second-class citizens imposed upon them because their skins are black. We must fight the spreading virus of anti-Semitism. We must make our democracy work at home and display that democracy abroad. We must demonstrate it in the way we conduct our affairs and in the consideration we constantly show all the peoples with whom we come in contact. We must make sure, through conscious efforts in our educational system, that a new generation of Americans grows up fully appreciative of the significance of the democratic concept of human relations and prepared to live and act on a plane of equality of personal value with the lowliest both in our own society and in any society in the world.

Another means whereby we can work for a truly democratic revolution in China is higher education and its methods of delivering the impact of our ideas. Higher education can operate to this purpose through two clear-cut channels. First, America exerts influence through those who have come to this country for their advanced education. They have come in the past and they are likely to continue to come by the thousands for many decades in the future. Through these men American ways and ideals of democracy are interpreted to the youth of China. The second channel is through the group of American-supported colleges and universities now operating in China. Altogether there are fifteen such institutions, Protestant, Catholic, and private. Their impact on Chinese life and education has been incalculably great. But if they are to continue to keep pace in the future, these institutions must gain much greater aid from American education and philanthropy. They represent too valuable a means of teaching and demonstrating democracy to be permitted to wither through lack of understanding and support in America.

American individuals and groups can make far-reaching contribution to the rebuilding of China by continuing to support Christian missionary work, both Protestant and Catholic. There has been an enormous amount of misrepresentation of both missionaries and missionary work in the popular press. In cartoons the missionary, represented as long faced and stovepipe hatted, black umbrellaed, is out to force the details of religious practice as his group defines them down the throats of unwilling natives. The great mass of missionaries and missionary work, however, is far from the distorted picture so frequently given.

Until missionaries went to China there were no modern schools, no hospitals, no orphan asylums, no one to teach the deaf and the blind, no treatment for the insane. There was no modern science and no scientific medicine, and, of course, there was no Christian Church. The missionary movement deserves much of the credit for the development of all these things which are now deeply rooted in Chinese life and are steadily expanding their benefits.

Above all, however, is that contribution made by the Christian Church to China without which American policies in China must fail: the moral motivation for democracy. In channeling the intellectual and moral force of China's old religions into a morality which elevates the individual and asserts the dignity of all men, the Christian Church has laid the foundation for the social and political structure that must bear the stresses of China's conversion to a modern, productive, democratic state.

The picture of China today and the prospect of undertaking even partial responsibility for her rebuilding does little to ease the weariness of the world. There is a tragically powerful temptation to say "It's too much—too huge, too complex for me to do anything about. I'm going to take care of myself and forget the rest of the world."

The bitter truth is that there is no way to create permanent security for a unit of the human race while denying the problems created by that two-thirds of mankind which exists on the bare survival line. There is no easily discoverable, day-to-day policy for Americans, either as individuals or as a nation, that guarantees the ends desired. There is only a complex of policies which must be carefully shaped around facts, tested, modified or rejected, retried, and changed once again as we work our way toward the achievement of our goal. There is no escape from the necessity of making the effort to understand.

There are times when I wake and hear again the cry of the dying beggar who wakened me one night in Chungking.

I had seen him many times, a long, misshapen bag of discolored skin stretched over knotty, outsized bones, lying beside the stone-paved trail that led from the ferry landing up to the house where I lived.

The first time I saw him he was already too weak to

stand. He lay by the trail, well down the mountain near the upper edge of the village, begging between fits of coughing. The passers-by were none too generous, but there were always a few dirty bills in the old cap that lay beside him. With them he bought a little food from passing vendors, and gradually, as the days went by, he began to work his way up the hill, a few feet at a time.

After he was dead I heard his story. The only son of a family with a little property, he had, years before while still a young man, contracted tuberculosis. After spending most of its wealth on the ineffective treatments of old herb doctors, his family finally took him to a modern hospital where better care slowed the progress of his disease, although he was already too far gone for a cure to be effected. His parents died, and, to pay for his care as the years went by, he used up what was left of the family property. The hospital continued to care for him for many months after there was no money left to pay his ever-mounting costs. Finally, burdened by patients for whom there was some hope of cure, the needs of civilian and military war wounded, limited in income and pressed by rising expenses, the hospital authorities were forced to tell the old man that they could no longer keep him. An appeal was sent to the city welfare department. An official reply, belated as is the way with official replies anywhere, stated regretfully that there were no further funds available, and the pain-racked derelict left the hospital to beg in the streets.

As the weather turned colder he inched his way up the hill toward my lodgings. Several times I gave him money, yet I was ashamed to do it—ashamed because I knew that I was powerless to give enough to do anything more than prolong the slow pain of his dying—yet ashamed not to make some gesture of sympathy. Each time I saw him I was forced again to face the fact that there were thousands of shrunken creatures dying slowly beside the roads and trails of China. Dying uncared for because millions were living, barely able to survive in a society which did not produce enough to support all its people and yet was forced to burn huge quantities of its wealth in fighting for its freedom. At last he made his way to the shallow shelter of an old broken-down archway a few tens of feet from the back wall of our compound.

Then in the small hours of the night, when a light wind was blowing and a slow, cold rain was falling, I was wakened by the hoarse, pleading cry of the old tubercular beggar. He was calling again and again the name of the woman in whose home I lived, begging for help.

The rest of the night I lay there sleepless, trapped between the quavering human cry from the night and the cold facts that forced me to know I could not save him or the thousands of others whose cries I could not hear. The next morning they came and told us that the beggar was dead.

His cry will haunt me the rest of my days, stinging and goading me, even as the cry of others like him will haunt those who come after me, driving all of us who hear, to think and work and build until at last the time can come when no one in China—or in any other land—need die of disease and starvation, uncared for in the shallow shelter of a broken-down archway.

Index